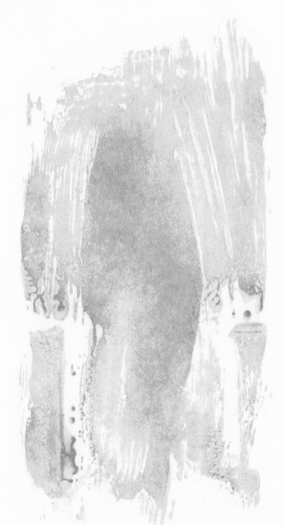

Comparative

Odontology

Comparative Odontology

by BERNHARD PEYER

Translated and edited by
RAINER ZANGERL

THE UNIVERSITY OF CHICAGO PRESS
CHICAGO AND LONDON

Library of Congress Catalog Card Number: 66–20578

THE UNIVERSITY OF CHICAGO PRESS, CHICAGO 60637

THE UNIVERSITY OF CHICAGO PRESS, LTD., LONDON, W.C. 1

Printed in the United States of America

Foreword

The late Dr. Bernhard Peyer,[1] distinguished zoologist and paleontologist, was deeply interested throughout his scientific career in the history of the dentition. A dozen years before his death, he began the preparation of a volume on comparative odontology. At his death in 1963 he had come close to the completion of this project; numerous excellent illustrations had been prepared and a draft of a complete text had been written. Although much still needed to be done, before the work could be readied for publication, it was clear that it would have been a scientific crime not to bring the extremely valuable results of Dr. Peyer's labors to fruition. Serious consultations were held as to how this might be accomplished. It was finally decided that the work be published in English, and the University of Chicago Press agreed to its publication.

Preparation of the volume for publication was undertaken by Dr. Rainer Zangerl. This task was a heavy one. The original manuscript was in German and the necessary translation of a technical work of this sort is difficult and time-consuming. Further, much of the manuscript was still in the form of a provisional draft, particularly with regard to the section on mammals, and throughout there was need of addition of new data regarding work which had not been published at the time when the various sections were written—for example, the development of the lepidomorial theory by the Stockholm school and Edmund's work on the mode of tooth replacement in lower tetrapods. All this has been done by Dr. Zangerl, taking care to produce a minimal amount of distortion of Dr. Peyer's original text. Those of us interested in the history of the dentition owe a debt of gratitude not only to Dr. Peyer but also to Dr. Zangerl for his labors in the production of this volume—labors undertaken in part, to be sure, purely in the interests of science, but in part also because of the affection (shared by many of us) which he felt for Dr. Peyer—a wonderfully fine person as well as an able scientist.

[1] Zangerl, Rainer, 1963. *Bernhard Peyer, 1885–1963.* News Bulletin, Society of Vertebrate Paleontology, No. 68, June 1963.

I think one may be justified in claiming that the publication of the present work is in many ways the most important landmark in the study of dental history since the publication of Sir Richard Owen's *Odontography* in 1845. During the century and more that has elapsed there have appeared several works on teeth which have treated odontography on a comparative basis. These, however, have been mainly concerned with mammalian dentitions, and have paid relatively little attention to lower vertebrates or to the fossil record. The present volume is unique in its broad coverage of the sweep of dental history, with much of an original nature as concerns the lower classes of vertebrates and fossil history.

ALFRED S. ROMER

Preface

The present work intends to provide a broad view of what is known of the teeth and dentitions of vertebrates, but it also embodies a great deal of original research by its author on the histology and histogenesis of the dental tissues. These are especially fascinating in the fishes and deserve more extensive treatment than is usually accorded them in books on dental morphology.

In translating the text of Professor Peyer's manuscript, I have taken care to retain, as much as possible, the flavor of the original. Since the work was not in final, publishable form throughout, I have added supplemental notes of material that seemed pertinent to me. For the most part, however, I confined my contribution to the mere addition of references to recent literature in order not to distort the overall concept of the work. In view of the fact that neither the translation nor my additions and editorial changes could benefit from scrutiny by the author, I must stand responsible for all shortcomings, though I claim credit for none of the merits.

The author meant, of course, to provide the manuscript with a foreword and to express his appreciation to the many persons who had been helpful in one way or another. He saved this for last, and it remained unwritten. This list would no doubt have included his old friend Professor Eberhard Ackerknecht, Dr. Rolf Schweizer, Murrhardt, Germany who served as assistant and made a large number of superb microscopic preparations, and Mr. Albert Mahler, Graphic Designer at the Faculty of Veterinary Science of the University of Zürich, who made the outstanding photomicrographs that are reproduced in the plates. Furthermore, many of Professor Peyer's colleagues and friends who provided him with study materials in Europe and North America would have been included.

My own thanks go to my colleagues at Field Museum of Natural History, Dr. Robert H. Denison and Mr. William D. Turnbull, for critically reading the translation; to Dr. Eugene S. Richardson, Jr., for his help with some illustrations; and to my secretary, Mrs. Winifred Reinders, for her efforts with the manuscript.

In Professor Peyer's name I wish to thank the many publishers and authors who permitted the reproduction of illustrations from their works.

Finally, many thanks are due to my wife, Ann, who patiently endured a year of "evening-absenteeism" spent in translating the text, and who helped me in proofreading the manuscript.

RAINER ZANGERL

Contents

Comparative
Odontology

Historical review

The development of odontology parallels—but to a limited extent—the history of dentistry, which has been comprehensively documented in the great works on the history of medicine. From these we learn that the treatment of diseases of the teeth gradually passed from the hands of market salesmen and bath house operators organized in guilds to those of dentists and became a science, which developed more or less closely with medicine. The history of this process is interesting in our survey only insofar as dentists have contributed to furthering our knowledge of teeth and dentition in general. Associated with the progress in odontological knowledge are also human anatomists, veterinary anatomists, comparative anatomists, zoologists, and paleontologists.

The body of information from the dawn of the oldest cultures is naturally skimpy.

In Chinese medicine, fossil bones and teeth are even today being ground to powder and used as therapeutics. This practice, however, has not resulted in more accurate knowledge of the different teeth, because the emphasis was directed solely toward their therapeutic value. Modern Chinese paleontology, on the other hand, although a young science in that country, has already made notable contributions.

The voluminous survival of written material of the old cultures of Mesopotamia can hardly be expected to contain special information concerning odontological knowledge.

In old Egypt, the circumstance that bodies not only of man, but of animals, were being embalmed might have led to a greater interest in the differences between their dentitions. This was, however, probably not the case; at any rate there is no evidence of a comparative study of the dentition in vertebrates.

Medicine in ancient India was, so far as known, not anatomically oriented, and could therefore not give rise to a morphological and comparative odontology.

The food prescriptions of the Old Testament emphasize, to be sure,

1

the particular character of the ruminant dentition, but they do not reach beyond the most general kind of information.

The first beginnings of an odontology not restricted to man is found among the old Greeks. Odontological information in the biological writings of Aristotle is mixed with errors, part of these originating in portions of the large work that have been added later; for example, a passage from Book VII of the *Animal History,* that states: "Furthermore, the animals are born with teeth, but in children the teeth begin to appear not before the seventh month. The teeth appear, however, all the faster, the warmer the milk of the wet nurses." Other errors might go back to Aristotle himself. Excellent, on the other hand, are the comparative considerations concerning the dentition. The section on teeth in the first chapter of the second book of the *Animal History* states: "Animals differ amongst themselves and from man also in many ways as regards their teeth. Provided with teeth are all blood-carrying and live-bearing four-footed animals, and these may or may not have complete tooth rows in both jaws. All horn-bearing animals, particularly, do not have complete tooth rows in both jaws, because the anterior teeth of the upper jaw are absent. But there are also a few with incomplete tooth rows that lack horns, such as the camel. Many have tusks, such as the boar, others do not. Furthermore, there are animals with carnassials, as the lion, panther and the dog. Carnassial teeth occur in those animals in which the pointed teeth of both jaws fit next to each other; in others, however, they do not overlap, as in the horse and cow. Tusks and horns together occur in no animal, and neither is there an animal with carnassials that possesses at the same time one of those two parts.

"In most animals, the anterior teeth are pointed, the posterior ones broad. In the seal, all teeth are carnassials whereby they approach, so to speak, the fishes, of which almost all have carnassials. None of the kinds of animals has double rows of teeth." (Cited after the German translation of H. Aubert and Fr. Wimmer, 1868.)

Regarding the replacement of teeth, Aristotle offers besides correct notes also incorrect ones, but states that further investigations are necessary with respect to these matters in the dog. The passage "In men, sheep, goats, and pigs the males have more teeth than the females" might possibly be genuine because the remark follows: "For the other animals no observations concerning this are as yet available."

Under Theophrastus, the successor of Aristotle in the direction of the peripatetic school, observation was probably cultivated more avidly than before, but we do not know what effects this had in the field of zoology. When, among the Ptolemaeans and later among the Romans, Alexandria became the center of learning and education, other disciplines were in the foreground of interest.

Some insight into the stature of Roman medicine and natural sciences just prior to and just after the birth of Christ may be gained from Celsus and from the elder Pliny. Neither was a professional scientist: Celsus was not a practicing physician, but a medical writer; and Pliny not a scientist, but a high Roman official who excerpted from a large amount of literature what seemed to him worthwhile for the officials of the state. In the matter of information regarding palliative remedies for toothaches, Pliny is nearly inexhaustible; but there is virtually no description of the teeth of man or animals.

While the Greek and Greco-Roman schools of medicine of late antiquity fought one another vehemently on the grounds of a variety of broad biological concepts, one of the most outstanding physicians of antiquity, Galen (A.D. 131–about 201), devoted himself, in addition to theoretical discussions, to extensive anatomical studies, primarily on the monkey *Macaca ecaudatus,* at that time still rather common in North Africa, and occasionally also on human bodies, for example, of highway robbers that had been beaten to death. With Galen the anatomy of antiquity reached the zenith.

The Middle Ages produced no progress in the fields of medicine and the natural sciences. But at least some of the works on natural sciences and medicine of Greek antiquity were retained, partly in the form of translations into Arabic, partly in the form of manuscripts that were produced in cloisters.

With the beginning of modern time, the most significant works were rapidly distributed all over Europe at the end of the fifteenth and the beginning of the sixteenth centuries as a result of the newly developed art of book printing, among them also the biological works of Aristotle. Under the influence of a new generation of scientists, the inherited body of knowledge experienced a change; it became the modern European medicine and biology.

Odontology assumes therein an almost infinitesimal space, although occasional odontological information is already contained in such large zoological encyclopaedias as the one by Conrad Gesner. Figure 1 shows that Gesner did not merely compile information, but that he clearly recognized, despite the small dimensions of the objects, the differences in the dentition of an insectivore and that of a small rodent.

From the beginning of the sixteenth until nearly the end of the eighteenth

FIG. 1.—Dentitions of a mouse and a shrew. From Conrad Gesner's *Historia animalium* (Zürich, 1551). The example shows that Gesner conducted not only complicated but careful investigations. From the Latin text it is apparent that he described a species of *Sorex*.

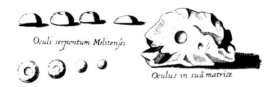

FIG. 2.—"Snake eyes" from Malta; in reality fossil pavement teeth of the fish genus *Sparus*, sometimes worn in finger rings as protection against poisoning. After Tudecius de Monte Galea (1680), from Peyer, *Geschichte der Tierwelt* (Zürich: Büchergilde Gutenberg 1950, by permission.

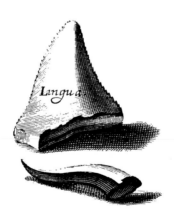

FIG. 3.—"Tongue stones" (glossopetri), in reality fossil shark teeth. After Tudecius de Monte Galea (1680), from Peyer, *Geschichte der Tierwelt* (Zürich: Büchergilde Gutenberg 1950), by permission.

century, it is not possible to speak of odontological research carried on in its own right. However, systematically conducted anatomical investigations, such as were carried out particularly in the second half of the seventeenth century in different cities by study groups involving many physicians and other interested persons, led also to an increase of odontological knowledge. Advances enjoyed by the whole field of biology naturally also affected odontology.

Among the newly founded academies, some furthered primarily the natural sciences. Their periodically issued publications contributed very significantly to the distribution of new discoveries. It is particularly to their credit that the discussions assumed international character and that a European standard of knowledge gradually developed in many fields. Among professionals it became possible to take this standard of knowledge for granted. In the early numbers of the periodical of the Leopoldinian Academy, the *Ephemerides naturae curiosorum,* for example, a certain quasi-science is still notably apparent that permitted recognition, with deep emotion, in accidental shapes of plant parts or crystal vugs, the image of the Savior, the Virgin Mary, or the imperial eagle, etc. When such locally highly prestigious views were subjected to the criticism of a broader public, interested in the natural sciences, they became soon untenable.

The differences of opinion concerning the character of fossils continued from Leonardo da Vinci and Bernard Palissy until late in the seventeenth century. Fossil shark teeth, common in Tertiary rocks, played here an important role. Some considered them as accidental natural shapes, curios, and called them "tongue stones" or—in learned terms—*glossopetri;* others, notably Fabio Colonna in Rome and Girolamo Frascastoro in Padua, insisted persuasively that these objects were the remains of sharks that actually had lived in the past.

In connection with the final chapter of the Acts of the Apostles, fossil teeth of the fish *Sparus (Chrysophrys)* on the Isle of Malta, thought to be fossil snake eyes, gained the reputation of being useful antidotes against poisonings of all kinds; this conviction was transferred also to the shark teeth that were found associated with them (Figs. 2 and 3).

The curio-of-nature theory was decisively overcome by Nicolaus Steno who, with his anatomical studies on sharks, concerned himself with the problem of the character of fossils and became thereby one of the founders of mineralogy, structural geology and stratigraphy. Figure 4 is taken from a paper by Steno from the year 1667, in which he described the head of a large shark, *Carcharodon carcharias,* captured near Livorno. Of odontological interest here is Steno's observation that the young replacement teeth are still soft.

Improved implements of investigation, especially optical instruments, and the gathering of collections (beyond the level of the curio cabinet), were important factors in the advancement of biological knowledge.

The growth of zoological systematics finally required closer attention to the dentition. While it is true that there are no notable odontological studies from the seventeenth and eighteenth centuries, there nevertheless were some excellent individual achievements, of which a few may be mentioned. In the *Philosophical Tranactions* for 1784, W. André published the figure of the dentition of a shark, probably *Galeocerdo,* here shown on Plate 1-a. This illustration has been reproduced by R. Owen (1840–45) in his *Odontography,* and again by J. H. Mummery (1924, p. 448, Fig. 225). The specimen is interesting because, in a cross row of teeth, the functional tooth and three following replacement teeth have been completely divided into two portions. A spine of the stingray *Dasyatis* that caused this injury is stuck fast in the jaw. It is, however, much too small seriously to have injured the functional tooth. Only a single tooth anlage was affected by the implacement of the spine. All succeeding anlagen of replacement teeth as they advanced toward their position of function were in succession divided by the implaced spine because they could not bypass it.[1] Also notable is the illustration of a tusk of a newborn Indian elephant (Pl. 2-a), published by J. Corse in 1799. It shows that the tooth is formed in the premaxilla and that it must thus be considered, Goethe's views notwithstanding, as an incisor tooth.

Toward the end of the eighteenth and at the beginning of the nineteenth century, Paris was the most outstanding center of research in the natural sciences and particularly in zoology. The large monographs of entire animal classes that originated there in this period, for example, those of fishes and mammals, brought an advance in the amount of all kinds of factual information, and of course also in odontological information. The increasing attention paid to the fossil vertebrates in research stimulated greater interest in the structural relationships of the teeth, as attested by the "Recherches sur les Poissons fossiles" by Louis Agassiz, issued from 1833 to 1844 in Neuchâtel.

In contrast to the fully differentiated hard substances that could be investigated easily in ground thin-sections, the study of developmental processes in teeth still presented very great difficulties, because the technical equipment of that time was far from adequate for the purpose. For these

---

[1] Injuries to the dentition in larger sharks and rays by *Dasyatis*-spines appear to be none too rare. Thus there were in the jaw of a specimen of *Rhina* (*Rhynchobatus*) no less than three spines of dasyatids. Probably such injuries occur when sharks or rays glide closely above the bottom and thereby disturb the stingrays.

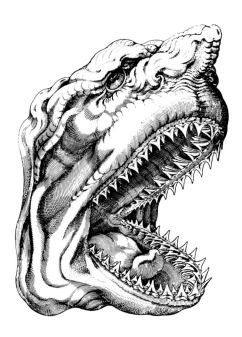

Fig. 4.—Head of a large shark. After Michele Mercati (1717); previously published 1667 by Nicolaus Steno, from Peyer, *Geschichte der Tierwelt* (Zürich: Büchergilde Gutenberg, 1950), by permission.

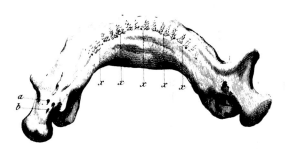

Fig. 5.—Tooth development in man according to the interpretation of Augustin Serres (Paris, 1817). While the structure of tooth hard substances based on ground thin-sections was already fairly well known in the first third of the last century, the state of the science of histology and the inadequacy of its investigative equipment did not yet permit a clear understanding of the developmental processes.

reasons, even leading scientists such as A. Serres in France and John Good-sir in England could not arrive at clear conceptions about tooth development (see Fig. 5).

The most significant event in the history of biology during the first half of the nineteenth century is the advent of the cell theory. Its application to odontology was advanced by Johannes Müller and by J. E. Purkinji, and later by A. Kölliker. Richard Owen's *Odontography* appeared between 1840 and 1845 in London. This masterful work has remained, for more than a hundred years, an indispensable aid to research, thanks to the wealth of excellent illustrations and the uniformly solid presentation of this large subject. It is noteworthy that Owen included in his investigation the fossil vertebrates that were known at that time.

With the publication of Darwin's *The Origin of Species* (1859), there began a period of lively, speculative discussion that also produced valuable comparative and ontogenetic investigations in odontology. For the elasmo-branchs, the sharks and their relatives, Oscar Hertwig could show that skin denticles (shagreen) are homologous to the teeth of the dentition.

During the nineteenth century another development of great significance was the addition of dental schools to the medical faculties. With this change, a large portion of the odontological research was taken over by professors of dentistry.

The development of veterinary medicine led in many universities to the creation of separate faculties for this discipline also. Veterinary anatomists have contributed richly to the advance of odontology by many studies. For a long time, physical anthropologists have also been concerned with de-tailed investigations of the human dentition and that of the modern and fossil primates.

Among other technical advances, including the perfection of selective staining methods and the microtome technique, we might also mention the method of plate model reconstruction. The latter had proved of very great value in the study of the embryology of the vertebrates, and was also used with particularly great success by C. Röse in odontological research.

An extremely useful tool for the practical demonstration of enamel in the teeth of many fishes, as well as for the demonstration of the fabric structure of mineralized hard substances in vertebrates generally, is microscopy in polarized light (Schmidt and Keil, 1958). X-ray pictures, today an indispensable diagnostic aid in dentistry, are used also for anatomical, ontogenetic and paleontological investigations. Teeth and other hard substances are now being investigated by microradiographic and auto-radiographic techniques also, as well as by the electron microscope.

Introduction

The word "tooth" (German "Zahn," French "dent," Italian "dènte") is used in English, as in other languages, in a variety of meanings. For example, it is understood to denote not only one of the hard structures in the mouth cavity that aid mastication of food but also the tooth of a gear or of a saw blade. In osteology, one speaks of an odontoid process of the second neck vertebra. The botanist speaks of denticulate leaves. There is a Dent Blanche, a Dent du Midi, and in the Tessin of Switzerland the Denti della Vecchia. Finally, there is in German "der Zahn der Zeit" ("tooth of time"), whose form relationships can hardly be defined precisely.

The derived meanings of the term "tooth" usually relate to function rather than to form. The original objects of reference were obviously not the teeth of the human dentition but the canine teeth of carnivores or those in the mouth of a crocodile or a pike. In this derived, purely formal sense, "tooth" means merely a conical or pyramidal elevation regardless of its substance. Originally, the word probably referred to those individual elements of the human dentition that produce discomfort in early youth as they erupt, that may make themselves disagreeably known in later years when injured or diseased, and that may eventually be lost in old age. Early man's observation of other animals probably led him to see a generally similar function of his own teeth and those of mammals in general.

In many invertebrates, the mouth is provided with hard parts that function as feeding structures—for example, the teeth of the radulas of many molluscs or certain parts of the biting mechanism of many sea urchins; these are also referred to as teeth.

These structures are, however, so different from the teeth of the vertebrates in their mode of development and in the structural material of which they are composed that it seems preferable to restrict the present treatment to the vertebrates. Comprehensive presentation of tooth structures throughout the entire animal kingdom could only be justified from a functional point of view.

Even among vertebrates there are two types of teeth, differing in their mode of development and composition: on the one hand the horny teeth of the cyclostomes (see p. 29) and of the anuran larvae (see p. 126) ; on the other, the teeth of all other vertebrates. These horny teeth originate within the ectoderm, and consist, as suggested by their name, of a hornlike substance. In the formation of all other teeth in vertebrates, both the ectoderm and the mesoderm are involved (see p. 19). The teeth in most vertebrates consist primarily of dentine often, but not always, covered by a layer of enamel. Especially among higher vertebrates, tooth cementum may also participate in the formation of teeth. Because dentine is always present, the anatomist Wilhelm von Waldeyer proposed the term "dentine teeth" (Waldeyer, 1871).

Such dentine teeth are found in modern sharks, rays, and skates and in certain fossil forms, not only within the mouth cavity but also attached to the entire skin. Because the mouth cavity represents, ontogenetically, an invagination of the external body skin—called stomodaeum (Fig. 6) —it is understandable that we find dentine denticles also in the epithelial covering of the mouth cavity much as in the rest of the integument. In part these dentine denticles retained their original character in sharks, rays, and skates as mucous membrane denticles; in part they established firm support on the underlying skeleton and thus gained a higher functional significance in feeding and became dentition teeth (Pl. 1-b). Skin denticles and dentition teeth correspond in their mode of development and in their composition to such an extent that they must be considered homologous structures. According to the different functions they perform, these denticles have become differentiated in various ways in the course of their phylogenetic history. Here we shall consider primarily the dentition teeth, the dermal denticles (of sharks), and the mucous membrane denticles of the mouth cavity.

Terminology

The first odontological investigations were devoted to the study of the dentition of man. Precise technical terms for the exact description of the human teeth were introduced by anatomists and dentists. These terms are also accurate for many mammals. But if investigation is extended to include the teeth of the lower vertebrates, it soon becomes apparent that the special terminology applicable to human conditions is inadequate and requires certain modifications and additions.

Morphology of human and mammalian teeth

As seen in Figures 7 and 8, it is possible to distinguish, in mammalian teeth, a crown, a neck, and a root. The tooth is composed of three different

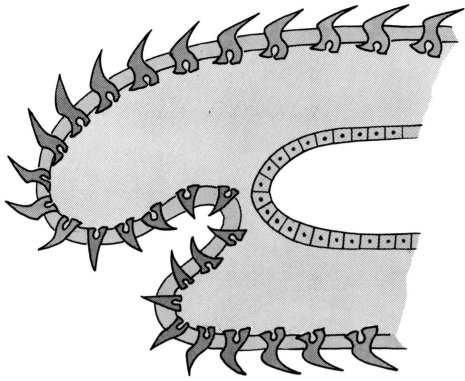

Fig. 6.—Stomodaeum and throat membrane (schematic). In early developmental stages the mouth cavity is merely an invaginated portion of the body surface; the intestinal tube is still closed at its anterior end. The two cavities become connected only after the rupture of the dividing partition, the so-called throat membrane. The outer skin of the sharks is set with skin denticles. Therefore, the portion of the skin that lines the stomodaeum is likewise equipped with denticles, from which there originate the mucous membrane denticles and the teeth of the dentition in the mouth cavity.

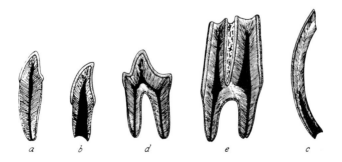

Fig. 7.—Vertical sections through different mammalian teeth. Pulp cavity, black; dentine, narrow crosshatching; enamel wide crosshatching; cementum, dotted: *a*, fully grown incisor tooth whose pulp cavity has become a narrow canal; *b*, incisor tooth in process of development with wide-open pulp cavity; *c*, incisor tooth of a rodent, covered with enamel only on its forward side and with persistent pulp cavity; *d*, double-rooted cheek tooth of man with broad, low crown; *e*, cheek tooth of an ox, with high crown and deep enamel folds whose interstitial spaces are filled with cementum; enamel cover on surface worn off. From Zittel, *Grundzüge der Paläontologie* (Munich and Berlin: Verlag R. Oldenbourg, 1923), by permission.

hard substances: enamel (*Glasurschicht, émail, substantia adamantina*), dentine (*Zahnbein, dentin, substantia eburnea*), and the tooth cementum (*caementum, substantia ossea*). The principal mass of the tooth is made up of the dentine, which surrounds the pulp cavity (*cavum dentis*) filled with a tissue rich in blood vessels and nerves. Basally, the pulp cavity narrows and forms the root canal. Its opening is called *foramen apicis (radicis) dentis*. Over the crown and the neck, the dentine is covered by a layer of enamel; the root is encrusted with tooth cementum. The structure and development of these three substances will be considered later.

According to form, position, and other criteria to be mentioned later, one can distinguish incisors, canines, and premolars and molars (the cheek teeth). The incisors in most mammals are chisel-shaped; in man the canines are simple cone-shaped. The human premolars possess two tubercles and are therefore also called bicuspids; the second lower premolar may have three tubercles. The molars are variably multituberculate. The roots of the incisors and the canines are simple. The premolars may have simple or more or less divided roots. The number of roots of human molars (and the mode of their differentiation) is not constant.

Comparison with other vertebrate teeth

If we compare the teeth of man with those of other mammals—for example, with the molars of the horse, cow (see pp. 255 and 268), or elephant (p. 283)—we can see that the molars of man, with their small number of simple tubercles, are much less complicated in construction. This brief suggestion may suffice for the present, because the many differences among mammalian molars will be discussed in a later chapter. Here I shall compare the mammalian teeth with those of other vertebrates—for example, with those of the reptiles. Thus we may note that to distinguish a tooth crown, neck, and root is possible only if the pulp cavity is narrowed basally to form a root canal (Fig. 8). This is typically true only in mammals, but not in all instances. In mammalian teeth that continue growing throughout life, the pulp cavity remains open at the base—as, for example, in the incisors of rodents and in the tusks of the boar. Even in molar teeth of certain mammals, root formation may either begin very late in life and remain incomplete or be entirely suppressed. Such teeth are known as "open-rooted" or teeth with continuous growth (Fig. 7).

In reptiles, amphibians, and fishes, the pulp cavity is generally open at the base, both in the fully differentiated tooth and in the ontogenetic tooth anlage (Fig. 8). If in exceptional instances a narrowing or a near closure of the pulp cavity occurs at the base, such narrowing is not, as in mammals, accompanied by a decrease in the transverse diameter of the tooth; instead,

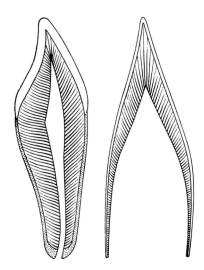

Fig. 8.—Section through human incisor with basally narrowed pulp cavity (root canal) and reptile tooth (schematic) with basally wide-open pulp cavity. From Peyer, *Die Zähne,* Verständliche Wissenschaft, vol. 79 (Berlin: Springer Verlag, 1963) , by permission.

the tooth is broadest in this basal area, as in the teeth of sharks. Narrowing of the basal part of the pulp cavity usually takes place differently.

In contrast to the crown, which is usually enamel-covered, the root of the mammalian tooth is surrounded by cementum. This hard substance, *substantia ossea,* is a form of bone (Fig. 8) . Cementum is absent in the teeth of many lower vertebrates.

Crown, neck, and root of a tooth cannot be distinguished outside the mammals; the differentiation of these three tooth regions is the result of the special way mammalian teeth are attached to the jaw—gomphosis, that is, anchoring in an alveolus: the tooth is attached to the jaw by one or several roots in such a way that the bone substance of the jaw fits closely around the roots (Pl. 2-b). Between cementum layer and wall of the alveolus there is an alveolar-dental membrane, also called the periodontium.

The crown of a mammalian tooth is not covered by the gingiva. In non-mammals, the size of the crown is not limited, because the tooth may be surrounded in varying extent by the mucous membrane of the mouth.

Clinically, the neck of the tooth is of great significance. In man, it is the narrow zone that borders the gingiva, and is also the boundary between the enamel cap of the crown and the cementum that covers the dentine of the root (Pl. 2-b) . The term "neck" applies only if the diameter of this area is smaller than that of the crown. [Thus the term does not always apply even among mammals.] In non-mammals, the tooth does not have a neck.

One may speak of a root only if the pulp cavity is basally narrowed to form a root canal and if the dentine of the part of the tooth that is embedded in the jawbone is covered by cementum. This structure occurs, at least among the living vertebrates, only in the mammals. To be sure, there are also forms among non-mammals in which the teeth are fixed in sockets of the jaw bones—as, for example, in many reptiles; in these instances, however, the pulp cavity usually reaches its greatest width at the opening, and the relationships of the tooth surface to the bony wall of the pit are usually somewhat different from those in mammals. The term "root" should be used only if conditions are similar to those in man. In most non-mammals, these relationships are very different from those in mammals, and the expression "basal portion" or "base" is to be preferred; "pedestal" should be restricted to instances in which the tooth rests on a bony projection, as in many amphibians.

Tooth attachment in non-mammals

Although the teeth of all mammals are anchored in alveoli of the jaws, many kinds of attachment occur in other vertebrates. If the teeth are in more or less deep pits that typically do not become narrower at the bottom, the condition is thecodont; if the pits are very shallow, prothecodont. In other instances, the teeth are on the surface of, and may fuse with, the jawbone (Fig. 9). Thus acrodont and pleurodont forms of attachment can be distinguished in reptiles. In a pleurodont dentition, the teeth are attached to the inner faces of the jaws; in an acrodont dentition, to the edges.

In primitive reptiles and amphibians, and in many fishes, nearly all bones that form the walls of the mouth cavity may be provided with teeth that rest flat on the bones. If the teeth are small, more or less rounded tubercles, the dentition is sometimes called shagreen. In contrast to the condition in mammals, the teeth in many reptiles, amphibians, and fish are firmly attached, by bone tissue, to the bones. This bone tissue may be distinguished from the tissue of the bony plates proper by the fact that it is resorbed whenever a tooth is shed. For the replacement tooth it is formed anew. This bone tissue, which is continually subjected to alternate destruction and renewal, may be remarkably extensive. Ch. S. Tomes was the first to recognize the wide distribution of such processes. He proposed for this type of bone the term "attachment bone," which I shall use in the following discussion. In rare instances, the large teeth of predatory fishes are not rigidly attached to the jaws but are jointed and may be tilted backward.

In the Chondrichthyes—the sharks and their relatives—the skeleton contains no bone;[1] instead, it consists of cartilage that may be strengthened

---

[1] Bonelike tissues and tissues indistinguishable from bone have been reported in modern sharks by Wurmbach (1932) and by Stephan (1900) in *Chimaera*. Real bone has recently been

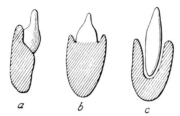

a   *b*   *c*

Fig. 9.—Cross-sections through tooth-bearing jaws for the schematic representation of the different modes of tooth attachment: *a,* pleurodont; *b,* acrodont; *c,* thecodont. After Wiedersheim, from Peyer (1937), in Bolk-Göppert-Kallius-Lubosch, *Handbuch der Vergleichenden Anatomie der Wirbeltiere* (Vienna and Berlin: Verlag Urban & Schwarzenberg, (1931–39), by permission.

by calcification. Accordingly, the attachment of the teeth is different. The teeth are anchored by a tough layer of connective tissue that covers the cartilaginous elements of the jaws. I have never found any evidence of resorption in shark teeth that had been used and shed.

Topographic terminology of individual teeth

In man, the tooth row describes an arc in each jaw (Fig. 10). Accordingly, the outer surfaces of the anterior teeth, toward the lips, face forward; the corresponding surfaces of the teeth behind the canines, toward the cheeks, face laterad. The inner surfaces of all the teeth face the tongue and are thus called "lingual" surfaces in all vertebrates, regardless of whether a fleshy tongue is present. To consider comparatively all vertebrate teeth, a generally acceptable term is needed also for the external tooth surfaces, regardless of the specific shape of the mouth. I shall use the term "labial" (from *labium,* "lip"), even though true lips are not universally present in vertebrates. The term "buccal" (from *bucca,* "cheek") will be restricted here to conditions in mammals; the term "vestibular" is often used in the literature as a synonym of "buccal."

In man, the anterior teeth have medial and lateral neighbors; those behind the canines have anterior and posterior neighbors. The vertical surfaces of two adjacent teeth that face one another are called contact surfaces (*facies contactus*). Dentists usually call the surface of a tooth that faces mediad in an incisor but anteriorly in a cheek tooth, the mesial contact surface; the one opposite it facing laterad in front and posteriorly in the cheek region is known as the distal surface. The terms "mesial" and "distal"

discovered in the form of a partial armor in the skull of a Pennsylvania shark of the family Edestidae (Zangerl, 1966). The bases of complex scales of Permian edestid sharks are said by Ørvig (1951) and Stensiö (1961, 1962) to consist of bone. Unpublished material at my disposal suggests, however, that the matter requires further study.—Translator

Fɪɢ. 10.—The meaning to the terms "labial," "lingual," "mesial" and "distal" explained with the example of the human upper dentition.

will be generally used in the following discussion, not merely for teeth that contact each other but also for teeth that stand isolated.

The objection has been raised that the expression "distal" is used differently in comparative anatomy. For this reason, Ch. S. Tomes (1923, p. 6), used the designation "distal" for the contact surface that in human incisor teeth faces mediad, in the post-canine teeth anteriorly. This usage, however, did not prevail over the established clinical practice of the term "distal."

The chewing surface (*facies masticatoria*) is the surface of the human and mammalian crown that comes into contact with an antagonist. Such a sharply definable crown surface occurs only in mammals and a few extinct reptiles, because only in these forms do upper and lower teeth meet in precise occlusion. In the greatly varied types of dentition found among all the other vertebrates (except in a few isolated instances that will be discussed later) nearly the entire crown comes into action. Thus upper and lower teeth often far removed from one another may act together in a meaningful way.

Jaw action

Differences in feeding habits led not merely to the evolution of different tooth forms but required a variety of types of jaw action and special forms of articular joints. These differences are most noticeable among mammals.

The simplest jaw movement, a mere opening and closing of the lower jaw, is called ginglymic (from *ginglymus*, "hinge joint") or orthal. In the corresponding joint the articular head of the mandible consists of a cylinder, moving in a conforming joint cavity, whose long axis is at a right angle to the longitudinal axis of the skull. Examples of this kind of jaw movement are found among the carnivores, most strikingly in the badger. Recent investigations of chewing motions in carnivores have revealed that slight lateral movements of the mandible are not only possible but are an important factor in the chewing act (Scapino, 1965).

In rodents, the mandible describes primarily an antero-posterior motion, called propalinal. The joint head is laterally compressed and fits into a longitudinal groove. In the rather complicated jaw motions of ruminants and horses, a lateral movement, called ental-ectal plays the major role.

The joint of the lower jaw of the mammals is not homologous to that of the non-mammals. The lower jaw in non-mammals does not bear a joint head but rather a joint cavity. Among reptiles, a variety of jaw mechanisms corresponds to the variously constructed temporal region of the skull. The jaw motion in amphibians is ginglymic. The construction of the fish skull is determined mainly by the requirements of gill breathing, which affects the differentiation of the visceral skeleton that in turn serves as firm basis for tooth attachment (Fig. 20). This results in certain peculiarities common to all fishes. But the detailed morphology of the mouth parts and their action is so greatly varied that to characterize them requires several separate presentations.

Tooth categories

In the dentition of man and of most mammals, we can distinguish a number of tooth categories—incisors, canines, premolars, molars. Dentitions of this sort are heterodont, in contrast to the homodont dentition which, as in the dolphin, consists uniformly of teeth of similar shape. Great differences among the teeth of a single dentition, such as occur in mammals, are not observed outside this class. But differences of form of individual teeth of a dentition are nevertheless remarkable in certain reptiles and fishes. A sharp distinction betweeen homodont and heterodont dentitions is not possible.

Distribution of tooth-covered area of mouth

The distribution of the tooth-covered area shows vast differences among vertebrates. In the mammals and in certain reptiles the dentition is restricted to the edges of the jaws. In other reptiles and amphibians, especially among the ancient, extinct forms, nearly all bones that take part in the formation of the mouth cavity may be covered with teeth. The tooth-covered area of the mouth may be even more extensive in fishes, where the posterior visceral arches, which support the respiratory membrane, serve respiration and often simultaneously also feeding. They border the throat cavity. Because of this position, the mucous membrane teeth of the posterior mouth-throat cavity could find places of attachment on the skeleton, and could evolve into powerful pharyngeal teeth.

Tooth generations

Man has two succeeding generations of teeth, the milk teeth (lactating dentition) and the permanent teeth (permanent dentition). His dentition is thus *diphyodont* (Pl. 3-a). Most mammals are also diphyodont. In some cases one of these tooth generations may become more or less suppressed in that the milk teeth fail to reach functional state and are being resorbed even prior to birth. This evolutionary trend results ultimately in *monophyodonty*. Despite the fact that the permanent molars appear much later than the milk teeth, it is not *a priori* clear to which tooth generation they belong, because the question arises: are they permanent teeth not preceeded by milk teeth, or are they belated milk teeth that have no permanent successors? In the prevailing view they belong to the lacteal dentition. In the marsupials only a single premolar is being changed. The question of the relationship of the dentition of the marsupials to that of the higher mammals is still under debate.

Reptiles, amphibians and fishes have, as a rule, not merely one or two tooth generations, but many. They are *polyphyodont*. In reptiles and amphibians a replacement tooth in advanced state of differentiation is found on the lingual side of the functional tooth; even further linguad, there is an anlage of the tooth that will replace the replacement tooth. Still greater is the number of simultaneously present replacement teeth in the "revolver" dentition of the sharks (Pl. 3-b). Since the replacement tooth is at the lingual side of the functional tooth, it and the replacement teeth that follow it form a row extending crosswise over the edge of the jaw (Pl. 3-b).

For the designation of such a row we shall use, in addition to the expression "cross row," the term "tooth-family" as proposed by L. Bolk (1913–

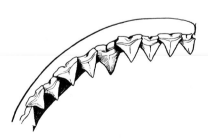

Fig. 11.—Section of the tooth row of the shark *Carcharhinus* in outside view. The teeth alternately stand a little farther outward and inward. The alternation is not perfectly regular, however. 1:22. After Landolt (1947).

1919). The functional teeth occupying the edge of the jaw form a longitudinal row. In many cases, for example in certain reptiles and in selachians, the individual teeth of such a longitudinal row are not perfectly aligned in a straight line or a bowline, but assume alternately a more labial and more lingual position (Fig. 11). These positional relationships in connection with the so-called concentration hypophysis formed the basis of L. Bolk's broad speculative theory that will be briefly mentioned in a later chapter (p. 184).

Histogenesis and histology of the teeth

Even a superficial survey of the teeth in vertebrates shows the presence of notable structural and histogenetic differences, but because emphasis of differences risks neglecting features that apply to all dentine teeth, a brief characterization of their common aspects will precede systematic presentation.

In all dentine teeth the place of origin and the earliest stages of tooth formation are the same. This was already noted by Oscar Hertwig (1874). Tooth formation always takes place at the boundary of ectoderm and mesoderm. Although bone may be formed far from any ectoderm, teeth originate only in this boundary zone. It applies also for the teeth of man and the mammals, whose early anlagen are deeply buried in the jaws; sections show readily that the ectoderm involved in the formation of the tooth has grown into the depth of the jaw. Thus mammalian teeth likewise originate at the boundary of ectoderm and mesoderm. In an inclusive presentation of tooth formation in all vertebrates, this topographic complication that has taken place in mammals may be ignored at this point, since more primitive tooth structures such as the denticles of the integument and the mucous membrane denticles of the mouth cavity of elasmobranchs, the pharyngeal teeth of osteichthyes, and, as Röse (1893) has shown, the first tooth generation in crocodiles, all originate superficially.

In early embryonic stages there are no indications of the impending formation of teeth. The basal layer of the epidermis, the *stratum Malpighii*, is multilayered in vertebrates in contrast to all invertebrates. The mesodermal portion of the integument derived from the somatopleura lies immediately beneath the epidermis, separated from it only by the basal membrane *(membrana propria)*. While the mainly morphologically oriented research of the latter part of the nineteenth and the early part of the twentieth century investigated these relationships and the morphology of the ontogenetic history, the problems of experimental zoology more recently concern primarily physiological events. The results of these experiments led, convincingly, to a loosening of the dogma of germ layer specificity; that is, of the idea that a given tissue can originate only from a specific germ layer. Especially with respect to the formational tissues of the tooth hard substances, it was demonstrated that the cell material of the mesodermal tooth papilla may originate as so-called mesectoderm from the neural crest, and furthermore that enamel-forming cells may descend not only from the ectoderm, but also from the entoderm (De Beer, 1947).

Experiments designed with precisely thought-out problems and with high levels of technical refinement enable investigation of the influence exerted by different parts of organs or tissues on one another during different phases of development. In odontology the so-called tooth chimeras are particularly interesting. They are produced by xenoplastic transplantation, that is by transposition of specific germ material of a donor to an approximately equally developed stage of a host animal that belongs to a different genus, family or even order.

Thus G. Wagner (1955) obtained such chimerical tooth anlagen by transplantation of material from the neural crest of *Bombina pachypus* to *Triton alpestris* (Pl. 3-c). These experiments showed that the *Bombina* implant brings about the formation of *Bombina*-like mesectodermal tooth papillae and tooth "shards" ("Zahnscherbchen") consisting of predentine in the *Triton* host.

In the following, the expressions "ectodermal" and "mesodermal" will be used in their traditional sense in the description of the developmental tissues of the tooth hardsubstances, even though, as mentioned, enamel cells may in exceptional cases originate from the entoderm, and the mesoderm of the tooth germs would be designated, more accurately, as mesectoderm. For the very primitive chagreen denticles, distributed all over the body of sharks, the two last-mentioned modes of development do not apply.

Formation of enamel and additional tasks of the ameloblasts: [1]

In the integument of shark embryos the loci of future denticle formation are not morphologically marked, at first, either by an elevation beyond the surrounding territory, nor by particular cell size; instead, the cells of the Malpighian layer of the ectoderm covering the mesoderm beneath it are all of equal size, and in the mesoderm no concentrations of mesenchyme cells are visible. But then the situation changes.

---

[1] Besides the name "ameloblasts" for the enamel-producing cells, there are also the terms "adamantoblasts" and "ganoblasts." The term "ameloblasts" introduced by J. L. Williams (1882) is neither Latin nor Greek, but an Old French derivation from *amel* ("émail"). We prefer it to "ganoblasts," because it is generally used, and because *ganos* has been used for a long time in a somewhat different sense to designate the external hard substance of ganoid scales (comp. Lehner, J., and H. Plenk, 1936, p. 568).

The boundary line between ectoderm and mesoderm no longer appears straight in section but outwardly convex. This protrusion is faint at first; then it becomes more pronounced. A point develops, and finally the shape outlined by the basal membrane, aside from the still unfinished basal part of the tooth, corresponds to the form of the future tooth. The height of the cells of the basal layer of the ectoderm increases notably in the area of tooth formation. Thus they become enamel cells or ameloblasts. For some time it has been suspected, probably correctly, that one of the tasks of the ameloblasts is to determine the species-typical shape of the teeth. However, experimental investigations suggest that the tooth germ does not have merely a passive role in this; perhaps a system of mutual influence operates.

Deposition of enamel generally begins soon after the beginning of dentine deposition. Even prior to the formation of enamel the ameloblasts have already passed the height of their size increase.

In contrast to dentine, the enamel layer, according to the position of the formational tissue, increases in thickness from the basal membrane outward: the last formed enamel layer lies outermost. The outer cover is formed by the enamel surface membrane (*cuticula dentis,* Nasmyth's membrane). It is important for the protection of the teeth because of its resistance to chemical agents, especially acids.

Dentine

In the area of future tooth formation a cell concentration occurs in the mesoderm prior to any deposition of hard substance. The tightly crowded modified mesenchyme cells are arranged in more or less steep cones. The apex and the upper portion of the cone become enclosed by the cells of the epidermis. Basally, the concentration of mesodermal cells increases in breadth and fades into the mesenchymal tissue beneath. From the latter it is clearly distinguishable as something special by the crowding of the cells into a small space, whereas the mesenchyme cells in the vicinity are spaced much farther apart. This concentration of mesodermal cells is called "tooth papilla" or "tooth germ" (Pl. 8-a).

The shape of the cells in this papilla is spherical and at first their arrangement is more or less irregular. Soon, however, the cells beneath the basal membrane group themselves into an epithelium-like formation, and change their shape from spherical to ovoid. Their longitudinal axes are often oriented at right angles to the surface of the basal membrane. Because these cells are involved in the formation of dentine, they are called "odontoblasts."

Prior to the deposition of any hard substance, the mesodermal layer of odontoblasts and the ectodermal layer of ameloblasts are closely aligned on either side of the basal membrane. The formation of dentine precedes the precipitation of enamel. Certain exceptions to this rule, as noted by a number of authors, are subject to question. It is suspected that in these cases the hard substance identified as enamel belongs to the dentine. Dentine begins to form with the deposition by the odontoblasts of an organic ground substance along the inner surface of the basal membrane. Into this ground substance, which also contains fibrilles, carbonate salts are deposited. In this way a little tooth "shard" ("Zahnscherbchen") consisting only of dentine has arisen between the basal membrane and the surface of the tooth papilla.

The cells of the tooth papilla, arranged in a cone and now enclosed beneath a coat of dentine, have become pulpa cells. New layers added to the inward face of the first formed dentine reduce the lumen of the originally very spacious pulp cavity. The dentine thus increases in thickness from the outside inward: the last formed dentine layer lies innermost.

The formation of dentine is in many cases periodically interrupted by periods of quiescence. On sections this produces concentric growth lines. In contrast to bone, in which the bone-forming cells, the osteoblasts, are being entombed by the hard substance they produce, the cell bodies of the odontoblasts generally retreat from the just formed dentine toward the center of the pulp cavity. Dentine forms, at first, so that over the entire inner surface of the very first formed dentine, additional layers are successively added. In the vast majority of cases this modus is retained as long as the formation of dentine continues. For dentine formed in this regular pattern, we shall use the term "orthodentine." In all cases a coat of orthodentine is deposited first. Then, however, the pattern of deposition may change: the remaining wide pulp cavity may be reduced by a different arrangement of the dentine substance. Dentine in process of formation, before the deposition of carbonate salts has been completed, is called "predentine" (Pl. 9-a).

Cementum

Tooth cementum may be found also in the teeth of certain reptiles, but it gained greater significance only in the mammals, where it has become an integral part of the tooth. As its name *substantia ossea* indicates, tooth cementum is ordinary bone. Hence some of the cells that produce it become entirely enclosed by the substance, although they remain in contact with one another by *canaliculi ossium*. If the layer of cementum is very thin, however, it does not contain bone cells, or, in fossil condition, cell spaces (*lacunae*).

As root cementum the substance coats in mammalian teeth the dentine of the root; as crown cementum it occupies—in teeth with folded enamel crowns—the deep valleys of the crown surface outside the enamel. Deposition of cementum is complicated by the fact that, during much of the tooth formation, both the enamel of the crown and the dentine of the root are surrounded by the ectodermal epithelial sheath. Before any deposition of cementum on top of the enamel of the crown and the dentine of the root is possible, part of the epithelial sheath must be destroyed. This process begins with a sieve-like penetration. The osteoblasts (often called "cementoblasts," in this case) originate from the tiny "tooth sack" that surrounds each primitive tooth anlage.

Terminology of tooth hard substances

The terminology of the different hard substances of teeth is unfortunately not used in the same sense by all authors. Opinions differ not only about the variety of modifications of dentine; there is also no unanimity as to what is to be regarded as dentine and what as enamel. Furthermore, the relationship between dentine and bone is not yet fully understood, hence opinion either overrates or underrates the differences between them. The lack of uniformity in the use of terms results primarily from choosing different criteria for their identification. It seems thus unavoidable to define the terms used in this work by stressing the criteria that seemed to me the most significant.

In the early period of odontology the outermost layer of the tooth crown, if it had an enamel-like luster and was very hard, was simply called enamel. For investigating tooth structure ground thin-sections from modern and fossil teeth were already used extensively by Louis Agassiz and Richard Owen. In such thin-sections they could find a sharp boundary line between enamel and dentine in teeth of mammals and reptiles. In many fish teeth this boundary was not found, however. In fish teeth the boundary was drawn arbitrarily according to subjective criteria. Microscopic technology had not yet advanced sufficiently to permit a successful investigation of the formational tissues of the tooth hard substances and of the processes of formation. Thus the distinction of enamel and dentine at that time was based exclusively on the characters of the fully differentiated hard substances. Histogenetic viewpoints could not yet be taken into account. Later, however, progress in microscopic techniques affected the study of teeth also. Oscar Hertwig demonstrated that all tooth formation is bound to the presence of an ectodermal dental lamina. The enamel, at least in mammals and reptiles, is formed by ectodermal cells, the dentine always by mesodermal cells. Corresponding to the topographic position of the formative cells, enamel increases in thickness from the basal membrane outward. The last formed dentine layer, however, lies innermost. Considerations of this sort led C. Röse (1897) and others to the view that selachians do not possess enamel. This interpretation was not generally accepted. Without considering the different mode of formation of enamel, several authors designate the outermost layer of selachian teeth as enamel. On the other hand, J. W. Schmidt (1949) denies that the teeth of any fishes possess an enamel layer.

Th. Kvam (1946, 1950) investigated the behavior of the different hard substances of teeth in terms of their response to acids. The differences thus found were emphasized as distinguishing characters between enamel and dentine without adequate acknowledgement of the different modes of development.

The great importance of the mode of development of the tooth substances may be inferred from the fact that the beginnings of tooth development are the same in all vertebrates. That the apposition of future growth layers of the hard substances must take place outwardly in enamel and inwardly in dentine results from the positional relationships of the developmental tissues. In modern mammals and reptiles it may be directly observed that the apposition takes place in this manner. In the teeth of fishes whose hard substances are being interpreted in such diverse ways, histogenetic studies are the major basis for tissue identification, but even this approach may be misleading if broad comparative histogenetic insights are neglected. A case in point is a recent study by Moss, Jones and Piez (1964) where the increase in the size of the ameloblasts is interpreted as reflecting an actively functioning area of amelogenesis, in a developing fin spine of a shark. As will be shown below (p. 92), this interpretation is subject to grave doubt, if viewed against the broader comparative background.

The relationship between dentine and bone has received attention by many authors, foremost among them Weidenreich (1926, 1929) and Ørvig (1951), who has presented a detailed review of this literature. Although the two hard substances are easily distinguishable in mammals on morphological and histogenetic grounds, exceptions to all but one of the well-known criteria may be found among the teeth and dermal denticles of lower vertebrates. So far as is presently known, formation of dentine is always topographically related to the outer body cover, the epidermis and its derivative in the stomodaeum. Bone, on the other hand, shows no such restriction to its distribution in the body.

Most authors generally agree that the two hard substances are closely related, that there are no fundamental differences between them, and that the formation of dentine is somehow related to the proximity of the scleroblasts to the epithelium of the skin or the mouth cavity. In the case of trabecular dentine, however, there is no evident proximity relationship between scleroblasts and the epithelium of the enamel organ, and this matter is further complicated by the fact that a cell-containing tissue, indistinguishable from bone, may sometimes be found to form the cores of dentine trabecules. Hence the question remains as to what determines the differentiation of an osteoblast or an odontoblast from a mesenchymal cell in a tooth papilla.

Teeth and dentition in the different groups of vertebrates

As late as the beginning of the nineteenth century the vertebrates appeared to be separated from the other phyla of the animal kingdom by an unbridgeable chasm. As certain lower vertebrates that were thought to be fishes became better known, the situation changed. The lampreys (Petromyzontoidei) and the hagfishes (Myxinoidei) were found to be so different from the remaining fishes that they were placed in a separate *class,* Cyclostomata. Even more profound were the differences from fishes in the lancelet, *Amphioxus,* an animal that had been known for a long time but misinterpreted in its systematic position. Although it possesses no vertebrae, it has often been included among the vertebrates because it possesses as the only organ of support an axial notochord, a structure universally present in vertebrates. This notochord consists of a very fluid tissue filling the space enclosed by the tough notochordal sheath, which by exerting pressure against the sheath creates an elastic rod.

The developmental history of some marine groups of invertebrates, the sessile ascidians and the pelagic salpae, shows that their youth stages also possess a notochord, and that the positional relationships of this notochord to the central nervous system and to the main vessels are the same as in *Amphioxus* and in all vertebrates. The same applies to the appendicularians; in these the notochord persists throughout life. In the three groups, the ascidians, the salpae, and the appendicularians, the notochord does not extend the entire length of the body, but remains restricted to the tail region. The three groups of tunicates are therefore united as Urochordata from *ura,* "tail"), to contrast with the Cephalochordata in which the notochord, as in *Amphioxus* and the vertebrates, extends the entire length of the body forward to the head region.

The tunicates, a group in which many forms are sessile and many form colonies, differ greatly in outer appearance and mode of life from the vertebrates. Because both possess notochords, they are now generally classified together in the more inclusive group of chordate animals, or Chordata. Chordata have one important character in common with echinoderms, one

26

of the largest phyla of invertebrates: in both groups the mouth opening does not represent the forward opening of the primitive gut (*Urmund*) during early development but is a new structure. The two large groups are therefore grouped together as Deuterostomia.

The phylogenetic history of both the echinoderms and the chordates is analogous in that the food of both originally consisted of minute, planktonic organisms and that geologically younger forms of both (starfishes and many sea urchins, and many fishes) became capable of subduing larger prey.

Except for the lowly organized Porifera, the sponges, the outer body cover of invertebrate Metazoa, including *Amphioxus*, consists of a single-layered epithelium, which may ultimately be why enamel, dentine, and bone are skeletal tissues restricted to the class Vertebrata (Peyer, 1949).

AGNATHA

Among Craniata two main groups may be distinguished: Agnatha, which do not have movable jaws, and Gnathostomata, which have them. The differences between these groups are not restricted to the organization of the mouth, but extend to the visceral skeleton, the metameric composition of the skull, the nervous system, and many other features. The modern representatives of the Agnatha are the cyclostomes: the parasitic lampreys and the hagfishes. The visceral skeleton of *Petromyzon* consists of a gill basket whose staves surround, on each side, seven gill openings. We search in vain, however, for a clearly differentiated mandibular or jaw arch, as found in all the more highly organized vertebrates.

The skull of the hagfishes (*Myxine*) is built rather differently from that of the lampreys.

By very detailed study of the morphology of the modern cyclostomes and their ontogenetic development, and by investigation of certain Paleozoic forms by means of serial thin-sections, the Swedish paleontologist Erik A:Son Stensiö demonstrated conclusively that a number of Paleozoic genera are at the level of organization of the cyclostomes: the ostracoderms, with the orders Anaspida, Coelolepida, Heterostraci, and Osteostraci. The Osteostraci, as their name implies, already possess bone in their skeletons.

Characteristic for the structure of the visceral skeleton of the ostracoderms is the notable uniformity of the visceral arches, which suggests that their food probably consisted of plankton. Dentition teeth were absent in ostracoderms, but the integument bore true dentine denticles (Fig. 12).

That the modern cyclostomes (lampreys and hagfishes) are derived from Paleozoic ostracoderms may be taken as firmly substantiated, despite the

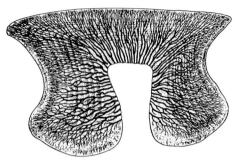

Fig. 12.—Vertical section through a dermal denticle of the ostracoderm *Thelodus scoticus*. After Röse, from Peyer (1931), in Bolk-Göppert-Kallius-Lubosch, *Handbuch der Vergleichenden Anatomie der Wirbeltiere* (Vienna and Berlin: Verlag Urban & Schwarzenberg, (1931–39), by permission.

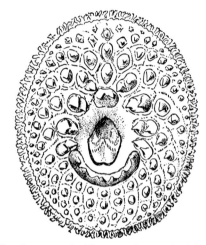

Fig. 13.—Horny teeth of cyclostomes. Sucking mouth armed with teeth of the lamprey *Petromyzon marinus*. From Bigelow and Schroeder, *Fishes of the Western North Atlantic*, Part I (Fig. 5c, caption modified), New Haven: Sears Foundation for Marine Research, Yale University, (1948).

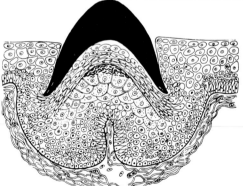

Fig. 14.—Section through a horny denticle of the lamprey *Petromyzon marinus* and a replacement tooth in process of development. From Peyer (1937), in Bolk-Göppert-Kallius-Lubosch, *Handbuch der Vergleichenden Anatomie der Wirbeltiere*, (Vienna and Berlin: Verlag Urban & Schwarzenberg, (1931–39), by permission.

absence of any fossils from the very long span of time between the end of the Devonian (when the last ostracoderms lived) and the Present to bridge the gap in the record. Undoubtedly the few remaining modern cyclostomes have undergone all manner of modifications in their organization since Devonian time, but their vitality seems unimpaired, as indicated by the disastrous destruction of lake trout in the Great Lakes of North America by *Petromyzon* (Fig. 13).

The teeth that accomplished this tremendous feat, are, as mentioned, not dentine teeth, but rather horny teeth, formed by the epidermis. They consist of corneal cells; replacement teeth are furnished beneath the functional ones (Fig. 14).

The hagfish *Myxine* has, instead of a circular sucking mouth, a "tongue" armed with recurved horny teeth and a single horny tooth on the roof of the mouth cavity pointed down and back. In both *Petromyzon* and *Myxine* a very powerful musculature, for which cartilage bars provide extensive origin and insertion surfaces, actuates these horny teeth.

GNATHOSTOMATA

As indicated previously, the Agnatha (that is, the modern cyclostomes and their fossil relatives) differ from the gnathostomes particularly in that all their visceral arches are more or less similar. In the gnathostomes one of these arches, the one innervated by the second and third branches of the trigeminal nerve, became markedly modified. It became a jaw, or mandibular arch, that serves primarily for food intake. With this change go hand in hand other profound changes in organization that cannot be discussed here.

Comparative anatomical investigation has led to the conclusion that the transition from agnathous to gnathostomous organization represented one of the most significant events in the phylogenetic history of vertebrates. Fossils that might provide insight into the mode in which this transition took place are not known. It is therefore uncertain from which group of ostracoderms the gnathostomous forms originated. A. S. Romer suggests that the ostracoderms known so far might not represent generalized types that could be considered as ancestors, but rather represent end forms of an early vertebrate phylogeny.

Among the modern gnathostomes two large groups may be distinguished: Chondrichthyes, whose skeleton consists of cartilage that often contains calcifications, and Osteichthyes, or bony fishes, that have both bone and cartilage in their skeletons. Until recently it was thought that bone never occurred in Chondrichthyes, a view that is no longer tenable, but bone is not a significant structural material in this group (see p. 59).

PLACODERMI AND ACANTHODII

Several Paleozoic groups of gnathostomes with bone in their skeletons differ so greatly from the Osteichthyes that they cannot be united with them and are presented as separate classes, the Placodermi and the Acanthodii.

The name "Placodermi" (from *plax*, "plate" and *derma*, "skin," because of the presence of plate-shaped dermal hard substances) was used for a long time as a name for the ostracoderms (for example see Zittel, 1923). It was realized, however, that "Placodermi" applies only to the following forms (for details see Denison, 1958).

In contrast to the ostracoderms, the placoderms are all more or less clearly gnathostomous. In the skeleton, bone is present besides cartilage. Paired extremities are usually present.

Placoderms probably existed as early as the Silurian period; in fact they have been discovered in rocks of latest Silurian or earliest Devonian age in Bohemia. Entire skeletons of placoderms are known from early in the Devonian period. To this day the phylogenetic relationships among the different groups of placoderms have not been satisfactorily clarified; their relations to the ostracoderms and to the other major groups of gnathostomes are also unsettled.

Classified among the placoderms are the Arthrodira and Ptyctodontia, the Antiarchi, and the Stegoselachii.

The Acanthodii (from *akanthos*, "spine," for their numerous, often large, fin spines) have a certain superficial similarity of the sharks. They differ from sharks, however, by the structure of their scales, by having bone in their skeleton, and perhaps by the structural relationships of the visceral skeleton.

For the genus *Acanthodes*, D. M. S. Watson suggested that the visceral cleft between jaw arch and hyoid arch was not yet reduced to a spiracular opening and that the hyoid arch was entirely separate from the jaw arch (see Fig. 15). More recently Watson's evidence has been questioned (R. S. Miles, 1964).

The geologically younger acanthodians, for example, the genus *Acanthodes* (Devonian to Permian), have become toothless. Of particular interest are peculiar tooth whorls, first described by Traquair (1898), then by A. S. Woodward (1915), under the name *Protodus*, which have recently been studied more closely by W. Gross (1957). Besides these spiral whorls there occur also single conical teeth with broad bases (Pl. 4-c). Enamel is absent.

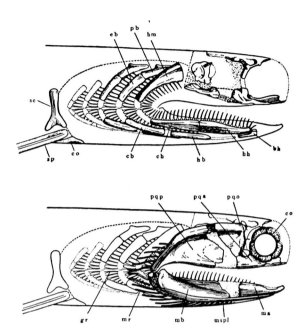

FIG. 15.—Skull of the acanthodian *Acanthodes* in lateral view: *top,* after removal of the scales and the membranous bony plates; *bottom,* after removal of the jaws also. The hyoid arch without connection with jaw arch. *pqo, pqa, pqp,* ossifications of the palatoquadrate; *ma, mb,* ossifications of Meckel's cartilage; *hm, ch, hh, bh,* bones of hyoid arch; *pb, eb, cb, hb,* bones of the first gill arch. After Watson, from Romer (1945).

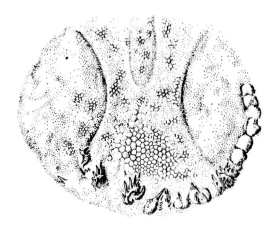

FIG. 16.—Dorsal view of the skull of the acanthodian *Protodus scoticus* with tooth spirals, generally in natural arrangement, 2.2:1 From Gross, *Palaeontographica,* Abt. A, vol. 109 (Stuttgart: E. Schweizerbart'sche Verlagsbuchhandlung, 1957), by permission.

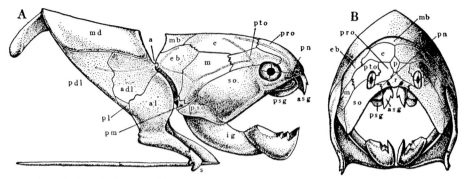

Fig. 17.—Skull and thoracic shield of the arthrodire *Dunkleosteus. A*, in lateral view; *B*, in anterior view. The serrations along the edges of the jaws are bony structures. From Romer (1945).

In each jaw there were a number of tooth whorls that occupied the edge of the jaw (Fig. 16). According to Gross, the teeth of such a spiral were formed not successively but simultaneously. During growth of the individual, thus, entire tooth whorls were probably replaced by larger ones. These peculiar structures (Pl. 4-c) differ markedly from other spiral tooth arrangements to be discussed among the teeth of elasmobranchs.

The genus *Onychodus,* known only from tooth-bearing jaws, and formerly tentatively placed among the acanthodians, belongs to the crossopterygians according to Gross, whose views I can confirm on the basis of first-hand evidence (see p. 114). For a recent review see Jesson (1966).

The arthrodires possess a head shield (Fig. 17), attached by joint to the thoracic armor that surrounds the anterior portion of the body. The arrangement of the bony plates of this head armor is not homologous with that of the fishes. The posterior portion of the body and the tail region were either sparsely covered with weak scales or lacked scales altogether. The jaw mechanism above consists of two sets of paired bones arranged one behind the other, sometimes with a cutting edge deeply notched in the anterior pair. In the lower jaw there is only one ossification on each side. In many genera, for example in the giant *Dunkleosteus,* whose skull reached a length of over one meter, the protruding jags of the jaws are merely bony protuberances. Another, fairly common genus of arthrodires, *Coccosteus,* has dentine teeth firmly connected to the jaws throughout life.

The still incompletely known ptyctodonts are grouped among the arthrodires. The jaws in many bore heavy tooth plates that evidently were used for crushing hard shells. The jaws in another group of placoderms, the Antiarchi, are extraordinarily weak. The Antiarchi were originally placed among the ostracoderms because of a superficial similarity to cephalaspids. In contrast to these, the Antiarchi have a pair of anterior appendages that are movably attached to the thorax and are totally encased in bony plates. A. S. Romer (1945) suspects that the Antiarchi, with their small mouth openings and the weak development of their jaws, were probably limited to eating water plants and small invertebrates. They are not known to have possessed teeth.

Also placoderms are a number of forms (*Gemuendina, Stensioella, Pseudopetalichthys*) which, because of their external similarity to rays and skates, have been called Stegoselachii. They are among the oldest gnathostomes, since their remains are of lower Devonian age. The similarity to rays and skates lies in the notable enlargement of the pectoral fins. In contrast to the elasmobranchs, their integument does not contain individual skin denticles, but rather plates in which are set pointed, denticle-like structures, a distinction that does not appear to be as basic as was thought until a few years ago (see edestid sharks, p. 59). The mouth is terminal and provided with pointed, star-shaped teeth. The jaw mechanism is notably different from that of the selachians. In a number of other genera that presumably also belong to the placoderms, there are forms that did not possess dentine teeth, and others known from rare specimens only, in which a dentition might have been present in life, but was not preserved. They may here be ignored.

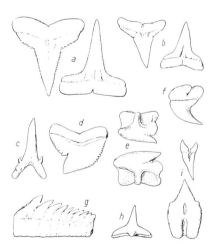

FIG. 18.—Tooth forms of sharks, *a, Carcharhinus limbatus,* fourth upper and lower teeth; *b, Negaprion brevirostris,* fourth upper and second lower teeth; *c, Carcharias taurus,* third lower tooth; *d, Galeocerdo cuvier,* fifth upper tooth; *e, Squalus acanthias,* third upper and lower teeth; *f, Rhincodon typus,* lateral view of a tooth; *g, Hexanchus griseus,* first lower tooth; *h, Squatina dumeril,* fifth lower tooth; *i, Dalatias licha,* middle lower tooth. Compiled after Bigelow and Schroeder (1948), from Peyer, *Die Zähne* Verständliche Wissenschaft, vol. 79 (Berlin: Springer Verlag, 1963), by permission.

CHONDRICHTHYES

The living Chondrichthyes may be grouped into two divisions of very unequal size: the elasmobranchs, represented by numerous genera and species of sharks, rays, and skates; and the holocephalians, whose modern representatives are the chimaeroids. The holocephalians have never been numerous.

ELASMOBRANCHII

The dentitions of the two modern groups of elasmobranchs, (sharks, or Selachii, and rays and skates, or Batoidei), show so many corresponding characters that they must be discussed together.

When talking about sharks many people think primarily of the man-eating sharks and of the news accounts of the injuries inflicted on bathers by sharks. Already Schiller lets his diver report: "Und dräuend wies mir die grimmigen Zähne der entsetzliche Hai, des Meeres Hyäne." Many species of sharks attain great dimensions; *Carcharodon carcharias* may reach a length of 13 meters. Such giants have no difficulty in subduing man, but probably the danger to man of large, predaceous sharks has been overrated.

In their work on the fishes of the Western North Atlantic, H. B. Bigelow and W. C. Schroeder (1948) investigated this question for pertinent species. They found that some species suspected of attacking man may not do so. Certainly attacks on man by the blue sharks (carcharinids), which in German are often directly referred to as "man sharks" ("Menschenhaie"), cannot be proved. Many forms with dentitions and swimming abilities such that they might endanger man do not do so because man is not among the prey to which they are keyed. *Carcharodon* is correctly thought to be the most dangerous shark. Tiger sharks *(Galeocerdo)*, large hammerheads, and large isurids have also been known to injure man. Along the coasts of warmer seas, danger from sharks seems much greater than in temperate latitudes. Among the gastric contents of *Carcharodon* there have been identified not only other large fishes, such as sturgeons and tunas, but also sea lions, seals, and sea turtles. These sharks have sharp, often stiletto-like teeth with cutting edges that are finely denticulate (Fig. 18), for example those of *Carcharodon* and of many species of *Carcharhinus*.

Corresponding to the various modes of life of the elasmobranchs are notable differences in the form of the mouth and its dentition (Fig. 19). The mouth opening generally lies on the ventral side of the body as a transverse cleft. This relation has led to the term "Plagiostomata," formerly often used to designate the combined group of sharks, rays, and skates. Only rarely is the mouth opening in terminal position, as, among the modern

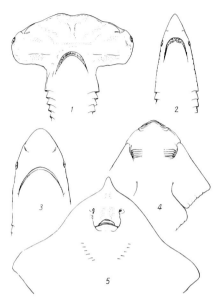

Fig. 19.—The shapes of the mouth in sharks and skates. 1, hammerhead *Sphyrna bigelowi;* 2, *Isurus oxyrinchus;* 3, *Carcharhinus limbatus;* 4, *Squatina dumeril;* 5, *Raja marginata.* Compiled after Bigelow and Schroeder (1948 and 1953), from Peyer, *Die Zähne,* Verständliche Wissenschaft, vol. 79 (Berlin: Springer Verlag, 1963), by permission.

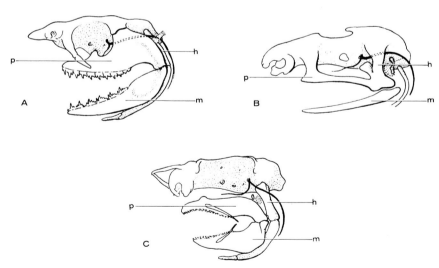

Fig. 20.—Modes of attachment of the jaw arches to the neurocranium. *A,* amphistylic connection *(Hexanchus); B,* holostylic connection (frog); *C,* hyostylic connection *(Scyliorhinus). p,* palatoquadrate; h, hyomandibular; *m,* Meckel's cartilage. Redrawn from Goodrich (1909).

forms, in *Chlamydoselachus anguineus* and in *Rhincodon typus;* in the latter it is probably an adaptation to the mode of filter feeding. Among the extinct elasmobranchs, the ancient and primitive genus *Cladoselache* has a terminal mouth opening. In the late Paleozoic fresh-water shark *Pleuracanthus* the position of the mouth is nearly terminal. The ventral position of the mouth was brought about by the development of a rostrum in front of the neurocranium proper, supported by three cartilage arches and housing the nasal capsules. As a rule the mouth opening is rather broad, reaching a relative maximal diameter in the genus *Rhincodon*. In rays and skates the mouth lies as a transverse cleft in the middle of the belly side of the dorsoventrally flattened body. This position results from the giant enlargement of the pectoral fins that completely frame the head and may even unite in front of it. Related to this extreme flattening of the body is the ventral position of the gill clefts, but the spiracular opening is on the dorsal side. Elasmobranchs with ray-like broadened bodies, in which the gill openings remain in a halfway position on the lateral sides, are considered sharks; on the other hand, forms whose gill slits are on the ventral side, but lack ray-like lateral expansion of the body, are placed among the rays and skates.

The jaw arch is attached to the neurocranium in various ways in Chondrichthyes. As Figure 20 shows, an amphistylic, a hyostylic, and an autostylic (or holostylic) connection are distinguished.

Many medium-sized sharks with pointed teeth are primarily fish eaters. In some sharks and in the rays and skates a special differentiation of the dentition permits the fish to eat hard-shelled prey. Two of the largest sharks, the basking shark *Cetorhinus maximus* and the whale shark *Rhincodon typus,* resemble baleen whales (see p. 272) in their mode of feeding.

The variety of form in shark teeth is notable (Fig. 18). This variety is related not only to the variety of modes of feeding, but also to the fact that teeth of very different shapes and sizes may exist in a single dentition. Furthermore, age differences and sexual dimorphism of the dentition have been reported in elasmobranchs.

Tooth form and mode of feeding

Usually the tooth crown in sharks is differentiated from the tooth base by the smoothness of the surface and by enamel-like luster. In fossil shark teeth the crown often, although not always, is stained darker than the base, the result of post-mortem changes. As will be discussed in the section on the ontogenetic development of the teeth (p. 53), the tooth crown reaches toward the tooth base only to the extent that the mesodermal papilla in the anlage is covered by the ectodermal enamel epithelium.

The tooth bases are generally large in shark teeth, thus even isolated fossil shark teeth are easily recognized. This peculiarity of form in selachian teeth is related to the character of the selachian jaw skeleton, which contains no bone (in modern representatives) but at best only calcified cartilage. Therefore, rigid attachment of the teeth to the jaws is not possible in sharks, rays, and skates. The selachian tooth is held in place by connective tissue that pads the jaw cartilages. To guarantee adequate resistance to functional abuse in such a mode of attachment, it is necessary for connective tissue fibers to have ample attachment surfaces at the tooth base (Pl. 10-b). Accordingly, the tooth bases of selachian teeth are generally extensive.

We shall use in our presentation the term "tooth root" only for structures that correspond in form and genesis with the characteristic conditions in man and the mammals. In this sense we cannot speak of a tooth root in elasmobranchs. We prefer the more indifferent terms "tooth base" or "basal portion" of the tooth.

In numerous descriptions of shark teeth the term "tooth root" has been used. There is no serious objection to this usage, if it is understood that the "root" of a shark tooth is a structure totally different from that of a mammal tooth. The selachian tooth base was studied intensively by E. Casier (1947), largely in fossil material. Casier distinguished different stages and types on the basis of the arrangement and the course of the vascular canals that lead to the pulp cavity and the development of the furrows that divide the "root" into two or more sections. He proposed special designations for such stages and types.

In Casier's anaulacorhizous stage, the basal tooth portion is entirely uniform. In the hemiaulacorhizous stage there is a differentiation of the base into two parts by formation of an incomplete furrow. In the holauricorhizous stage the tooth base is divided into two portions by a deeply penetrating, labiolingual furrow. Finally, in the polyaulacorhizous stage there are many furrows; consequently the tooth base consists of numerous, separate lamellae.

Except for those giant sharks that can even eat sea lions and sea turtles, most sharks are fish eaters. Their teeth serve not just as wound-inflicting, offensive weapons; perhaps primarily they are used to hold a struggling prey that is to be swallowed whole. For such a purpose recurved, pointed hooks are adequate, but cutting edges are also rather common. Sometimes they may be developed as razor-sharp blades, for example, in the extinct genus *Sphenodus* (*Orthacodus*) (G. de Beaumont, 1960). That this form of tooth was retained entirely unchanged for almost all the Jurassic and Cretaceous periods—an interval of some 80 million years—suggests that it was a perfect adaptation to a particular kind of prey. The prey was prob-

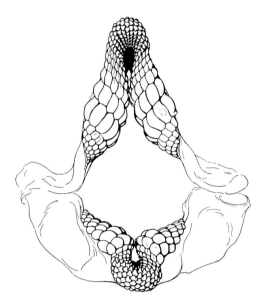

Fig. 21.—Dentition of *Heterodontus philippi*. About 1:2. From Peyer (1946).

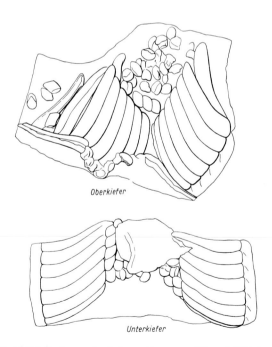

Oberkiefer

Unterkiefer

Fig. 22.—Dentition of *Bdellodus*, a shark from the upper Lias of Württemberg. Dedrawn after Quenstedt (1882).

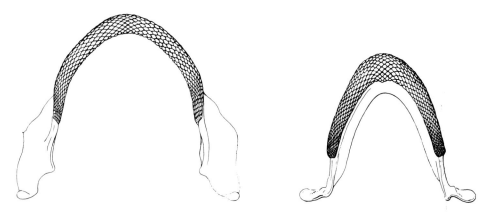

Fɪɢ. 23.—Dentition of *Mustelus* sp. *Left,* upper jaw; *right,* lower jaw. About 1:1. From Landolt (1947).

ably among the invertebrates, possibly Mesozoic dibranchiates, since such extraordinarily fine cutting blades would not have been suitable for penetrating bony fish scales or the shagreen of the skin of other selachians.

Durophagy led to the formation of more or less perfect tooth pavements that serve for crushing shells. In the Port Jackson shark, *Heterodontus,* tooth plates are found only in the posterior half of the dentition; the anterior half shows pointed teeth, hence the name *Heterodontus* (Fig. 21). Similar dentitions, although more highly specialized in the durophagous direction, are recorded for extinct genera *Asteracanthus* (Peyer, 1946) (Pl. 4-b) and *Bdellodus* (Quenstedt, 1882) (Fig. 22). *Mustelus* (Fig. 23) and numerous skates have a closed pavement of teeth of rhombic outline. Among the elasmobranchs, the most perfect differentiation of a shell-cracking dentition is found in the family Myliobatidae. Their tooth pavement either may consist of relatively small polygonal components of equal shape and size or may be formed of enlarged individual teeth (Pl. 20-a). In the eagle ray *Aetobatus* the tooth pavement is composed of a single median row of enlarged teeth. Upper and lower teeth are in contact over an extensive surface, which results in a corresponding wear pattern.

In the genus *Rhina* a precise occlusion between upper and lower parts of the dentition develops in a unique way (Pl. 5-a). In the lower jaw there arises along the midline a ridge covered with teeth that fits perfectly into a depression in the upper jaw that is likewise paved with teeth. Laterally, there follows on either side in the upper jaw a flat ridge that fits into a corresponding depression in the lower jaw. More laterally a projection of the lower jaw again occludes with a groove in the upper jaw, and at the outermost edge a flat protrusion of the upper jaw fits into a corresponding pit in the lower jaw.[1]

The described configuration of the dentition seems to reach full development only postembryonically, so that *Rhina* is theoretically interesting for its occlusion between upper and lower teeth, which has not been achieved, as in mammals, by differentiation of form in opposing teeth. To be sure, the teeth that occupy the elevated portions of the *Rhina* dentition are somewhat larger than those that pave the depressions. Sections through jaws show, however, that the slight differences in size of the teeth are not adequate to account for the elevated and depressed parts of the dentition; these ridges are brought about by pads of connective tissue that are being formed in certain areas between the basal surfaces of the teeth and the jaw cartilage.

The cochliodonts, which existed during Carboniferous time, were doubtless also durophagous (Fig. 24). So far only their dentition is known. A. S. Woodward assumed that the larger tooth plates had originated by the fusion of smaller ones. Against this interpretation, however, is the finding of P. Treuenfels (1896) that the growth increase of enlarged tooth plates of *Myliobatis aquila* does not take place by fusion but by enlargement of individual teeth.

Two of the largest sharks, the basking shark *Cetorhinus maximus* and the whale shark *Rhincodon typus,* eat food similar to that of the baleen whales: all feed on planktonic organisms. In the baleen whales the wier in which the small prey is retained is formed by horny baleen blades; in the sharks the gill openings have become wiers (*Cetorhinus*) or sieves (*Rhincodon*) formed by highly specialized mucous membrane denticles (Fig. 25) extending from the gill arches.

Form differences due to the position of the teeth in the dentition

The shape of a tooth varies with its location within the dentition, both between anterior and posterior teeth and between upper and lower teeth. Differences between teeth situated in the anterior and posterior parts of the dentition are often observed; most notably in the dentitions of predacious forms in which the large fang teeth are in front and in which there is a gradual decrease in tooth size toward the angle of the mouth (Fig. 26). *Isurus nasus* and other isurids are minor exceptions; they have a third tooth of the upper jaw that is smaller than the next posterior fourth tooth (Fig.

[1] It may be mentioned in passing that in the legend to Plate 23 of R. Owen's *Odontography* (1840–45), the captions for upper and lower jaws have been erroneously interchanged. Figure 123 in the *Vertebrata Craniata* of E. S. Goodrich (in Ray Lankester's *Treatise on Zoology*, Part 9) is correctly oriented.

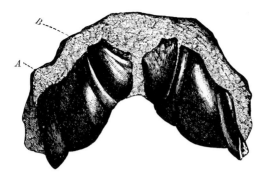

FIG. 24.—Dentition of *Cochliodus contortus*, Carboniferous elasmobranch. Slightly reduced. From Zittel, *Grundzüge der Paläontologie*, Verlag R. Oldenbourg, München-Berlin (1923) by permission.

FIG. 25.—*Cetorhinus maximus*. Mucous membrane denticles that have become modified to form the retaining rods of a gill wier. 1:3.4. After Bigelow and Schroeder (1948), from Peyer, *Die Zähne*, Verständliche Wissenschaft, vol. 79 (Berlin: Springer Verlag, 1963), by permission.

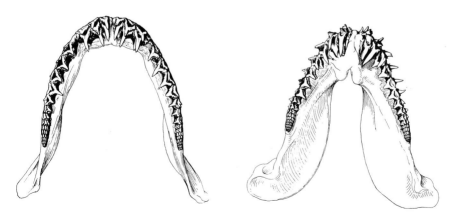

FIG. 26.—Dentition of *Carcharias* sp. *Left*, upper jaw; *right*, lower jaw. 1:4. From Landolt (1947).

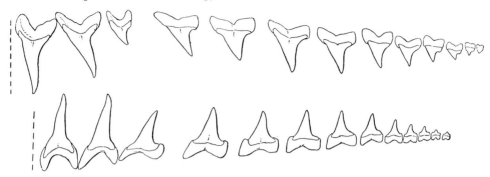

FIG. 27.—*Isurus oxyrinchus.* Upper and lower tooth rows. The fourth tooth of the upper row is larger than the third. From Bigelow and Schroeder, *Fishes of the Western North Atlantic,* Part I (Fig. 19a, legend modified) (New Haven: Sears Foundation for Marine Research, Yale University, 1948).

27). The most posterior teeth are extraordinarily small in isurids and are also arranged differently from the teeth in the forward region of the dentition. Differences in form include changes in tooth proportion and the relative sizes of side cusps from front to back, for example in *Carcharias taurus,* and changes in tooth symmetry, for example in carcharinid and sphyrnid sharks (see Bigelow and Schroeder, 1948).

Differences between the teeth of the upper and lower jaws are particularly pronounced in a few families, for example in Notidanidae (Fig. 28) and Dalatiidae (Pl. 7-a), which have upper jaws that harbor slender, acutely pointed teeth that are smaller than those in the lower jaws. In these sharks the teeth differ both in shape and in arrangement.

Single pointed and multicusped teeth

Many shark teeth are single pointed. Others have one or several accessory points mesial and distal to a dominant main point. Still other teeth, for example the lower teeth of *Hexanchus* (Fig. 28) and *Heptranchias,* have a series of adjacent points that impart to the tooth a saw-like appearance. The existence of these differences in form raises the question of whether such differences are morphologically significant. The following reasons tend to deny the deeper morphological significance of the presence or absence of accessory cusps.

The anlagen of both single-cusped and multicusped teeth are entirely uniform formations. It would thus seem that the development of side cusps results from the differentiation of the enamel organ of a primarily uniform anlage.

There are isurids, for example *Lamna nasus,* in which the teeth of certain cross rows are single cusped in juvenile specimens, and the replacement teeth of the same cross rows in older individuals have small accessory cusps.

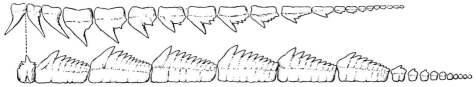

FIG. 28.—Upper and lower tooth rows of *Hexanchus griseus*. From Bigelow and Schroeder, *Fishes of the Western North Atlantic*, Part I (Fig. 8*f*, legend modified), (New Haven: Sears Foundation for Marine Research, Yale University, 1948).

Furthermore there are teeth, for example those of the fossil shark *Hybodus,* in which there is no certain distinction between mere surface granulation and minute accessory cusplets.

That separate tooth shards may develop on accessory cusps during tooth formation cannot be used as argument for a deeper morphological significance of side cusps, because mineralization of the tooth anlage in single as well as multicuspid conditions begins generally at the crown points, which remain isolated until progressing mineralization leads basally to a unification of the separately formed shards. The process of mineralization, however, cannot be regarded as being as significant as the uniformity of the anlagen.

An alternative view is expressed in the lepidomorial theory of Stensiö and Ørvig (Ørvig, 1951, Stensiö, 1961, 1962). According to this theory, the teeth of elasmobranchs, teleostomian fishes, and tetrapods are composite structures consisting of an indeterminate number of primordial entities, called lepidomoria, and their aggregates that are said to have fused at the papillary stage of odontogenesis. During the papillary stage the simple (lepidomorial) and complex (synchronomorial) elements of which a tooth may be composed might undergo certain modifications in position, length, and shape of their crown portions; these modifications would result in corresponding changes in the fully grown tooth. The lepidomorial theory endeavors to explain multicusped teeth in this manner.

The difficulty in this theory lies in the tacit assertion, entirely unsupported by evidence, that a primary morphological entity such as a lepidomorium is incapable of phylogenetic differentiation into a larger, ornamented or multicuspid structure except by amalgamation with other lepidomoria and fusion at the papillary stage. Even the dermal denticles of the elasmobranch integument are considered composites (synchronomoria) of lepidomoria. This view is hardly tenable in the light of new evidence now available for elasmobranchs of Pennsylvanian age (p. 59), which shows clearly that lepidomoria not only occur in different sizes on the same individual, but also occur in different shapes, and that in the edestid sharks these lepidomoria may combine to form composite scales of variable complexity. These lepidomoria (Fig. 32) are no different in basic morphology from the shagreen denticles and the mucous membrane denticles of modern elasmobranchs, as should be amply demonstrated by the ontogeny of the latter (Pls. 15-b, 16-a; Color Plate I, a, d, e). It would thus seem that shagreen and mucous membrane denticles and dentition teeth are highly differentiated single lepidomoria.

Age differences

Age differences in shark teeth concern first their size, since at any given age the dimensions of the teeth correspond to the body size of that particular stage. Every replacement tooth surpasses the size of its predecessor as soon as it is fully developed. Since a number of replacement teeth in a cross row are visible simultaneously besides the functional tooth, differences in size of the successive teeth of a cross row might be thought to be easily determined. Such is not so, however. I only rarely noted macroscopically detectable differences in size. Measurement is difficult because the bases of the replacement teeth usually have not yet reached full development. Better knowledge of the size differences during successive stages in the life of a shark would be of some interest, because such differences would provide a way of estimating the number of tooth generations between the youngest and the oldest stages. The number arrived at in this way would probably be very large for most sharks, but it should be considered that during periods of accelerated growth notable differences probably do occur and that increase in size of the teeth is a function not only of age but also of circumstances of life.

The best example of age differences in the tooth shape is offered by *Heterodontus,* justifying its name also in this regard. The anterior teeth of very young specimens are clearly multicuspid; tooth plates have not yet developed at that stage (Pl. 5-b). In older individuals the anterior teeth show, in addition to a strong main cusp, only weak indications of side cusps, and these may be entirely absent in the upper jaw.

It may be generally true in all cases of durophagy that specialization of the dentition is less pronounced in juvenile animals than it is in the adult.

Minor differences not only in size but also in shape of the teeth of juvenile sharks may well prove to be common. In older specimens of *Lamna nasus,* already mentioned (p. 42), there develop in front and behind the main cusp small side cusps that are not present in teeth of young animals.

Sexual dimorphism in the dentition

Sexual dimorphism in the teeth of sharks is rare. It has been described in certain batoids (Pl. 6) (Clark, 1926), and among the rays and skates of the Western North Atlantic the phenomenon seems to be widespread (Bigelow and Schroeder, 1953). The differences between the dentitions of male and female animals involve arrangement as much as form of the teeth. In males the cross rows of teeth in the symphyseal region and in the adjacent portions of the dentition are separated from one another, whereas in females they are more closely spaced. Whether these differences have a functional significance is not known.

The number of teeth in the dentition

The question of the number of teeth in the dentition of a shark may be easily and accurately answered for those in which only one tooth in each cross row is functional, and replacement teeth are still covered by a fold of the mucous membrane. If, however, several teeth in each cross row function simultaneously, as for example in *Mustelus* and in many rays and skates, then it is not possible to distinguish sharply the functional teeth from the replacement teeth.

In isolated fossil teeth, for example of isurids, that occur in vast numbers in sediments of Tertiary age, it is often impossible to determine whether the tooth had been functional or was a replacement tooth well advanced in its development without investigating the structure. This relatively insignificant matter would have to be considered, however, in an estimate of the number of individuals that are represented by the isolated teeth of a given fossil occurrence.

Tooth formulae of the dentitions

A tooth formula is used to express the number of teeth in a dentition. Unlike the conventional form used for the dentition of mammals, the

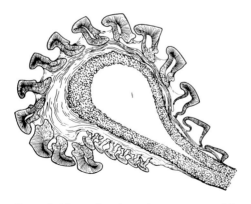

Fig. 29.—*Mustelus* sp. Ground thin-section through a cross row of functional and replacement teeth of the lower jaw, and through adjacent dermal denticles. The jaw cartilage is somewhat deformed by drying. 7:1. From Landolt (1947).

formulae for sharks usually include both the right and left halves of the jaws because occasionally small differences occur in the number of teeth of the right and left sides. But more important, such a formula indicates at once the presence or absence of an unpaired, symphyseal row of teeth. In rays and skates the tooth arrangement often does not permit sharp distinction of right and left sides. Hence the tooth formulae merely state the observed range of variation in the upper and lower jaws. The number of teeth among selachians may vary considerably: the whale shark *Rhincodon typus* has about 3,600 teeth per jaw, whereas the eagle ray *Aetobatus* has only a single row of about a dozen median teeth in each jaw. The following examples are taken from the work of H. B. Bigelow and W. C. Schroeder (1948, 1953):

Species	Left	Median	Right
Hexanchus griseus	16–20 / 12–16	1 (or 0)	16–20 / 12–16
Prionace glauca	14 / 13–15	0–1 / 1–4	14 / 13–15
Scyliorhinus boa	24 / 22		24 / 22
Scyliorhinus retifer	21 / 20	0 / 1	21 / 20
Lamna nasus	24–32 / 14–20		24–32 / 14–20
Pristis pectineatus	88–128 / 84–176		
Himantura schmardae	28–36 / 30–38		
Rhinoptera bonasus	33–36 / (48–52) / 36–39	11–12	33–36 / 36–39 / (48–52)

The number of replacement teeth of a cross row varies not only with genera and species, but also with position in the dentition.

Arrangement of the dentition teeth

The arrangement of the dentition teeth in rows was mentioned already in connection with the different numbers of teeth in the dentition of the selachians. Longitudinal rows can be distinguished as running parallel to the edge of the jaw, and cross rows as usually extending slightly obliquely to the edge (Fig. 23). Often only the most labially situated tooth in each cross row is functional. This tooth is the most advanced in its development whereas the youngest replacement tooth anlage lies in the most lingual position. Particularly among rays and skates, and in *Mustelus*, several to many teeth in each cross row function simultaneously. In such instances a sharp boundary can rarely be determined between functional and replacement teeth, the transition being gradual. Cross-sections through selachian dentitions of this type have suggested the term "revolver" dentition (Fig. 29). L. Bolk proposed the term "tooth family" for the designation of the teeth present in a cross row: the functional tooth or teeth and the succeeding replacement teeth. We shall use this term purely descriptively, in the sense of transversal row as an inclusive designation of the set of teeth present in a cross row at any given moment. But it is applicable also for the designation of all teeth that are being formed in one cross row during the life of an individual, thus including the teeth that have already dropped out and those that are yet to be formed.

If in each cross row only a single tooth is in function—which is often the case—the simultaneously functioning teeth of upper and lower jaws form a longitudinal row extending from the symphysis to the angle of the mouth. This row of teeth runs in an arched line parallel to the edge of the jaw. Such, however, is not absolutely true: the line is rather a flat zig-zag line since the teeth of neighboring cross rows do not stand at the same height but alternate with one another. Thus, among the functional teeth of a longitudinal row, alternate teeth assume a more labial position and those in between a more lingual position. This alternation is, however, not absolutely regular (Fig. 26).

The cross rows are either at a slight distance from one another or so close together that the teeth of one row fit, with lateral processes, into spaces bounded on each side by two teeth of the neighboring cross rows.

Mode of replacement of the dentition teeth

The mode of tooth replacement may be studied particularly well in the dentition of the selachians, because in each cross row there are simultaneously present a varying number of tooth generations in different stages of development (Landolt, 1947). The movements that take place in the process of tooth replacement may not be observed directly. But the line of movement and the distance traveled by a particular tooth from its first anlage to its position of function and finally to the point from which it is shed may be readily ascertained from the regular arrangement of the teeth in different stages of development. Already toward the end of the seventeenth century, W. André (1678)) had, according to Owen (1840–45), interpreted in this sense an observation that he had made on a specimen of *Galeocerdo* in which a tail spine fragment of a stingray had penetrated the jaw (Pl. 1-a).

I have not been able to find reliable information concerning the tempo of the tooth replacement. It probably differs among genera and species, according to the intensity of use of the dentition, but it might also change with the age of the individual.

All observations show with certainty that a tooth that had its anlage at the lingual end of a cross row must often traverse a notable distance, but we do not know how long it stays at the different stations along this way before it reaches the position of function on the edge of the jaw or how long it functions in its last position. Breder (1942) reported that *Carcharias* took two to eight days to shed a tooth.

That tooth replacement actually involves movement in a linguolabial direction is seen in a thin-section, ground crosswise through a jaw of *Mustelus laevis* (Fig. 29). The tooth about to fall out is no longer anchored in its natural substrate, the connective tissue pad lining the jaw cartilage; it literally went "on the rocks," moved onto the pavement of the skin denticles. A lower jaw of *Rhina* likewise shows that teeth about to be shed override the shagreen of the integument.

The ways by which tooth anlagen are displaced and teeth are replaced are in controversy. Thus far it has been assumed that the tough connective tissue layer covering the jaws glides over the jaw with its always firmly anchored teeth. James (1953), in a detailed investigation, suggested that the movement is brought about by growth pressure of the ectodermal cells that lie between the teeth of a cross row. This attempt at explanation is primarily based on the relatively simple tooth replacement dislocations seen in rays and skates and in *Mustelus*. Whether it suffices also for the more complicated conditions remains doubtful.

Except for those instances in which several teeth of a cross row function simultaneously a replacement tooth can only become functional after its predecessor has been shed. When cross rows are well spaced, a single, functional tooth prevents its successor from moving into its place. When the latter has been shed, the replacement tooth can move into the vacant spot. If, however, the cross rows are so close together that the tooth bases extend into the interstices between the tooth bases of the neighboring cross rows, a replacement tooth can only move into position of function if the labially situated teeth of the neighboring cross rows have also been shed and so cannot prevent its progression. In extreme cases, for example in the lower jaw of *Dalatias,* the positional relationships are such that the entire row of functional teeth must be shed in rapid succession, at once so to speak, in order to enable an entire row of replacement teeth to move into position of function (Pl. 7-a). Separated cross rows in which the advancement of the replacement teeth is not dependent on the teeth of the neighboring cross

rows occur, for example in the Carchariidae and the Isuridae, and dependence on the position of the teeth of neighboring cross rows is found, for
example in the family Carcharinidae. Among the rajids there are, often
within a single dentition, transitions from separated to crowded cross rows;
separated positioning is seen primarily in cross rows near the symphysis.
When noticeable sexual dimorphism of the dentition occurs, loose position
seems to occur more often in males than in females.

Even if the anterior cross rows are separated from one another, as in
isurids, the rows at the mouth angle, which contain only few, extremely
small teeth, may be interlocked.

In Osteichthyes and in tetrapods the shedding of teeth is usually initiated
and prepared for by the appearance of resorption phenomena. No such
resorption phenomena may be observed in selachian teeth about to be shed
or already dropped out. On the other hand, it must be assumed that the
connective tissue fibers that hold the tooth firm in its position undergo
reduction. In jaws of *Carcharodon*, for example, preserved in a dry condition, the places where teeth evidently have been shed shortly before the
death of the animal are marked by flat, shallow scars.

In the youngest replacement teeth the point of the tooth or, when none
such occurs, the apical portion of the tooth faces ventrad in the lower jaw
and dorsad in the upper jaw. The replacement tooth must therefore not
only travel a certain distance in linguolabial direction to reach its position
of function, but also must change its attitude. This change may take place
in various ways. In *Mustelus* and in most rays and skates the attitude
changes in many small successive steps while the tooth travels the road to
the edge of the jaw. In others the initial changes of attitude are insignificant.
Even in the oldest replacement tooth, next to the functioning one, the apex
faces in the opposite direction. The main change in attitude does not take
place until immediately before the time the replacement tooth becomes
functional.

For the schematic representation of these differences the concept of the
"angle of attitude change" was used by my student H. Landolt (1947)
(Fig. 30). This angle is obtained by comparing the attitude of the functional
tooth or teeth to that of the successive replacement teeth of the same cross
row. Naturally, this angle can only be determined approximately. Nevertheless, the schematic presentation serves well to illustrate the different conditions. The replacement tooth must undergo particularly complicated
movements when the last change of attitude amounts to nearly 180 degrees.
It must travel over the edge of the jaw. With its base directed dorsad, the
tooth creeps upward along the lingual face of the lower jaw, then tips over
and applies itself with the lingual face of its base to the outer face of the

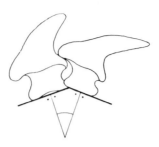

Fig. 30.—Change-of-position angle, indicating the magnitude of the successive movements of rotation that a replacement tooth of an elasmobranch must carry out while traveling linguo-labially to the site where it will function. From Landolt (1947).

jaw (Fig. 31). There it is fixed solidly. The great height and the small labiolingual diameter of the bases of the lower teeth of notidanids and of *Dalatias* are related to this condition. James (1953) suggested that it may be correlated with the narrow cross-section profile of the jaw.

For teeth of notidanids from the uppermost Jurassic of Nusplingen, R. Schweizer (Tübingen), in a study still in progress, has shown that the labiolingual diameters of the bases of these teeth are relatively much larger than those in teeth of modern genera. From the form of the tooth bases it seems absolutely impossible that replacement of the teeth could have taken place by the same mode as in the modern forms (see also G. de Beaumont [1960]).

The change of tooth attitude, brought about in many, small successive steps, certainly represents the more primitive condition. It appears that the movements related to tooth replacement took place in this way in the Mesozoic genus *Acrodus,* and probably also in the late Paleozoic sharks. The same is true of the generalized modern genus *Heterodontus.*

Delay of the greatest step in the change of attitude until immediately before replacement seems to be a specialization. Perhaps it offers the advantage that the crowns of the replacement teeth remain protected against mechanical injury until the teeth become functional.

Histology and histogenesis of the elasmobranch teeth

As already briefly mentioned, the mode of development of the teeth is of fundamental significance in the interpretation of their hard substances. The dentition of the sharks and their relatives is particularly favorable for the study of the ontogenetic development of the teeth, because throughout its life a selachian has a series of replacement teeth in different stages of development in addition to the functional teeth. Investigation of these stages, however, cannot fully replace the study of embryonic conditions of

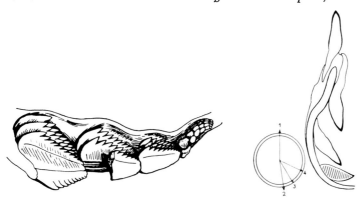

Fɪɢ. 31.—Tooth replacement in *Hexanchus griseus. Left,* interior view (1:2); and *right,* schematic cross-section of the lower jaw. From Landolt (1947).

tooth development: for this study I had available embryos of *Squalus acanthias* and of *Scyliorhinus canicula.*

Embryos of *Squalus acanthias:* The embryos used in sectioning were of about the same overall length, approximately 100 mm.

According to Bigelow and Schroeder (1948) the length of *Squalus acanthias* at birth is usually about 220 mm, occasionally they are only about 180 mm and sometimes as large as 330 mm. Adult males reach 600 to 800 mm, females 700 to 1,000 mm.

The low-power illustration of a sagittal section (Pl. 7-b) shows the entrance to the mouth cavity, the palatoquadrate and Meckel's cartilages, and the extent of the dental laminae from which the tooth anlagen have originated. As a rule two or three anlagen are seen in a section; in the majority two in the upper jaw and three in the lower jaw, although, sometimes, three are recognizable above and two below. Instructive overall pictures result only with favorable section orientation. The illustration (Pl. 8-a) shows the lower jaw of the same embryo at high magnification. Lingual to the youngest tooth anlage lies the end of the dental lamina as an insignificant, rounded projection that is sharply delimited from surrounding connective tissue. At this point the inner enamel epithelium turns into the outer enamel epithelium (Pl. 8-a). Between the two epithelial layers a number of spherical cells correspond topographically to the cells of the enamel pulp of higher vertebrates. Sometimes it is difficult to delimit the end section of the dental lamina from the youngest tooth anlage. The terminal portion thus presents a zone of cell proliferation that gradually changes into a zone in which the cells of the inner enamel epithelium have increased a little in height but do not as yet cover a mound of mesenchymal cells. At this early stage they are still arranged in a plane.

Often there occurs a rather flat but sharply defined cone of mesenchymal cells, enclosed by ameloblasts that have not yet reached their full height but are already cylindrical. In contrast to the following stage, the mesenchymal cells with their large nuclei entirely fill the space bounded by the ameloblasts; a cell-free zone, occupied only by ground substance and fibers, is not yet present.

The middle one of the three tooth anlagen (Pl. 8-a) is distinguished in its form from the youngest one in that the apex of the future tooth is already clearly indicated. The ameloblasts have nearly reached their maximum size. Their cytoplasm, which stained reddish with azan [1] and hematoxylin-eosin in the previous stage, now appears light and nearly colorless when stained. The ameloblasts thus are in sharp contrast to their surroundings. The large nuclei do not lie in the middle of the cylindrical cells but are slightly peripheral. The cell boundaries appear very distinct, as does the basal membrane.

The cells of the future pulp cavity do not extend to the apical portion of the tooth in this anlage; the triangular space (as seen in section), which is surrounded by ameloblasts, is here filled with a cell-free ground substance in which fine fibers may be observed. Basally the mesodermal cells are still in contact with the basal membrane. A differentiation of odontoblasts has not yet taken place. The interior of the pulp cavity is tightly filled with cells.

The oldest tooth anlagen in the present embyonic stage are characterized by the presence of a few odontoblast processes, entering a predentine-like layer. This substance, probably restricted to embryonic stages, seems somewhat different from true predentine in its staining characteristics.

Adult *Squalus acanthias:* The section used for the illustration (Pl. 8-b) was cut in labiolingual direction near the symphysis of the lower jaw through a cross row. Six teeth and tooth anlagen were cut entirely; these were two functional teeth, a fully developed tooth, a less advanced replacement tooth, and two younger stages.

Between the second and the third tooth anlagen two additional anlagen are not completely visible in the section; one of these belongs to a neighboring cross row. Lingually beyond the youngest stage follows the end of the dental lamina. The youngest tooth anlagen of the adult specimen differ from the youngest anlagen of the embryos particularly in that the ameloblasts already are cylindrical. Otherwise, the two are similar. The space beneath the ameloblast layer is solidly filled with undifferentiated cells.

In the next stage of the adult specimen the ameloblasts have reached their

[1] Azan is a German acronym comprising the first letters of Azokarmin B and Anilinblau W to identify colloquially a stain made from their combination (Lillie, *Histopathologic Technique and Practical Chemistry*).

maximum size. Furthermore, there is already a layer of predentine, although it is very thin. The following tooth anlage already has a moderately thick dentine layer. The pulp cavity is no longer uniform at the base, but is divided by coarse struts. The fourth tooth is a fully developed replacement tooth; the following two are functional teeth. In the upper jaw the same relations apply.

Embryos of *Scyliorhinus:* I had available embryos of *Scyliorhinus* that were 61, 65, and 90 mm in overall length. The youngest stage generally shows the same relations as that of *Squalus.* In the older embryos the anlagen of the dentition teeth are a little further developed, but the differences are not significant. Much more notable is the age difference in the skin denticles, whose development is well advanced in the older embryo; at the corresponding area of the skin of the younger embryo no shagreen is present.

Adult *Scyliorhinus:* In sections through jaws of adult specimens, the most lingual tooth anlage, next to the end of the dental lamina, sometimes represents a very early stage of development (Pl. 9-a). In sections through the symphyseal portion of the lower jaw predentine begins to occur in the third anlage from the lingual end. In the fourth anlage there is already much dentine peripheral to a narrow predentine zone. In this stage a certain complication occurs in the basal pulp cavity in that the latter is subdivided into a number of smaller cavities. The sixth tooth (Pl. 9-b) is fully developed, but has not yet begun to function. Teeth numbers seven, eight, and nine were functioning when the animal was alive.

The example of *Scyliorhinus* shows clearly that in sharks the inner dental epithelium does not cover the entire future tooth as in man but only its upper portion. The latter becomes the smooth, shiny crown; the lower part, anchored in the connective tissue without epithelial cover, becomes the tooth base whose surface is somewhat rough and dull. This difference in the genesis between tooth crown and tooth base makes possible a sharp distinction between them. The situation also suggests that the term "tooth root," as it applies to mammalian teeth, should be avoided in sharks.

Mustelus mustelus: In Plymouth, England, I obtained two young specimens of *Mustelus* for histological study. A single section may contain denticles of the skin, functional and replacement teeth of the dentition, and mucous membrane denticles (Pl. 1-b). The tooth anlagen next to the end of the dental lamina often represent early stages of development (Pl. 10-a). The dentine is a normal orthodentine. The pulp cavity is correspondingly simple, although sometimes it may be moderately complicated near the tooth base (Pl. 1-b; Fig. 29).

Raja clavata: As part of the study of the mucous membrane denticles I examined much material of *Raja* while in Plymouth, England. I investigated vertical sections cut in labiolingual direction through cross rows of upper and lower teeth especially. Except for the region of the mouth angle, each cross row contains a large number of teeth of which many are fully functional. Between the teeth of the dentition of *Raja* and the shagreen denticles that are relatively sparse on the ventral side of the body there is a rather broad denticle-free zone. For the study of the youngest stages of tooth development, postembryonic specimens of *Raja* are less satisfactory than those of many other forms, because even the youngest anlage present is usually already in a somewhat advanced stage. The teeth of *Raja* are particularly interesting for several reasons: their extraordinarily regular orthodentine structure; the unusually strong anchoring of their tooth bases by connective tissue fibers, Sharpey's fibers (Pl. 10-b) ; their special usefulness in the study of whether shark teeth have enamel (see p. 68) .

Carcharodon carcharias: In a large specimen of *Carcharodon carcharias,* sections of entire cross rows of dentition teeth were made that show the development from the youngest anlagen to the fully developed replacement tooth (Pl. 17-a). These sections served particularly well for the study of trabecular dentine (see p. 61) .

Isurus: As supplement to the examination of *Carcharodon carcharias,* sections of the related genus *Isurus* were studied; *Isurus* has the same type of tooth construction (see pp. 68, 70) .

Mucous Membrane Denticles

In contrast to many Osteichthyes, the tooth-bearing area in the mouth cavity of the elasmobranchs is usually restricted (often only apparently) to the jaws, that is, to the inner faces of the palatoquadrates and Meckel's cartilages. But the teeth that are attached by connective tissue to these skeletal elements often are not the only dentine teeth of the mouth cavity. Extensive areas of the mucous membrane of the mouth cavity may also bear teeth. These mucous membrane denticles are generally very small.

O. Steinhard (1902) showed that frequently these denticles of the mouth and throat cavities display great similarity to the skin denticles (shagreen) of the particular species investigated. He thus called them "placoid scales" of the mouth and throat cavities. We prefer the designation "mucous membrane denticles" because it conveys at once the fact that the structures in question are located in the mouth and that they are true teeth. For the designation of the dermal hard structures of the elasmobranchs I also consider the English term "dermal denticles" preferable to the name "placoid scales," because, according to the view here presented, they are morphologically discrete tooth structures; in contrast the scales of the Osteichthyes, most strikingly those of the Paleozoic crossopterygians, certainly represent complex structures.

There cannot be the slightest doubt that the teeth of the mouth cavity and the denticles of the outer body integument of elasmobranchs are homologous structures. Ontogenetically the mouth cavity is an invagination of the outer body surface (stomodaeum) (Fig. 6). Since the entire integument in elasmobranchs is covered with dermal denticles, it is readily understandable that such denticles should also be present in the wall of the mouth cavity as an invaginated portion of the body surface. Some of the denticles of the mouth cavity gained support on underlying skeletal elements. Because of this advantageous position they acquired functional importance in the grasping of food. Phylogenetically they increased in size and their form became adapted to the new function, thus becoming elements of the dentition. The other denticles of the mouth cavity remained small. Despite their modest functional significance they were retained in many species.

Except for brief mention, for example by Hertwig (1874), the shapes and distribution in the mouth and throat cavities of mucous membrane denticles have been described only by Steinhard (1902), Imms (1905) and Fahrenholz (1915) for a number of genera and species.

Individual mucous membrane denticles may be isolated by treatment of small pieces of mucous membrane with potassium hydroxide. The best overall preparations were obtained by removing the mucous membrane of one side of the mouth-throat cavity and drying it in taut (pinned) condition. In addition, I used selectively stained sections, cut in various directions.

The number of mucous membrane denticles and their arrangement vary greatly among families of selachians. In some they are tightly crowded; in others they are more or less widely scattered. They may occur directly behind the dentition teeth and reach to the esophagus; they may be restricted to the posterior portion of the mouth-throat region, or they may be almost or completely missing.

In *Lamna nasus* and in the common hammerhead, *Sphyrna zygaena,* the mucous membrane denticles are very small compared to the size of the animals. They are so crowded that individual denticles are hardly visible to the naked eye. Stroking such a denticle pavement with the finger from front to back one feels no resistance; but there is strong resistance stroking from back to front because the freely protruding portion of the mucous membrane denticles consists of posteriorly directed points. One of the best whole preparations of the shagreen of the mucous membrane of the mouth cavity was obtained from an adult specimen of *Hexanchus griseus,* in which the denticles, distributed over the mouth cavity, are separated from one another (Pl. 11-a). This preparation shows clearly that the denticles of different areas of the mouth vary notably in size and shape.

In *Raja clavata* the shagreen of the mouth cavity is sparse; it is restricted to the posterior portion of the mouth cavity. The points of the individual denticles are as thin as hair, and the denticles are broadly spaced (Pl. 11-b).

I studied the dentition and the mucous membrane of a specimen of *Carcharodon carcharias* in Zürich, Switzerland [1] (Pl. 12-a). X-ray pictures were made of the available piece of mucous membrane. Counts revealed the presence of about 600 to over 1,200 denticles per cm². The available surface of mucous membrane was about 1,900 cm². A conservative estimate suggests a total number of over 2 million denticles, and a missing strip of membrane probably contained additional hundreds of thousands of denticles (toward the esophagus a strip about 8 to 10 cm wide could not be preserved). Greater numbers of denticles occur probably in large individuals. The greatest length recorded for *Carcharodon carcharias* is 12 meters; its skin and mucous membrane denticles were probably not much larger, but instead much more numerous than in smaller specimens. The size of the mucous membrane denticles of *Carcharodon megalodon,* of late Tertiary and early Quarternary age, which had dentition teeth 15 cm high, are not known.

Where projections of the mucous membrane fold that covers the anlagen of the replacement teeth border the teeth of the dentition, the mucous membrane denticles of *Carcharodon* have a shape (Pl. 12-b) differing from that of the denticles of the rest of the mouth cavity (Pl. 13-a). The denticles in *Mustelus* are about as crowded as those in *Carcharodon*. Because of the much smaller size of this shark (about 80 cm in total length), it was possible to cut a single section containing dentition teeth, shagreen of the integument, and mucous membrane denticles (Pl. 1-b). Mucous membrane denticles consist of a basal portion, anchored in the mucous membrane, and a crown part that reaches into the mouth cavity. The crown usually is directed backward, and often has the shape of an oval, posteriorly pointed plate. The surface of this plate may be ornamented with one or several longitudinal keels. Isolated denticles, as well as sections of denticles, show that the pulp cavity may have two small lateral openings near the base in addition to the main basal opening, much as do those of the skin denticles (Color Plate I, f). The mucous membrane teeth of *Heterodontus* are large considering the modest size of this shark (Pl. 13-b). In *Prionace* the crown plates of the denticles have posteriorly rounded points and three longitudinal keels, as is true for several other genera (Pl. 14-a). The microscopic structure of the mucous membrane teeth will be discussed later (p. 58). Here it may merely be noted that it is similar to that of the shagreen denticles of the skin.

---

[1] Through the courtesy of Prof. J. de Beaumont, Director of the Natural History Museum of the University of Lausanne, Lausanne, Switzerland. This institution had obtained a specimen of *Carcharodon carcharias* 4.5 meters long from Sête, France.

cles that oftei
bone tissue fc
scales. Moreo\
sheath the snc
layer of bone.

Ørvig (1951
of the nature (
Their theoreti
pound scales (
plex scales are
but also amor
subholosteans,
mary conditioi
primordia, cal
tend to form (
still recognizab
of modern and
to be the prodi
of developmen

According ti
thin-walled cor
bony base. A si
this structure \
neck region (i

Denticles of
bony bases, do
32) .[1] The dent
as belonging ti
served so far ir
from the center
is extremely th:

The single d
stages of shagr
branchs (Color
of shape, with
(Pl. 11-b) .

The evidenc
denticles of mo

1 This material is
yet been described.

Mode of replacement of the mucous membrane denticles

A further agreement between the mucous membrane denticles and the shagreen of the integument lies in the mode of replacement. On dry preparations of the skin and the mucous membrane of the mouth, and especially on X-ray pictures of the mucous membrane of the mouth of *Carcharodon carcharias* (Pl. 12-a), there appear areas, distributed irregularly over the surface, where denticles must have fallen out. With higher magnification under the binocular microscope young denticles may be seen to occur in such places in dry preparations. Even where the space in the pavement of denticles has already been fully closed by the new denticle, the latter may be recognized by their lighter color compared to the somewhat darker denticles of the surroundings. On sections the newly formed denticles are of course clearly discernible. I was unable to detect any kind of pattern in the replacement of these denticles.

The anlagen of the replacement denticles are formed not at a depth within the mesoderm, but roughly among the bases of the functional denticles. During growth the replacement denticle hardly changes its location; its apex attains the level of the apices of the functional denticles by being raised as a result of the formation of the base of the denticle. The increase in size of the ameloblasts, which takes place early, and the change in their staining qualities are the same as in the dentition teeth (see p. 52) .

Systematic significance of the mucous membrane denticles

The notable differences in the shape and arrangement of the mucous membrane teeth probably could contribute to a more complete taxonomic characterization of the various groupings of selachians. Even a cursory survey reveals that these denticles show a certain similarity in closely related groups of elasmobranchs. A systematic collection of dry preparations of the mucous membrane of the mouth of as many different elasmobranchs as possible would additionally be of significance in micropaleontological investigations.

Structure and development of the mucous membrane denticles with notes on the shagreen denticles in elasmobranchs

As seen in Plate 1-b, the dentition teeth and mucous membrane denticles of *Mustelus* have similar size and shape. Even greater similarities exist between mucous membrane denticles and shagreen denticles, which extend to the microscopic structure of their hard substances.

The fully developed mucous membrane, or skin denticle (Pl. 14-b and Pl. 15-a) consists in its simplest form of a tiny cone or orthodentine that encloses basally a small pulp cavity. A vascular canal leads to the pulp cavity

fron
post
D
The
shag
the
exce
spec
othe
den
15-k
Ii
cyli
Cole
oute
in tl
in e
tion
d ar
Ii
repi
the
cle,
part
Hei
tissι
fere
U
prei
den
inte
Botl
ope
opm
dep
amc
that
irre
H
case
wig

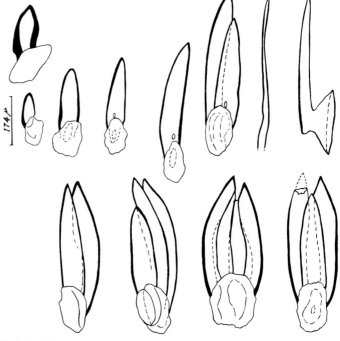

Fig. 32.—Single lepidomorial denticles of different sizes and composite scales from the remains of the skin of an individual of a Carboniferous shark, *cf. Agassizodus* sp. For photographs of these denticles and scales, see Zangerl (1966). The walls of the denticles which enclose hollow and air-filled pulp cavities as now preserved are extremely thin and consist of dentine only. Note the presence of a neck canal just above the basal funnel in several of the denticles. Two or more of these lepidomoria may partially fuse to form scales of varying complexity. Drawn by microscope projection from isolated denticles on slides.

as maintained by Hertwig and most subsequent workers. These denticles are themselves more or less highly differentiated lepidomoria (as are all dentine teeth of vertebrates, see p. 55), subject to variation in size (Fig. 32), shape (Pl. 12-b, 13-a), histological complexity (single and complex scales of *Ornithoprion* that have bony bases, see p. 59), and ability to form loose (Fig. 32) to highly complex aggregates (Stensiö, 1961, Fig. 1, Q to X; Zangerl and Richardson, 1963, Pl. 25).

Dentition Teeth

Orthodentine

Orthodentine is formed as follows: The odontoblasts, after having formed the first layer of dentine on the interior side of the basal membrane, leave behind in this dentine, thread-like cell processes, and the cells themselves retreat in closed formation toward the center of the pulp cavity.

The wall of the dentine that encloses the pulp cavity increases in thickness by successive apposition of new layers of dentine (at the time of formation in the form of predentine, which later changes to dentine) to the inner surface of the already formed dentine. In contrast to many osteoblasts which, except for their canalicular communications with neighboring cells, are entirely enclosed by the bone substance they produce, odontoblasts (almost without exception) retreat from the hard substance they deposit. Pulp cavities surrounded by orthodentine generally present undivided, simple spaces with more or less smooth walls.

It must be particularly emphasized that in elasmobranchs a very regular coat of orthodentine is always formed first, surrounding a wide, uniform pulp cavity, even when the mode of formation of dentine changes in the further development of the tooth. The dentition teeth of *Mustelus, Raja,* and other skates possess typical orthodentine, as do the mucous membrane denticles of the mouth cavity of even those forms whose dentition teeth have another type of dentine beneath a coat of orthodentine. The shagreen denticles of modern sharks also have typical orthodentine. Orthodentine is broadly distributed among most bony fishes, amphibians, reptiles, and mammals.

Trabecular dentine

In *Raja, Mustelus,* and other elasmobranchs whose teeth consist of orthodentine, the genesis of dentine progresses during the entire period of its formation in a rather uniform way, as it does in mammals. Where trabecular dentine occurs, there is a sudden, non-transitional change in the mode of formation. Even macroscopically this change may be seen in the replacement tooth of an isurid (Pl. 16-b). As shown in sections (Pls. 17-a, 18-a), the change is brought about by the odontoblasts which, instead of retreating in closed formation toward the center of the pulp cavity, suddenly show a seemingly irregular alignment throughout the pulp cavity. The layers of odontoblasts can thus assume any possible orientation to the inner enamel epithelium.

Ørvig (1951) states that the morphology of the trabecular dentine is determined by the vascular pattern in the pulp cavity. This relationship is unmistakable in the fully formed condition, but it remains to be demonstrated that the vessel pattern always determines the course of the first-formed trabecles.

Positional relations of the forming cells to their hard substances correspond in orthodentine and trabecular dentine. In both, the odontoblasts retreat as they form dentine, leaving behind only cell processes called Tomes' fibers. Furthermore, both form predentine first, which later becomes dentine. Plate 17-a shows the non-transitional occurrence of trabecular dentine in the tooth development of *Carcharodon carcharias*.

Ørvig (1951) adopted the term "osteodentine" because of the cylindrical deposition around vascular tubes, resembling primary osteonal bone. According to Ørvig these dentine cylinders are always connected by interosteonal bone that may or may not contain bone cells (or lacunae, in the fossil condition.[1] Ørvig assumes that a system of bony trabecules forms first and that dentine is deposited on this bony framework and from it in concentric lamellae toward the vessels.

This generalization could not be confirmed in the present study. Early stages of formation of trabecular dentine in *Prionace glauca* (Pl. 17-b) do not reveal any bone; rather they show an initial thin layer of predentine that soon becomes dentine. Thus, it is uncertain that cell-free interosteonal hard substance can automatically and properly be called bone. It is true, however, that a hard substance resembling bone (thus including cell spaces) is found as the central material of dentine trabecles in many Paleozoic vertebrates. If this substance is, indeed, bone, the intriguing question arises why some modified mesenchymal cells of the pulp cavity first become odontoblasts, producing an outer coat of orthodentine, are succeeded by others that differentiate into osteoblasts to form a bony pulpal sponge work, then, in a third episode of cell specialization, are followed by a new set of odontoblasts that lays down the circumvascular dentine? This matter involves the question of the histogenetic relationship between dentine and bone; it requires further investigation.

We may thus distinguish two types of trabecular dentine. In one kind the central material of the trabecles consists of a hard substance that lacks osteocyte-like cell spaces; in the other type cell spaces are present. Whether they are to be called dentine and bone, respectively, is a matter that requires additional work.

Between elasmobranch teeth that consist entirely of orthodentine and those that have the entire interior space within a coat of orthodentine filled with trabecular dentine are forms with many transitional conditions in which only the apical portion consists of orthodentine, whereas the basal tooth region has an originally uniform pulp cavity that is subdivided into diverticula. It is possible to arrange a series of teeth according to complexity, from those with incipient and poorly defined trabecular dentine restricted to the basal part of the tooth, to those in which the orthodentine is present only as a very thin layer and the remainder of the tooth consists of trabecu-

---

[1] Among exceptions, namely osteodentine lacking interstitial bone, are mentioned the tooth plates of *Diodon latus* (Ørvig, 1951, p. 335). In material of *Diodon sp.* (FMNH No. PF 4518) the tooth plates consist exclusively of *orthodentine (see p. 109)*.

lar dentine. A faint beginning is seen for example in *Mustelus* (Fig. 29).
An intermediate condition is offered by the teeth of *Sphyrna zygaena*
(Pl. 18-a), in which the meshwork of the dentine partitions is somewhat
less tightly joined than in the isurids. Typical trabecular dentine is present
in the basal portion of the teeth in *Prionace glauca* (Pl. 18-b).

Thin sections through dry jaws of *Heterodontus philippi* likewise show
that the trabecular dentine originates within a first-formed coat of compact
orthodentine (Fig. 33). The filling of the pulp cavity with dentine struts
increases in density in the course of formation of the replacement teeth
toward the functional stage (see Marquard, 1946, Fig. 5).

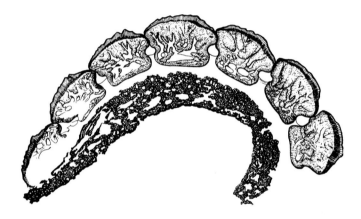

FIG. 33.—*Heterodontus philippi.* Labio-lingual vertical ground section through the eleventh
cross-row of functional and replacement teeth of the upper jaw. At the left, the youngest tooth
anlage; beneath the row of teeth, the calcified jaw cartilage. 1.6:1. From Marquard (1946).

The dentine types that occur in elasmobranchs

Plicidentine

Plicidentine has the histological characteristics of orthodentine. Whether
one may speak of plicidentine in elasmobranchs depends on the definition
of this term. Plicidentine in its restricted sense designates the folded wall
of the basal region of the tooth surrounding the pulp cavity, as in *Lepisosteus* (Pl. 28-b). Many authors, however, among them Mummery, speak of
plicidentine even when the tooth base is not entirely folded but rather has
projections that extend from an externally smooth wall into the interior of
the pulp cavity, as in the large pavement teeth of *Myliobatis aquila*. It seems

advisable, however, to use the term "plicidentine" only in its restricted sense.

Trabecular dentine

For the type of dentine characterized on p. 61, Röse (1897) proposed the term "trabecular dentine" (*Bälkchenzahnbein*) from *trabecula*, "strut," which will be used in the present volume. The shortened version of this designation, "trabeculin," suggested by Burckhardt (1906), has not been widely accepted. Röse proposed the new term rather than accept an existing name because earlier authors had used such names for very different hard substances, a practice that persists and causes confusion, especially with the names "vasodentine" and "osteodentine."

The name "vasodentine" was used by Owen (1840–45), based on views no longer tenable, for the hard substance here called "trabecular dentine" following the practice of Röse. Tomes (1923) used the name "vasodentine" sensibly for a kind of dentine (not occurring in elasmobranchs) that is traversed by tubules containing blood capillaries.

For the substance Owen called "vasodentine," Tomes used the expression "osteodentine" (Tomes, 1923, "osteo-dentine" or "trabeculo-dentine"). A hard substance defined by Owen as "osteodentine"—"a kind of dentine where the cellular basis is arranged in concentric layers around the vascular canals and contains radiated cells, like those of osseous tissue"—does not occur in selachians.

Röse used the expression "osteodentine" in an entirely different sense than did Owen or Tomes: for a narrow boundary zone between dentine and bone, where dentine and bone occur mixed together (see p. 94). To simplify and clarify the nomenclature we shall avoid the name "osteodentine" not only as Röse used it, but also as Owen, Tomes, and Ørvig used it. The expression "vasodentine" will not be used in Owen's sense, rather we shall follow Tomes' terminology for a dentine that is penetrated by tubules containing vascular capillaries (see p. 99).

In the extinct genus *Hybodus*, which was already widely distributed in Triassic time, the space inside the coat of orthodentine is usually entirely filled with trabecular dentine. When the tooth possesses a slender high point, however, the pointed part consists of orthodentine only.

The trabecular dentine of *Myliobatis aquila* is of interest because the trabecles in the early tooth generations do not show the predominantly vertical arrangement that characterizes the later generations (Pls. 19-a, 19-b, 20-a). This seems to indicate that vertical orientation of the struts in trabecular dentine is not a character of fundamental significance but is probably related to the external shape of the tooth. Vertical struts usually occur primarily in teeth of somewhat square or rectangular outline, bordered by more or less flat surfaces.

Two peculiarities of *Myliobatis* may be mentioned. Size differences among successive tooth generations are great in a very young specimen (Pls. 19-a, 20-a). Although in general the calcifications of the jaw cartilages are restricted to a zone located immediately beneath the perichondrium, there occur in *Myliobatis,* probably in connection with the considerable functional requirements, calcifications also in the interior of the cartilages (Pls. 19-a, 20-a) .

Orthodentine

The outermost coat of compact dentine is present in all elasmobranch teeth. In durophagous dentitions it may be removed by wear. The outer zone of this orthodentine coat often contains few dentinal tubules and assumes a glass-like hardness and shiny surface. This outermost zone is often referred to as vitrodentine, although many authors call it enamel (see below) .

Vasodentine in this sense does not occur, as already mentioned, in elasmobranchs. If in the literature the name "vasodentine" is used in connection with elasmobranch teeth, it is to be understood in the sense of Owen, which Tomes and Ørvig call "osteodentine" and for which we prefer the term "trabecular dentine."

The question of enamel in elasmobranchs

In the early period of odontology, a superficial tooth layer, if it was hard and displayed enamel-like gloss was traditionally called enamel. This assumption was revised when O. Hertwig pointed out the significance of the histogenesis. His idea was later supported, in particular by C. Röse who concluded, based on histogenesis, that the elasmobranch tooth is covered by a superficial enamel membrane (*Schmelzoberhäutchen*) but no enamel layer.

Even today opinions on this question are divided. In the textbook by Tomes (1923, p. 62, Fig. 37) the designation "enamel" is applied to selachian teeth, but Tomes stated that he used it "to avoid multiplication of terms." Mummery's textbook (1924, pp. 72–73, Figs. 38 and 39) also speaks of enamel in selachian teeth, referring to Tomes, and clearly setting forth the factual relations. Authors attributing enamel to the selachian tooth include Weidenreich (1926, 1929), Lison (1949), and Moss *et al.* (1964). Kerr (1955) in his paper on selachian teeth also speaks of enamel but with absolutely accurate presentation of the mode of formation of the hard substance in question.

The views of Röse were accepted by Peyer (1937). Schmidt (1948) denied the presence of enamel not only in selachians but in fish teeth generally. Kvam (1950) proposed for hard substances of certain fish teeth the name "mesodermal enamel." Since this is, however, primarily related to Osteichthyes the matter will be discussed later (see p. 90).

To discuss what must be regarded as enamel, it seems best to start from the conditions in mammals and reptiles, because the term "tooth enamel" was used first for hard substances of mammalian teeth. In mammals, distinguishing enamel from dentine offers no difficulties. The enamel of mammalian and reptilian teeth corresponds in all general aspects so that we may consider both as genuine enamel, although some special peculiarities of the mammalian enamel are absent in reptilian teeth.

For our definition the genesis is most fundamental: enamel is formed by cells of the inner enamel epithelium, the ameloblasts. This determines the direction of growth: the last-formed layer of enamel lies outermost.

Where a hard substance is formed may also be significant for its interpretation. If it can be demonstrated that it is formed in mesodermal territory, the substance in question cannot properly be called enamel.

The direction of apposition is evident on preparations of teeth of elasmobranchs. As soon as a hard tissue is recognizable, its growth is without doubt centripetal, and therefore it must be designated as dentine.

Lison (1949), on the basis of positional changes affecting certain melanophores during the growth of a tooth anlage in *Scyllium*, believed that a hard substance must have been formed that increased in thickness centrifugally, suggesting to him that this hard substance was enamel. In his argument he assumed that a space, that plays an essential role in his topographic considerations, had been filled by enamel that was lost during decalcification of the preparation. Contrary to this I could never observe the dissolution of the organic ground substance of already formed hard substance among hundreds of section preparations covering different families of sharks, rays, and skates. Probably the mentioned space never contained hard substance but developed as a result of shrinkage during fixation of the specimen.

Moss, Jones, and Piez (1964) in referring to Lison's study presented two sections through a dorsal fin spine of a fetal specimen of the spiny dogfish, *Squalus acanthias*, in support of the contention that enamel is here being deposited in a centrifugal direction. If these sections are compared to pertinent developmental stages of better fixed material, for example Plate 20-b, it becomes apparent at once that the purported enamel layer is the outermost fibrillar layer of the dentine, forming as usual in centripetal direction (see below). The statement: "the cytodifferentiation of the inner

enamel epithelium is typical of active vertebrate amelogenesis" is an infer-
ence not at all warranted by our broad comparative observations and is
refuted by a look at Plate 20-b, where the highly differentiated ameloblasts
of the third tooth anlage (an3) lie next to a thin layer of predentine (stained
blue in all azan preparations), whereas the ameloblasts of the second tooth
anlage (an2) are not particularly differentiated, yet lie next to a zone that
might be mistaken for enamel. It contains fine fibrils and thickens inward
from the basal membrane (see below). In ground thin-sections of fully
grown teeth this zone is seen as a thin peripheral layer; nothing has been
apposited to the outside of this zone.[1]

Before deposition of any substance, the ameloblasts and the cells of the
future pulp cavity lie close together, separated only by the basal membrane.
Already during embryonic life the first formation not of a tooth hard substance but of a soft ground substance takes place. Into this ground substance
delicate fibers are inserted (see below). The region into which this mass is
deposited lies between the basal membrane and the large mesodermal cells
of the pulp cavity. Particularly free of cells (with their marked nuclei) is the
conical point of the tooth anlage, which is surrounded by the inner enamel
epithelium. The sections show furthermore a cell-free zone that diminishes
rapidly in width toward the base on either side of the tip of the tooth.

Investigation of this region and the processes that take place therein is
essential to the question of whether shark teeth possess enamel. To characterize this region with an unmistakable, unprejudiced expression, I shall
call it "peripheral initial zone" (from *initium*, "begin," because a ground
substance is first deposited in this region, and because of the peripheral
position of the region to the mesodermal tooth germ). Such an indifferent
expression avoids making a decision on the name of the hard substance that
later forms in this region.

The development of a peripheral initial zone, characterized by particular
features and typical of elasmobranchs, begins, as we have seen, with the
deposition of a zone free of nuclei but containing fibers from the beginning,
between the layer of ameloblasts (underlain by the basal membrane) and
the superficial cells of the mesodermal tooth germ. The basal membrane,
because of its fiber-containing nature, is considered a mesodermal structure
(Lehner and Plenk, 1936). In the stages that follow deposition and in still
incompletely developed teeth, the zone of the initially deposited ground

---

[1] The legend to the illustrations of Moss, *et al.*, contains further inaccuracies: "Fish lack any
stratum intermedium or *stellate reticulum*. The outer enamel epithelium is often difficult to
see. . . ." This is all too true in poorly fixed material, but the reader is invited to examine Pl.
8–a: the outer enamel epithelium is very well organized, and there is a well developed *stratum
intermedium*. *A stellate reticulum* has not been observed in sharks, but is beautifully developed
in *Lepisosteus*, for example (Pl. 31–b).

substance remains a different tissue from the other tooth substance by its particular structure and by its particular stainability. It may be distinguished from orthodentine by its lack of dentine tubules; it contains fibers, among which Kerr (1955) distinguished reticular fibers that orginate from the basal membrane and collagenous fibers that originate from cells in the pulp cavity in *Squalus acanthias* and in *Scyliorhinus*.

As may be seen in the illustrations, notable differences exist among sharks in the development of the peripheral initial zone. In *Isurus* (Pl. 21-a) and in *Carcharodon* the outermost fibers, that border the basal membrane and are arranged at approximately a right angle to its surface, appear very clearly. Inward from this layer is a region in both genera in which are found fiber bundles extending parallel to the tooth surface with other bundles standing at a right angle to them. Into this region radiate coarse fiber bundles from the pulp cavity, which are oriented at right angles to the tooth surface. Dentinal tubules are not present in the early stages. During further development, however, the peripheral initial zone is soon delimited internally by the occurrence of dentine tubules. The tubules are first surrounded by incompletely mineralized predentine, not by fully developed dentine.

In *Raja clavata* the peripheral initial zone is clearly visible, even in already functioning teeth, in preparations stained with azan (Pl. 21-b). The zone is more simply constructed than in *Isurus* in that it is occupied almost exclusively by fibers tapering off peripherally and standing at right angles to the tooth surface. Only the outermost layer shows a slightly different

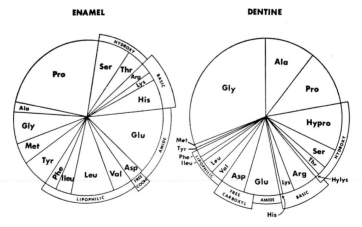

FIG. 34.—A comparison of the composition of proteins from the enamel and dentine of developing human deciduous teeth. 1° = 2.78 amino acid residues per 1,000 total residues. *Ala,* alanine; *Arg,* arginine; *Asp,* aspartic acid; *Glu,* glutamic acid; *Gly,* glycine; *His,* histidine; *Hylys,* hydroxylysine; *Hypro,* hydroxyproline; *Ileu,* isoleucine; *Leu,* leucine; *Lys,* lysine; *Met,* methionine; *Phe,* phenylalanine; *Pro,* proline; *Ser,* serine; *Thr,* threonine; *Tyr,* tyrosine; *Val,* valine. From Eastoe, *Bone and Tooth,* ed. H. J. J. Blackwood (Oxford: Pergamon Press, 1964), by permission.

fiber arrangement (Color Plate I, g). In *Prionace glauca* the fiber course is subject to notable changes during tooth development (Pl. 20-b). Tooth anlagen of embryos of *Scyliorhinus* and of *Squalus acanthias* show that the deposited ground substance already contains fibers in very early stages.

Kerr (1955) calls "enamel" the structure here designated as "peripheral initial zone," arguing that it could not be called "dentine" according to his definition of this tissue. According to our definition of enamel, derived from the situation in mammals and reptiles, the substance in question cannot be called enamel because:

1. The growth direction is not centrifugal, since the peripheral initial zone receives no addition of substance on its outside; the layer with the radial fibers that are outwardly delimited by the basal membrane lies in all stages of development (and in finished teeth insofar as still recognizable) at the tooth surface. Kerr himself pointed out that the organic base of the substance he calls "enamel" does not receive any later addition of material to its outer surface.

2. The hard substance that arises in the region of the peripheral initial zone by mineralization does not show the kind of negative birefringence characteristic of enamel.

3. The outermost layer of the hard substance in selachian teeth forms in a different way than in mammals. Among mammals the enamel originates by the mineralization of cell processes of ameloblasts. Such is not the case in selachians, as evidenced by the entirely different character of the organic bases of their outermost tooth layer (Fig. 34).

These reasons strongly suggest that the outermost layer of the teeth of selachians should not be called "enamel;" this is all the more indicated because the definition of enamel, as derived from observation of enamel in mammals and reptiles, may properly designate this tooth hard substance in the fishes of the class Osteichthyes.

With the proposed name "peripheral initial zone" for the outermost layer of selachian teeth the inapplicable term "enamel" may be avoided; furthermore, the special conditions of its formation may be indicated.

The characteristic birefringence of the enamel has generally proved a practical, reliable criterion in mammals, amphibians, reptiles, and numerous Osteichthyes. As may be readily demonstrated in thin-sections through fossil shark teeth, this type of birefringence is absent in all elasmobranchs.

The striking increase in size which the ameloblasts display temporarily in early stages of development of the tooth anlagen (Pl. 8-a) suggests particular functions. For a long time it has been suspected that the ameloblasts—present in every kind of tooth development, even when ultimately no enamel is formed—might influence attainment of the species-typical tooth form. Experimental investigations (see p. 20) showed, however, that the cells of the mesodermal (mesectodermal) tooth germs also contribute to this form.

An additional function of the ameloblasts is suggested both by the correspondence of the extent of the crown of the shark tooth to the extent of the cover of the mesodermal tooth germ by the inner enamel epithelium and by the previously mentioned increase in size of the ameloblasts in early stages of development. Because of my observations, to be described later, of the development of enamel-like so-called modified dentine in certain Osteichthyes, I have come to think that the ameloblasts exert some influence on the developing dentine also in elasmobranchs. In some Osteichthyes the ameloblasts attain an amazing increase in size, but only where they border the developing modified dentine. This suggests that they contribute to the modification of the dentine (Pl. 30-a). It is thus possible that the temporary size increase of the ameloblasts in early stages of selachian tooth development (Pl. 8-a) might likewise be connected with an effect on developing dentine. Without knowledge of this parallel observation, Tomes (1923) and Mummery (1924) have come to similar conclusions. Mummery (1924, p. 176) stated: "While this organic matrix is beyond question furnished by the mesoblastic dentine papilla, the epiblastic ameloblasts over it are in a state of development which implies that they take an active part and that the tissue is a joint production."

Folding of the outer enamel epithelium in certain developmental stages of *Isurus nasus:*—A surprising feature not hitherto known in any selachian is seen in a few young tooth anlagen of *Isurus nasus*. These are not the youngest, but, counted from the lingual end of the cross row, are the fourth, fifth, and sixth tooth anlagen, which, counting from the labial side, correspond to the sixth, seventh, and eighth anlagen. The inner and the outer enamel epithelium are folded, most notably at the tooth apex (Pl. 22-a and b). Except for a few places, the connection of the enamel epithelium (io) with the adjacent mesodermal tissue (ct) has been lost in the preparation. Between the two formations there is an artificial gap (s) that probably originated by shrinkage during fixing of the specimen. Where the gap is not very wide, projections of the mesodermal tissue lie opposite folds of the enamel epithelium, and each of these mesodermal projections contains a blood-filled capillary. It may be assumed that the protruding portions of the mesoderm fitted into the depressions of the folded enamel epithelium. The few places where enamel epithelium and mesodermal tissue remained in contact in the preparation confirm the view that there is a papillary intertonguing of the vascular mesoderm with the non-vascular epithelial portions of the tooth anlage, by which means the ameloblasts are furnished substances necessary for building the tooth from the outside of the tooth germ, via the bloodstream. The hard substance, to whose construction the ameloblasts probably contribute material in this instance, is the very hard outermost crust of the tooth, the peripheral initial zone that, when fully mineralized is usually called "vitrodentine." In the similar situations to be mentioned under *Lepisosteus* and in several labrids and sparids the substance is not real enamel but rather an enamel-like modified dentine.

General aspects concerning shagreen denticles, mucous membrane denticles, and dentition teeth of sharks

The peculiarity of the elasmobranchs evident from many important features of their organization is reflected also in the hard substances of their integument. Using these shagreen denticles as the criterion, Louis Agassiz has grouped the Recent and fossil forms that possess them under the term "Placoidei." The most significant difference between these integumental structures and those of the Osteichthyes is that the shagreen denticles are dentine teeth which, according to the view here represented, are morphologically simple units.[1] Although the dermal scales of early Osteichthyes, such as the cosmoid scales of Devonian crossopterygians, must be considered complex formations, the scales of the modern Teleostei have presumably originated from ganoid scales by simplification of the histological structure.

If we compare the shagreen denticles of the elasmobranchs with their dentition teeth that have, no doubt, originated from them, it seems obvious that differentiation took place in both according to functional requirements.

The shagreen denticles are protective devices. In benthic forms, such as *Raja,* some denticles achieve notable size. Increase in size does not affect all denticles equally, instead groups of denticles of moderate size develop in certain places of the body. Even less numerous are the very large denticles that likewise occupy specific sites. In fast-swimming forms the shagreen denticles remain small, even in huge specimens, probably because of the selective disadvantage of surface friction. For example, in a sub-adult specimen of *Oxynotus centrina* about 1 meter long the shagreen denticles are decidedly larger, in a *Heterodontus* 80 cm long they are about as large as in a specimen of *Carcharodon carcharias* 4.5 meters long.

Many sharks such as *Squalus acanthias* and *Heterodontus* possess fin spines whose construction is not as simple as that of the large shagreen denticles of *Raja clavata*. In several fossil forms, such as *Asteracanthus*

---

[1] These units may, however, combine to form composite scales in Paleozoic sharks, but in all cases known to me (R. Z.) the individual component denticles remain clearly discernible.

(*Strophodus*), *Ctenacanthus*, and *Nemacanthus*, these spines are covered with denticles. Based on the ontogeny of the dorsal fin spine of *Squalus acanthias*, investigated by Markert (1896), it may be suspected that these spines have originated from the fusion of a much enlarged central skin denticle with a multitude of smaller denticles (Peyer, 1946 and 1957).

Although the dentition teeth have become differentiated in many ways in connection with different modes of feeding, the functional significance of the mucous membrane denticles has remained rather modest. It appears, however, not always to have been the same, since these denticles may be almost or completely absent in some selachians, whereas in others they pave, in vast numbers, almost the entire mouth-throat cavity. If the area dotted with mucous membrane denticles reaches as far back as the esophagus, as often it does, the distribution of the denticles is greater than should be expected from the posterior extension of the throat membrane that delimits the stomodaeum. This distribution probably results from boundary displacements during embryonic development and perhaps even subsequent to it. Mucous membrane denticles are often present near the gill arches, even when they are virtually absent elsewhere. Already mentioned were the rare cases in which extremely elongated mucous membrane denticles form a wier that screens the gill clefts. This apparatus retains small food organisms, and thus assumes vital importance for its bearer (Fig. 25).

Survey of the forms

The following Recent and fossil examples were chosen because of the condition of their dentitions.

Because of the application of the rules of priority many generic names of sharks stand today for something other than they did even a few decades ago. Thus it is to be remembered that *Odontaspis taurus* must now be called "*Carcharias taurus* Rafinesque." The name "*Carcharias*," in the sense in which it was used in the past, has been replaced with the earlier name "*Carcharhinus*" (also spelled "*Carcharinus*"). The former "Lamnidae," to which *Carcharodon* and *Isurus* belong, are now generally called *Isuridae*. *Scyllium* has become *Scyliorhinus*. The large works of Bigelow and Schroeder (1948 and 1953) readily orient one to the present state of the nomenclature.

Among the oldest fossil selachians known are single teeth of Devonian age that have been described under the name of *Cladodus*. Whole skeletons of a shark with similar teeth found in the late Devonian Cleveland shales were given the name *Cladoselache*. The teeth (Fig. 35) show a strong middle point and smaller lateral points. A later, late Paleozoic shark, *Pleuracanthus*, of which the entire skeleton is known, had teeth with strong lateral points and middle points that usually were very small (Fig 35). In the construc-tion of the paired fins the two genera differ profoundly, and are considered representatives of different orders. *Pleuracanthus,* furthermore, is a typical element of late Paleozoic freshwater faunas.

The rather varied group of Carboniferous Chondrichthyes that have been gathered in recent systematic work under the term "Bradyodonti" are thought related to holocephalians and are probably a very heterogeneous group. Some probably are more closely allied with selachians than is gen-erally assumed. Among these forms are the cochliodonts, known so far only from the dentition and large numbers of isolated teeth. These indicate a durophagously specialized shell cracker (Fig. 24). A. S. Woodward (1889) assumed that the larger tooth plates had originated from fusion of smaller elements. Such, however, is improbable since the large tooth plates do not arise from fusion of smaller ones in the eagle ray. Treuenfels (1896) demonstrated in *Myliobatis aquila* by investigation of different age stages that increase in the size of tooth plates takes place by more intensive growth, not by fusion. The same probably applied in the cochliodonts. From the Kohlenkalk, giant teeth similar in shape to those of *Acrodus* have been described under the name *"Orodus"* (from *oros,* "mountain") (Fig. 36). Also of Carboniferous age are the widely distributed, single tooth plates of *Psammodus.* These have rounded rectangular outline and may attain notable height. It has been suspected that the Carboniferous ichthyodorulites of the genus *Ctenacanthus* might belong with the teeth called *"Psammodus"* and that these fishes might have been selachians in the narrow sense.

Hardly understandable in its mode of function is the dentition of the Carboniferous to Permian Edestidae *Edestus, Helicoprion, Campodus, Sar-coprion),* which possess, in both the upper and lower jaws, rows of sym-physeal teeth that are firmly connected with one another (but not fused) (Fig. 37). A pavement of small teeth lateral to the symphyseal row is present in some genera *(Sarcoprion).*

In *Edestus* the tooth bases reach enormous size and combine to form tooth-bearing spines that protruded medially from the snout and the lower jaw and presumably functioned as serrated tweezers or scissors.

Janassa bituminosa from the Permian Kupferschiefer of Thüringen ex-hibits a peculiar condition: The worn teeth did not fall off but buttressed the succeeding teeth (Fig. 38).

Aside from the early period, which is not yet clarified, twice during earth history changes of great import took place in the composition of the shark fauna: once before the beginning of the Mesozoic era and once during the Jurassic and the beginning of the Cretaceous periods. The many varied

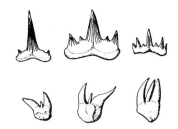

FIG. 35.—Teeth of paleozoic sharks. *Top, Clado-selache*, late Devonian of Cleveland, Ohio; *Bottom, pleuracanth* teeth, latest Devonian to Permian of Europe and North America. From Romer (1945).

FIG. 36.—*Orodus ramosus* a shark of large size from the Carboniferous of Armagh, Ireland. From Zittel, *Grundzüge der Paläontologie* (Munich and Berlin: Verlag R. Oldenbourg, 1923), by permission.

FIG. 37.—Tooth spiral of *Helicoprion ferrieri*, a Permian edestid shark. Such spirals constituted the symphyseal tooth row in *Helicoprion* and related genera. The lateral teeth were small bars with low crowns that formed a pavement. About 1:3. From Eaton (1962).

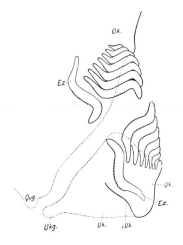

FIG. 38.—Section across the denticulate jaws of *Janassa bituminosa* from the Permian Kupferschiefer. The worn teeth did not fall off but formed a buttress for the successors. As in many modern sharks, the replacement teeth reached their functional position only after notable changes in attitude. Compare Fig. 31. After Jaekel from Zittel, *Grundzüge der Paläontologie* (Munich and Berlin: Verlag R. Oldenbourg, 1923), by permission.

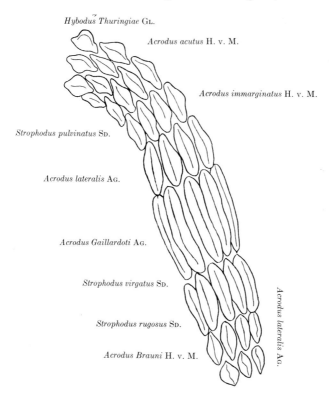

Fig. 39.—*Acrodus.* Arrangement within one dentition of the tooth shapes of this shark genus, which were described as different species. After Jaekel (1889).

early lines of sharks nearly all became extinct before the end of the Paleozoic era. In the Triassic and in the lower Jurassic a few genera dominated in Europe, of which *Hybodus* and *Acrodus* may be mentioned. In both genera the males possessed a pair of head spines that originated from enlarged skin denticles. Anterior and posterior dorsal fins were provided with fin spines. The tooth replacement took place in a way similar to that in *Mustelus.*

For the genus *Acrodus,* as in many other fossil genera, too many species were described in the past, all on the basis of teeth. O. Jaekel (1889) thus delighted in showing in a schematic illustration of the dentition of *Acrodus* (Fig. 39) how many of the superfluous "species" could be united without difficulty in a single dentition. The identification of isolated fossil shark teeth is difficult not only because teeth of very different size and shape may occur within the same dentition, but also because age differences may occasionally lead to form differences within a given species.

For statistical reasons it has been assumed that the fin spines called

"Nemacanthus," which are rather common in deposits of Rhaetic age, might belong with *Acrodus*-like teeth that are extremely common in the same deposits.

Although *Hybodus* and *Acrodus* were still rather common in the lower Jurassic (*Hybodus* extends into the late Cretaceous), new elasmobranchs occur beside them from the Lias onward. One of the earliest forms is *Sphenodus* (*Orthacodus*), of which teeth were found in the lower Lias (Lothringian) of Arzo, South Tessin. This genus is interesting because it is closely related to the isurids, and thus belongs to the modern sharks. These sharks, however, probably experienced their present radiation during the Cretaceous period. The teeth of *Sphenodus* possess razor-sharp cutting edges (p. 37).

In addition to *Sphenodus* there were also found teeth of *Notidanus* in the Lias of Arzo. Among the living representatives of this group *Hexanchus* and *Notorhynchus* possess six gill arches and *Heptranchias* seven, instead of the usual five. Six gill arches occur otherwise among sharks only in *Chlamydoselachus* and *Pliotrema*. For this reason the Notidanoidea are usually considered an ancient group of sharks. It has, however, also been suggested that the increase in the number of gill arches might be a secondary specialization. Although upper and lower teeth have the same form in the dentition of *Chlamydoselachus*, they have extraordinarily different shapes in *Hexanchus* and *Heptranchias* (Fig. 28). The dentition of the last two genera is to be regarded as specialized also in the mode of tooth replacement: The replacement teeth, immediately before they become functional, must undertake a complicated change in position (see p. 48, Fig. 31). As was mentioned previously, this cannot have been the case in the *Notidanus* teeth from the late Jurassic because of the form of their tooth bases (see p. 50). For fossil Notidanoidea the old generic name *Notidanus* is retained, because in the fossils available the number of gill arches which serves to distinguish the modern forms, is unknown.

The only modern representative of the Heterodontoidea, a group that reaches back to the Jurassic period, is the Port Jackson shark, *Heterodontus* (from *heteros,* "different," and *odus, odontos,* "tooth") (Fig. 21). The dentition of *Heterodontus* is interesting for several reasons: because of the different morphology of the teeth in the anterior and posterior portions of the dentition, because of the form differences between teeth of adult and juvenile individuals (Pl. 5-b), because of the mode of tooth replacement and the development of the tooth structure, and because of its robust mucous membrane denticles. *Heterodontus* helps explain the tooth structure of the extinct genus *Asteracanthus* (Pl. 4-b) and *Bdellodus* (Fig. 22) in which the durophagous specialization has evolved notably farther than in *Heterodontus*.

The studied material of *Asteracanthus* also illustrates frequent penetration of fossil shark teeth by organisms called collectively *"Mycelites ossifragus"* Roux. Infection usually took place after death but before burial in the sediment; however, it was determined in the modern *Raja clavata* that the attack of the boring organism can take place during the life of the host (Pl. 23-a).

To my knowledge *Bdellodus* appears suddenly in the Lias of Boll. This sudden appearance shows why great care must be taken in the interpretation of the temporal distribution of some rare fossil selachians. In the Cretaceous there began the evolution of Galeoidea, a group that later evolved into a great variety of forms that encompass a number of families. In Cretaceous deposits *Scyliocorax* is not at all rare. The genus *Hemipristis* was proposed on the basis of fossil teeth; later it was discovered that the genus is still extant and is represented by a species presently living in the Red Sea (Concerning *Galeocerdo*, see p. 34 and Fig. 18). The hammerhead *Sphyrna zygaena* is characterized by the peculiar position of its eyes (Fig. 19); its tooth structure is illustrated in Plate 18-a.

Much less numerous than the Galeoidea are the Squaloidea. *Squalus acanthias* could be discussed in more detail because embryos of this form have been available. To be mentioned also are the spinacid *Oxynotus* and the scymnorhinid *Dalatias*, which is of special interest because of its type of tooth replacement. The Pristiophoroidea with *Pristiophorus* and *Pliotrema* assume an isolated position. *Pristiophorus* has a rostrum resembling that of the pristids or sawfishes but is not closely related to them. The Angel sharks, *Squatina*, despite an amazing similarity in the over-all body shape to the rays and skates, are nevertheless considered true sharks; well preserved specimens are available from the late Jurassic.

In the dentition of the rays and skates, the Batoidea, numerous low-crowned teeth, often of rhombic outline, form a more or less closed pavement. In the rajids the dentition generally shows modest sexual dimorphism. *Rhina* is interesting because of the occlusal relationships of its tooth pavements (see p. 39). In the dentition of the myliobatids a progressive trend toward durophagous specialization may be observed (Fig. 40). In *Rhinoptera polyodon* the tooth pavement consists of numerous small teeth of about equal size. In *Myliobatis* the teeth of the median row become wider than the lateral teeth in the course of ontogeny. Finally, in *Aetobatus* only the enlarged median teeth are present. Among the cow-nosed rays, right-left asymmetrics have been observed in *Rhinoptera* (Bigelow and Schroeder, 1953, Fig. 108).

Although the teeth of the rajids have very regular orthodentine, those of the myliobatids contain trabecular dentine, the formation of which could be studied in replacement teeth of different ages.

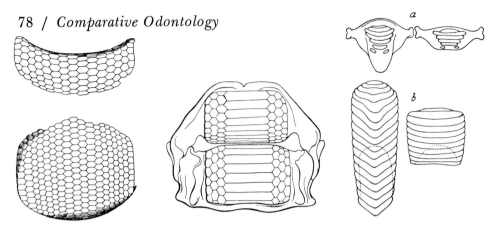

FIG. 40.—Dentitions of rays. *Left, Rhinoptera polyodon; center, Myliobatis aquila; right Aetobatus narinari (upper)* juvenile and *(lower)* adult. After Goodrich from Peyer (1937), in Bolk-Göppert-Kallius-Lubosch, *Handbuch der Vergleichenden Anatomie der Wirbeltiere* (Vienna and Berlin: Verlag Urban & Schwarzenberg, 1931–39), by permission.

The sawfish *Pristis* (p. 36) belongs to the Batoidea despite its shark-like shape. The teeth of its formidable rostrum are enlarged skin denticles; the numerous small dentition teeth are arranged in a tooth pavement.

HOLOCEPHALI

The second subdivision of the Chondrichthyes are the holocephalians, of which only a few genera are left today. Best known among them is *Chimaera monstrosa,* which is not especially rare in European coastal waters and lives at some depth. *Callorhynchus* is restricted to the southern hemisphere. A number of other genera are rarely collected deep sea forms.

The body structure of *Chimaera* shows clearly that the holocephalians are relatives of the elasmobranchs, but they display many characteristics of their own. The skeleton contains no bone, as in most elasmobranchs (see p. 59). In the notochordal sheath a series of limy rings are present. A skin flap covers the gill openings so that only a single opening is visible from the outside. The skull is holostylic, that is, the palatoquadrate is fused to the neurocranium. This feature is thought to be related, as in Dipnoi, to the fact that the dentition consists of but a few, large tooth plates that require notable muscular effort for their functioning, which, in turn, requires strengthening of the head skeleton.

There are two tooth plates on each side of the upper jaw, a smaller anterior and a larger posterior pair; in the lower jaws there is only one large plate on each side (Pl. 23-b). The posterior upper plates have rounded triangular outline. They are separated along the midline by a narrow strip of mucous membrane, which broadens anteriorly to form a papillary structure. These plates lie parallel to the roof of the mouth cavity;

their posterior ends are buried in soft parts that partly cover the plates (Pl. 24-a). The smaller anterior plates have a more oblique position and touch each other in the midline. Their ventral, abraded edges function as cutting shears according to Bargmann (1933). The surfaces of the upper plates that face the mouth cavity are concave. Behind the two lower tooth plates there is a glandular organ (Pl. 23-b).

The histological structure of the tooth plates is complex. Our sections (Pl. 24-a) show, where the outermost tooth layer has not been removed by wear, a superficial layer called "vitrodentine" by Bargmann (1933) and Schweizer (1964), and "enamel" by Brettnacher (1939), which is unmistakably similar to the outermost layer of the crown of shark teeth. The interior of the tooth plates is filled primarily by a wide-meshed trabecular dentine. Within this trabecular dentine there occur in *Chimaera* areas characterized by greater hardness, which form several rods resembling ball chains in section. The formation of these structures takes place by specially arranged odontoblasts. Bargmann (1933) calls these structures cosmine rods, comparing their dentine with the cosmine layer of cosmoid-scales of Devonian crossopterygians. The tritoral surfaces of the tooth plates that have been described in modern and particularly in fossil chimaeroids have falsely been assumed to have systematic significance; they are in reality the places where the cosmine rods of the tooth plates have been ground or cut by wear, as already pointed out by Dean (1906). The dentition of *Chimaera* has been studied primarily by Bargmann (1933) and Brettnacher (1939) and by Schweizer (1964, and work still in progress). Brettnacher appears to have missed Bargmann's paper, since he neither mentioned nor used it. The complicated histological structure of the tooth plates and especially the peculiar structures called "cosmine" by Bargmann and "hard substance of the odontoblastogeneous vacuoles" by Brettnacher, led the authors to different interpretations, as to the relative closeness of the phylogenetic relations between elasmobranchs and holocephalians. Thereby the fact was neglected that *Chimaera* possesses, besides the dentition teeth and the peculiar little dentine structures that surround the canal of the lateral line (Pl. 24-b), normal skin denticles in the tenaculum and in the mixopodia of the males. These skin denticles can hardly be distinguished in their form, size, and structure from those of the selachians. The correspondence with the skin and mucous membrane denticles of the sharks, which are no doubt less differentiated than are the dentition teeth in the same species, supports the view that in chimaeroids also the skin denticles are more primitive structures than the tooth plates that seem such highly specialized organs. To emphasize this consideration, skin denticles of *Chimaera* are pictured in Plates 25-a and b.

In view of work in progress by Schweizer, who has studied fossil holocephalians (Schweizer, 1964) and is interested in the morphological interpretation of the tooth plates of modern *Chimaera,* a detailed discussion of the different views seems superfluous.

In the geological past holocephalians are not particularly common in the Mesozoic era, but are to some extent documented by skeletons (C. Patterson, 1965) and more often by isolated remains of dentitions, especially in Jurassic and Cretaceous sediments. A discussion as to how many of the so-called Bradyodonti, generally allied with the holocephalians, are actually related to the holocephalians is beyond the scope of our task. Two unquestionable holocephalians may be mentioned: *Myriacanthus* from the Lias, which is characterized by pronounced development of the skin denticles, and *Ischyodus,* of which also whole skeletons have been found.

OSTEICHTHYES

In contrast to the Chondrichthyes, in which the skeleton consists of cartilage and contains no bone (but see p. 59), the fishes in whose skeletons bone occurs to a varying extent are grouped together as Osteichthyes. This division is still used today even though based on Recent fishes and not strictly correct if the fossil relatives are also considered. Unquestionable bone has recently been observed in an elasmobranch of the family Edestidae (Zangerl, 1966), and it has been known for a long time that bone already occurs on a low level of organization among the jawless fishes (Agnatha) in the cephalaspids and among the early gnathostomous Placodermi.

Whether the oldest Chondrichthyes, as is assumed by many paleontologists, also had bone that has been lost secondarily or whether they are derived from distant ancestors that never had bone, remains an open question; although the discovery of true bone in a very highly specialized family of sharks, the Edestidae, would tend to favor the second alternative. Certainly, however, the cleavage into Chondrichthyes and Osteichthyes reaches far back in time.

ACTINOPTERYGII

Two major groups, the Actinopterygii and the Choanichthyes, are distinguished among the Osteichthyes. Following Romer (1945) we use the term Choanichthyes despite the fact that not all forms included in this group have choanae. These Choanichthyes include the crossopterygians and the lungfishes (Dipnoi). Three large groups are distinguished among the actinopterygians: the Chondrostei, Holostei and the Teleostei. From the purely linguistic aspect of this terminology it might be assumed that a greater or lesser amount of cartilage or bone in the skeleton serves as a reliable criterion for the interpretation of the systematic position of these fish groups. This is not so, however; it has been learned that bone, phylogenetically, may undergo reduction in many cases. The above named well-known designations are retained, because they apply reasonably well at least in the broad sense, but particularly because the fishes that are grouped under these names appear to form natural groups characterized by a series of other anatomical characters.

In the construction of the teeth and the differentiation of the whole dentition there are notable differences among the Osteichthyes. It seems advisable, however, to provide first a general survey of the whole class.

As aquatic animals, Chondrichthyes and Osteichthyes correspond to the extent that the differentiation of the visceral skeleton is determined in both by the requirements of respiration by means of gills. Because of this dependence both groups share the same limitations of the possibilities of organization of the mouth.

FIG. 41.—Sea horse, *Hippocampus.* From Goodrich, *A Treatise on Zoology, Part 9: Vertebrata Craniata* (London: Adam and Charles Black, 1909) , by permission.

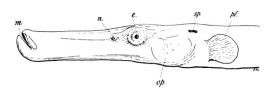

FIG. 42.—Head of the needlefish *Syngnathus.* From Goodrich, *A Treatise on Zoology, Part 9: Vertebrata Craniata* (London: Adam and Charles Black, 1909), by permission.

As in the sharks, the mode of life and particularly the type of feeding in the Osteichthyes is reflected in the mouth and the teeth. In German *"Raubfische"* (predatory fishes) are distinguished from *"Friedfische"* (peaceful fishes). This distinction is not very profound, to be sure, because when tiny planktonic crustaceans are swallowed by a so-called Friedfisch, their doom is as violent as when a Friedfisch faces death in the throat of a pike. The difference lies entirely in the size relationship between predator and prey. Accordingly the relative width of the mouth opening varies greatly. In the seahorse *Hippocampus* (Fig. 41) and in the pipefish *Syngnathus* (Fig. 42) the mouth has become a narrow pipette; in the angler *Lophius piscatorius* the mouth cleft is nearly as wide as the relatively broad body of this fish. Maximal size of the mouth cavity is seen in certain deep sea fishes, such as *Malacosteus, Macropharynx* and *Chiasmodon* (Fig. 43).

In contrast to sharks, the mouth opening lies generally at the extreme end of the head. Only exceptionally is it in a ventral position, namely where a large rostrum has developed, as in sturgeons and especially in *Polyodon, Xiphias* and *Histiophorus* and in the fossil *Aspidorhynchus* (Fig. 44). On the other hand, it may be the lower jaw that extends far forward beyond the tip of the upper jaw, as in *Ammodytes* and even more strikingly in *Hemirhamphus* (Fig. 43). Sometimes both upper and lower jaws contribute equally to the formation of a long, slender, pointed, snout, as in *Labichthys* (Fig. 43).

The differentiation of the mouth cavity is also related to the overall shape of the body. Dorsoventral flattening results in a broad mouth opening. The asymmetry in the body of the Pleuronectidae, which is related to the lateral flattening of their body and functional side position on the bottom, also involves the mouth.

While the jaws of sharks are only moderately protrusive, this apparatus has reached perfection in a variety of different groups of Osteichthyes (Fig. 45). This protrusiveness is apparently related to the different structure of the skeleton. Bone as the skeletal material permits constructions that would not be possible in cartilage. Accompanying this is a corresponding differentiation of the musculature of the visceral skeleton. The area covered by teeth varies greatly. Maximally, nearly all bones that line the mouth cavity may bear teeth; in other cases the dentition is restricted to the edges of the jaws, and in still others the dentition may be totally lost, but often not until the adult condition is reached.

In the mouth cavity of elasmobranchs, dentition and mucous membrane teeth may be distinguished according to their size and mode of replacement, but a similar distinction is not possible in Osteichthyes.

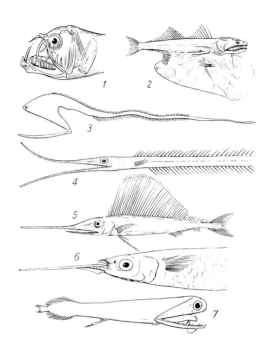

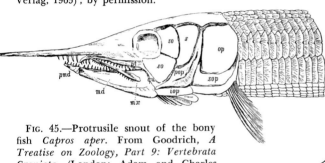

FIG. 43.—Mouth forms of bony fishes: 1, *Chauliodus;* 2, *Chiasmodon;* 3, *Macropharynx;* 4, *Labichthys;* 5, *Histiophorus;* 6, *Hemirhamphus;* 7, *Malacosteus*—1, after Günther; 2–7, after Goodrich (1909), from Peyer, (*Die Zähne,* Verständliche Wissenschaft, vol. 79 (Berlin: Springer Verlag, 1963), by permission.

FIG. 44.—*Aspidorhynchus acutirostris,* holostean from the late Jurassic. From Zittel, *Grundzüge der Paläontologie* (Munich and Berlin: Verlag R. Oldenbourg, 1923), by permission.

FIG. 45.—Protrusile snout of the bony fish *Capros aper.* From Goodrich, *A Treatise on Zoology, Part 9: Vertebrata Craniata* (London: Adam and Charles Black, 1909), by permission.

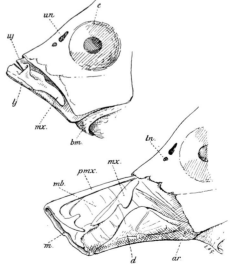

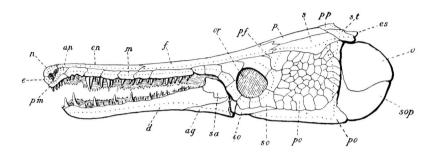

FIG. 46.—Skull of the modern gar pike *Lepisosteus viridis*, in lateral view. After Woodward from Goodrich, *A Treatise on Zoology, Part 9: Vertebrata Craniata,* (London: Adam and Charles Black, 1909), by permission.

FIG. 47.—Head of *Trichiurus armatus* Gray. 1:2. From Tucker (1956)

Tooth form

The variety of tooth form in the Osteichthyes is rather modest if compared to that of the much less numerous selachians. In most cases, a simple conical tooth form prevails. The effectiveness of dentitions that consist solely of pointed, conical teeth may be increased if individual teeth far removed from one another are notably enlarged and the spaces between them are occupied by numerous smaller teeth. This is the case, for example, in the North American predacious freshwater fish, the garpike, *Lepisosteus* (Fig. 46).

Pronounced cutting edges are relatively rarely developed on the teeth of Osteichthyes, for example in *Serrasalmus* and in *Trichiurus* (Fig. 47). Interesting in this connection are the large conical fang teeth of *Lepisosteus*, in which the apex of the tooth is a true lancet (Fig. 48), while the tooth

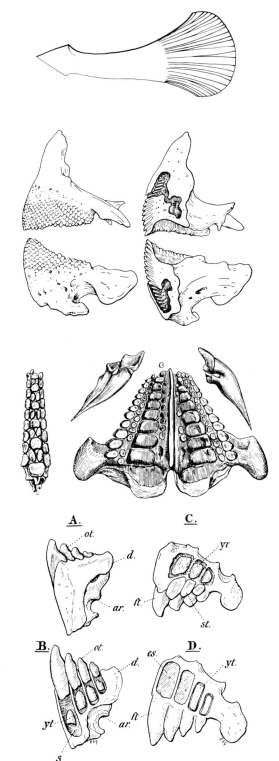

FIG. 48.—One of the large teeth of *Lepisosteus*. Point shaped like a lance. 2.2:1. From Peyer, *Die Zähne*, Verständliche Wissenschaft, vol. 79 (Berlin: Springer Verlag, 1963), by permission.

FIG. 49.—Upper and lower jaws of *Pseudoscarus muricatus* in outer view and in section. From specimens in the British Museum (Nat. Hist.). After Goodrich (1909), from Peyer (1937), in Bolk-Göppert-Kallius-Lubosch, *Handbuch der Vergleichenden Anatomie der Wirbeltiere* (Vienna and Berlin: Verlag Urban & Schwarzenberg, 1931–39), by permission.

FIG. 50.—Dentition of the pycnodont *Microdon elegans* from the late Jurassic. *Left*, vomer; *right*, lower jaw; in front of this, incisor-shaped teeth of the lower jaw viewed from inside and outside. After Zittel, from Peyer (1937), in Bolk-Göppert-Kallius-Lubosch, *Handbuch der Vergleichenden Anatomie der Wirbeltiere* (Vienna and Berlin: Verlag Urban & Schwarzenberg, 1931–39), by permission.

FIG. 51.—Dentition of the acanthopterygian *Balistes viridescens: A* and *B*, inside and outside views of the lower jaw; *C* and *D* inside and outside views of the upper jaw; *ar*, articular bone; *d*, dental bone; *es*, cavity from which a replacement tooth has been removed; *rt*, replacement tooth. After Goodrich, *A Treatise on Zoology, Part 9: Vertebrata Craniata* (London: Adam and Charles Black, 1909), by permission.

base has a circular cross section. Often numerous teeth are united by bone to form a functional unit that may act as a beak, as in *Pseudoscarus* (Fig. 49).

From originally conical teeth, semispherical teeth, robust cylindrical teeth with flatly arched or even gently curved surfaces, extensive tooth plates have evolved in connection with the use of "hard-shelled" food (Fig. 50). Such phylogenetic transformations took place entirely independently at different times of the geological past and in different systematic groups of Osteichthyes. That these are not cases of wear due to use, may easily be demonstrated by replacement teeth that have not yet been used (Pl. 26-a). The marginal teeth in dentitions that otherwise consist of pavements of half spherical or cylindrical teeth often retain their original conical shape. Sometimes they may assume the shape of incisor teeth, particularly strikingly in *Sargodon tomicus* from the Rhaetic (Pl. 26-b). The name of this holostean is meant to indicate that its incisiform teeth are very similar to those of *Sargus ovis,* the sheepshead (Pl. 26-c). The peculiar S-curved anterior teeth of *Loricaria,* an armored catfish, have a more or less two-lobed crown whose apical part, much as the front teeth of many rodents and insectivores, may be red-brown (Pl. 27-a). In some fishes the bones that line the mouth and throat cavity are covered with very numerous small, low, hemispherical or irregularly granular shagreen teeth, or "brush teeth," which are somewhat higher.

Number of teeth

The number of teeth varies widely. Often it is very considerable, particularly where nearly all the bones that line the mouth-throat cavity bear teeth. The number is especially great where "brush teeth" are present, as in the catfish *Silurus glanis.* One large specimen has an estimated nine thousand such teeth. Conversely, durophagous specialization has led to enlargement of individual teeth and reduction of their number. Thus *Balistes* (Fig. 51), for example, has in each premaxilla only seven teeth, in each dentary only four.

Tooth distribution in the mouth

The arrangement of the teeth of the Osteichthyes is related to the structural relations of their skeleton. In the selachians the dentition teeth are attached to the palatoquadrate and Meckel's cartilages, while the mucous membrane denticles, except for the proximity of gill arches and the base of the neurocranium, have no skeletal substrate. In the Osteichthyes the cartilaginous visceral skeleton has no relations to the teeth. These are fastened to the bones that surround the mouth and throat cavities. The

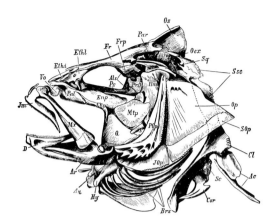

FIG. 52.—*Perca fluviatilis*, perch. Lateral view of the skull. Maxilla *(mx)* toothless, excluded from the rim of the mouth opening. After Cuvier, from Goodrich, *A Treatise on Zoology, Part 9: Vertebrata Craniata* (London: Adam and Charles Black, 1909), by permission.

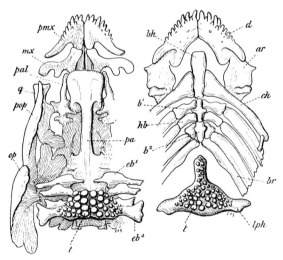

FIG. 53.—Dentition of the pharyngognathous fish *Labrus maculatus*. The teeth occupying throat bones that adhere above and below to the posterior—most gill arches are larger than the teeth of the premaxilla and the dentary. Maxilla *(mx)* toothless; *pmx*, premaxilla; *d*, dentary; *eb⁴*, fourth pair of pharyngobranchials; *t*, throat teeth. From Goodrich, *A Treatise on Zoology, Part 9: Vertebrata Craniata* (London: Adam and Charles Black, 1909), by permission.

presence of such bones and their arrangement vary greatly in the different groups of Osteichthyes. Thus the modern dipnoans lack both premaxilla and maxilla, for which reason all the rest of the Osteichthyes were placed apart from them as Teleostomi, until it was learned that in the oldest fossil dipnoans small, homologous ossifications are present in the proper places. In many actinopterygians the maxilla has been crowded out of its border position along the mouth cleft, and it became toothless (Fig. 52). Instead of a single maxilla in *Lepisosteus,* there are six bones arranged in series, all bearing teeth. These and many other examples show that the differentiation and arrangement of the bones about the mouth cavity are highly variable. The result is a correspondingly different organization of the dentition because of the mode of tooth attachment. Only those areas of the mouth-throat cavity which are underlain by bone are covered by teeth.

In connection with a particular differentiation of the bones, characteristic arrangements of the dentition have evolved and these are useful in taxonomy, for example among the Labridae and Scaridae (Fig. 53).

Tooth attachment

The most common mode of tooth attachment in Osteichthyes consists in a more or less rigid fixation of the tooth to the jaw bone by means of bone substance. As already mentioned, this connection has been closely studied by Tomes (1874–75), who showed that the connection is resorbed each time preparatory to the shedding of a tooth and rebuilt for the replacement tooth. In contrast to the jaw bone proper he called it "bone of attachment." This bone of attachment may sometimes form a pedestal for its tooth. Occasionally the teeth may sit in depressions of variable depth. In a few predacious fishes, such as in *Esox, Lophius,* and *Merluccius,* the large anteriorly situated fang teeth are movably attached so that they may be tilted backward when an animal of prey glides over them; afterward they reassume an erect position and prevent attempts at escape by the prey. These teeth cannot be tilted forward. The apparatus is most perfectly developed in *Merluccius* (Pl. 27-b), as Mummery (1924) has shown. Often the teeth are attached to the jaw by stiff connective tissue.

Throat teeth

An extraordinary wealth of forms, of which we can illustrate only a few, is encountered in the arrangement of the teeth of the gill arches. These teeth are not directly attached to the bone of the gill arches; instead they sit on separate little pieces of bone, that may assume all manner of shapes. In *Polypterus* the teeth adhere to flat bony platelets. In *Amia* they are carried by stout club-shaped bases. *Lepisosteus* differs from *Amia* in that

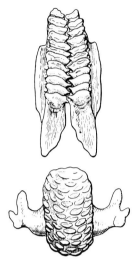

Fig. 54.—Upper and lower tooth-covered throat bones of *Pseudoscarus muricatus*. The tooth replacement above takes place from front to back; below, in reversed direction. From Goodrich, *A Treatise on Zoology, Part 9: Vertebrata Craniata* (London: Adam and Charles Black, 1909), by permission.

the denticles are extraordinarily small relative to the bony bases. Bones similar to those in *Amia* occur in *Sparus* and *Thymallus,* and in *Esox* flat bony platelets are studded with a varying number of stout teeth, depending on the size of the platelets.

Tooth replacement

Generally applicable statements about tooth replacement in the Osteichthyes are hardly possible, since it occurs in a variety of modes, depending on the organization of the tooth-bearing bones. In cases where the developing replacement teeth would be exposed to mechanical injury without adequate protection, their development takes place in special cavities within the jaw bones. Such cavities may occur in all manner of systematic groups, for example in *Lepisosteus, Pseudoscarus* and in *Myletes* (Fig. 54).

Histology and developmental history of the teeth of Actinopterygii

1. Fossil Subholostei and Holostei

In the following the histology of the teeth of the modern Osteichthyes will be preceded by an account of our investigations of some fossil ganoid fishes (subholosteans and holosteans), because this led to the discovery of relations that could subsequently be observed also in many modern forms.

Already Jaekel (1906) [see Hennig, 1906] described an enamel-like dentine in teeth of pycnodonts which he called tekodentin (from *tekein*, "to melt"). My study of *Sargodon tomicus* and *Lepidotes* (Peyer, 1919) showed that the teeth of these fossil ganoid fishes consist of three different hard substances: enamel, dentine, and a merely dentine-like substance which we shall call modified dentine. These two genera and other ganoid fishes were investigaged by me (1937) and by my student Guttormsen (1937). The following description rests primarily on these studies:

The optical differences between these three hard substances that show up especially well in polarized light cannot be documented as sharply on black and white as on color photographs (see Color Plates II and III, a; Pls. 29-a and 34-a).

For the moment, we restrict the discussion of our interpretation of these hard substances to the fossil ganoid fishes. Comparison with other vertebrates shows that the substance that surrounds the pulp cavity undoubtedly represents orthodentine. The nature of the modified dentine (which has generally been interpreted as enamel) and the enamel character of the so-called "email du collet" (Thomasset, 1930 and Peyer, 1919, 1937) are disputed, however. Schmidt (1949) and Schmidt and Keil (1958) particularly have disputed the enamel character of the latter substance.

Against the view that the substance here called modified dentine might be enamel, speaks its structure, which is altogether different from that of enamel; a further, although only gradual, difference is that the dentine tubules may enter the modified dentine in large numbers, but do not do so with the same frequency in the enamel of fish teeth.

For the enamel character of the hard substance that surrounds the basal part of the dentine, three arguments may be cited: the mode of its birefringence in thin-section, its topographic position, and the direction of growth. How sharply the basal enamel is set off both from the orthodentine and the modified dentine may be seen in the color pictures of thin-sections (Color Pl. II). In its position, the basal enamel of the mentioned holosteans corresponds to true enamel in that it lies superficially. It surrounds not only the orthodentine, but covers also the modified dentine, as is clearly seen in *Sargodon* and *Colobodus*. Its growth, therefore, must have taken place in an outward direction, as is determinable with certainty in highly magnified sections (Pl. 27-c).

While describing the dentition of the fossil holostean *Lepidotes maximus* (1954), I suggested in a discussion of the views held by Schmidt

(1949) the possibility of checking the debated question in the modern holostean *Lepisosteus*.[1]

2. Modern Holostei

Lepisosteus

Ground thin-sections reveal that the teeth of this fish are composed of modified dentine, orthodentine and basal enamel in the same way as in the described fossil ganoid fishes (Color Plate III, b). Selectively stained microtome sections show the following:

Enamel: in contrast to the enamel of mammal teeth *Lepisosteus* enamel is not totally lost during decalcification; its organic ground substance is retained throughout the extent of the enamel layer, as determined by comparison with the ground sections. In Teleostei, to be described later (p. 95), the organic ground substance of the enamel is characterized by staining qualities different from those of the orthodentine, which is generally not the case in *Lepisosteus*. It may be distinguished from that of the orthodentine by its structure: it consists of straight rodlets, oriented at a right angle to the tooth surface, and separated from one another only by very narrow spaces.

Orthodentine and plicidentine: it has been known for a long time that the basal portion of the tooth wall enclosing the pulp cavity is radially folded in *Lepisosteus*. As is clearly seen in photographs of ground sections, taken under polarized light (Pl. 28-a), the enamel layer takes part in this folding to some extent; externally this participation is manifested by a vertical ribbing of the basal tooth portion. The survey picture (Pl. 28-b) shows the basally increasing complication of the folding, that finally produces a labyrinthine structure. In the upper tooth portion the pulp cavity, which is narrow compared to the thickness of the tooth wall, is surrounded by orthodentine (Pl. 29-a). During tooth development, the pulp cavity remains wide and smooth-walled for some time. The folded basal portion develops in the later phases of tooth development. Histologically the plicidentine of *Lepisosteus* does not display any clear difference from the orthodentine; there is a gradual transition from one to the other.

Modified dentine: microtome sections through replacement tooth anlagen of *Lepisosteus* show the mode of development of the hard substance which,

[1] I have been able to undertake such an investigation thanks to the help of my American friends and colleagues. Dr. Rainer Zangerl of the Field Museum of Natural History (Chicago) and the late Dr. Frank E. Peabody of the Department of Zoology, University of California, Los Angeles, provided me with material of *Lepisosteus* properly fixed for histological purposes.

despite its enamel-like appearance in ground sections, is different from enamel, and which we call modified dentine.

The modified dentine which occupies the apex of the tooth as a cap is surrounded by the inner enamel epithelium (Pl. 29-b). Characteristically, those cells of the inner enamel epithelium that border the modified dentine are much higher than those cells of the same epithelial layer that are nearer the tooth base and which, as true ameloblasts, produce the enamel (Pls. 29-b, 30-a; Color Plate III, c and d). The enlargement as well as the differentiation of these cells indicates that they are in a state of great activity. Their task consists, in my opinion, in influencing the pre-stage of the hard substance formed in the adjacent mesodermal territory enclosed by these cells, so that modified, instead of ordinary, dentine develops. At the beginning of deposition of the pre-stage of this hard substance, the space between the grossly enlarged cells of the enamel epithelium and the odontoblasts, at the apex of the tooth anlage, is filled with a substance that stains blue in azan preparations (Color Plate IV, c and Pl. 30-b) as does predentine in all sections studied. In somewhat later stages (Color Plate IV, a and Pl. 31-a) a conical, empty space is seen at the corresponding place of the tooth anlage, above a blue zone that clearly represents the lower end of the modified dentine cap in ground thin sections of functional teeth. Since the modified dentine cap of fully formed teeth is entirely lost in the process of decalcification of the specimens, this conical space probably also represents loss due to decalcification. In the fully formed teeth as well as in older replacement tooth anlagen, the cap of modified dentine is dissolved during decalcification and disappears completely. Such teeth thus terminate not in a sharp point but in a rounded cusp whose outline in section corresponds to the boundary between orthodentine and modified dentine.

The ectoderm of the tooth anlage occupies a relatively very large space, especially in developmental stages of middle age. Between the inner and the outer enamel epithelium there is a true enamel pulp containing reticular cells (stellate reticulum) (see Color Plate III, d, and Pl. 31-b).

Differentiation of the boundary of the outer enamel epithelium and the surrounding mesoderm is especially interesting. The two tissues are interlocked so that mesodermal papillae containing capillaries interfinger with projections of the outer enamel epithelium (Pl. 31-b). The result is an obvious enlargement of the boundary surface between ectoderm and mesoderm, indicating increased procurement of material from the blood stream for the tooth anlage. Iron-haematoxylin preparations demonstrate especially well the large number of fine vessels in the connective tissue surrounding the tooth anlage (see also Color Plate IV, b).

Osteal dentine: this tissue occurs occasionally in *Lepisosteus:* see the description of the teeth of *Amia* (p. 94).

Tooth replacement: tooth replacement in *Lepisosteus* is very intensive. The replacement tooth anlagen seem to form, without apparent pattern, everywhere in places in which space has been made by resorption of bone of attachment of worn-out teeth. Active resorption is indicated by the characteristic Howship's lacunae (Pl. 30-b). The tooth anlagen arise at different depths, some rather superficially in broad connection with the mucous membrane of the mouth, some from deeper tissue. In the latter case they are connected by a strand of epithelium either with an older tooth anlage or directly with the mucous membrane of the mouth. During a large part of their development the replacement tooth anlagen remain free from the jaw bones. A firm connection, necessary if the tooth is to become functional, forms relatively late. The orientation of the young teeth varies; their apices may point upward, but they may also face in other directions. If the latter, they must change their attitude before they can reach the position of function.

Denticles of the gill arches: these denticles are very small in relation to the size of the fish, and compared to the throat teeth of many teleosts. They are barely visible to the naked eye, connected to small, approximately cubical ossifications that in turn are attached to the gill arches. The tiny denticles consist of a cone of orthodentine and a cap of modified dentine.

Amia Calva

As in *Lepisosteus,* the tooth is constructed of orthodentine, modified dentine, and a layer of enamel. The latter is notably thinner than in *Lepisosteus,* but its presence can be readily observed in polarized light. The modified dentine appears sharply delimited on ground thin-sections (Color Plate V, a). As also in *Lepisosteus,* it is largely or completely dissolved during decalification of the specimen (Color Plate V, b). The microtome sections usually contain many developmental stages of different age (Pl. 32-a). These show that the modified dentine is surrounded during its formation by an extensive cover of ectoderm (Pl. 32-b).

The connective tissue that encloses the outer enamel epithelium contains many capillaries whose arrangement seems to indicate a functional significance: probably structural materials are passed by diffusion to the inner enamel epithelium along the contact surface (Pl. 33-a).

Prior to and during the development of the hard substances, the cells of the inner and outer enamel epithelium differ notably from one another. The outer enamel epithelium is in close contact both with the connective tissue and its capillaries, and with the inner enamel epithelium; from which the cells of the outer enamel epithelium are distinguished by lighter toning (in stained microtome sections). Near the boundary against the connective tissue there are often vacuole-like cavities of different size. The tightly crowded cells of the inner enamel epithelium do not show a straight radial arrangement, but are slightly curved along the main cell axes (Pl. 33-a); their nuclei are clearly visible. During development, the modified dentine is sharply distinguishable from orthodentine.

The tooth anlagen often lie very superficially; they are seen in broad connection with the epithelium of the mucous membrane of the mouth. Paired occurrence is common, so that a younger anlage is connected with an older one by a strand of epithelium, clearly visible in horizontal sections (Pl. 32-a and b; Color Plate V, c). Resorption occurs but does not play as important a role as in *Lepisosteus.*

Amia is an excellent example for the presence of osteal dentine, that hard substance in which bone cells (or cell spaces, in macerated or fossil tissues) occur together with dentine tubules (Pl. 33-b). In thin sections of fully developed teeth there is no doubt about the bone-cell (osteocyte) character of these cells, with their longitudinal axes lying parallel to the surface of the tooth. These osteocytes are not present in the apical portion of the orthodentine and there is no discernible boundary between the orthodentine and the osteal dentine in the basal half of the teeth. The mode of development of this osteal dentine is not yet clear. That osteoblasts should enter the lower pulp cavity, become associated with the peripheral layer of odontoblasts and sometimes become incorporated into the dentine seems odd. In some sections an occasional cell may be observed at the instant of enclosure by predentine. But it is impossible to determine whether it is an odontoblast or an osteoblast. Moss (1964) has investigated this tissue without adding significantly to what is stated above. He calls the enclosed cells odontocytes and states that osteal dentine may occur in the apical region of the teeth of *Amia,* an observation that could not be confirmed by our material.

3. Teleostei

Enamel

A hard substance that must be recognized as enamel because of its topographical position, because of its direction of apposition, because of its structure, and because of the mode of its birefringence in thin-section, occurs beyond doubt not only in ganoid fishes, but also among the teleosts. It does not have as wide a distribution among teleosts as the enamel-like modified dentine which functionally substitutes for the enamel.

In its best differentiation, true enamel is found in the families Sparidae and Labridae, both acanthopterygians. Examples are the wrasses or lip fishes, *Labrus* and *Crenilabrus* (Labridae) and *Sparus auratus,* the sea breams *Dentex* and the sheephead bream *Sargus* (Sparidae).

As in many ganoid fishes, the orthodentine that makes up the main mass of the tooth is covered at the top by a rounded or cone-shaped cap of modified dentine, while the enamel surrounds the more basal part of the dentine cylinder. In polarized light the differences between enamel, orthodentine, and modified dentine are very clearly emphasized (Pl. 34-a, Color Plate V, d). In contrast to the enamel of mammalian teeth, that of the Sparidae and Labridae is not entirely dissolved during decalcification of the material: its organic ground substance remains preserved along its entire extent. That this is indeed true enamel is indicated by the following features: the layer in question in the microtome sections corresponds exactly in extent and position to the unquestionable enamel layer in the ground thin-sections, and the ground substance, after decalcification, shows an enamel-like structure. This layer is penetrated in its entire thickness by straight rodlets, oriented at right angles to the surface and separated from one another by but very small interstices. These rodlets probably represent the organic base of prismatic structures (Pl. 34-b).

Aside from the Sparidae and Labridae, the occurrence of basal enamel appears to be rather rare among the forms I have investigated.

Dentine (kinds of dentine in teleosts and vertebrates in general)

A discussion of the different kinds of dentine in vertebrates and a review of their terminology may best be attempted in connection with the description of the relations in teleosts, because here we find the greatest diversity in the differentiation of the dentine substance. In elasmobranchs only the general aspects of dentine formation could be emphasized, while the histological peculiarity of the shark teeth called for a separate description. The first portion of the discussion of the histology and development of the teeth in Osteichthyes dealt only with the fossil and modern ganoid fishes because the complicated tooth construction in this group required a separate presentation, which at the same time contribute to an understanding of the construction of the teeth of certain Teleostei. In the tetrapods orthodentine dominates to such an extent that the very few different kinds of dentine that occur among them may here be prematurely mentioned.

Orthodentine

In teleosts, as elsewhere, orthodentine forms generally the main mass of the tooth. It is always present, because even in cases where in the course of further development another kind of dentine follows in the interior of the pulp cavity, there always occurs, as the first hard substance formed, a coat of orthodentine. This is clearly seen in developmental stages.

The dentinal tubules and the cytoplasmic cell processes of the odontoblasts within them run parallel to each other. They usually branch only near the surface of the tooth, and in the rest of their course have weak side branchlets that anastomose with neighboring tubules. Often growth zones occur parallel to the tooth surface; these are seen as growth lines that appear darker in section (Pl. 34-a). The orthodentine forms a smooth-walled delimitation of the pulp cavity that is circular or oval in cross section.

Further investigation is required concerning our observations regarding the tooth development in the angler *Lophius piscatorius, Trigla,* and other teleosts. In cross sections of young tooth anlagen of *Lophius* there is near the periphery a system of lines oriented approximately vertical to the surface, and inside this a network of somewhat finer lines. These two structures extend almost across the entire thickness of the tooth wall at this stage (Pl. 35-a). In older stages normal dentine forms pulpward, soon gaining in thickness to such an extent that the first described dentine portion represents now only a relatively narrow seam along the edge (Pl. 35-b). The above-mentioned lines might represent reticular fibers that extend into the interior of the tooth anlage from its periphery. Observations on teeth of *Trigla* (Pl. 36-a) show a similar structure. Structures of this sort could probably be found in additional forms that possess modified dentine as do *Lophius* and *Trigla*.

In sparids and labrids, as well as in *Solea* and *Pomadasys,* an oblique streaking occurs in the basal part of the dentine coat in certain developmental stages, and which in azan preparations consists of alternating red and blue bars. Since azan stains weakly mineralized dentine blue (predentine, for example, is consistently blue in all preparations available for this study), the blue zones in this streaking might be zones of lesser mineralization (Pl. 36-b).

Modified dentine

As already mentioned, the teeth of sparids and labrids, in correspondence with those of the holostean *Lepisosteus,* do not consist of two, but rather of three different hard substances, namely enamel, orthodentine, and modified dentine. The mode of formation is the same in the sense that modified dentine is surrounded by the inner enamel epithelium during its development, and that we must assume that its cells contribute in the same way to the formation of an enamel-like modified dentine where an ordinary type of dentine would be expected. But there is also this difference from *Lepisosteus* (also applicable to *Amia*) : the nuclei and cell walls of the inner and outer enamel epithelium in adult specimens are discernible only in the early stages of tooth formation, and even then not very clearly. Apparently the processes by which the normal histological conditions are modified in young tooth anlagen take place very early. Unfortunately, I was unable to investigate young fishes and embryos regarding this point.

Plate 34-a shows the differences in the structure of the modified dentine and the enamel in *Labrus turdus*. While the enamel layer is composed of tightly crowded, straight rodlets that stand at right angles to the surface of the tooth anlage, there is, in most of the modified dentine a wild array of numerous crooked dentinal tubules. Only in the most superficial layer may straight dark lines that stand at right angles to the surface be present. During the necessary treatment with acid for decalcification of the specimens, the modified dentine is almost completely dissolved because of its high level of mineralization (Pl. 37-a) and disappears without a trace, as does mammalian enamel. The apical part of such teeth as well as older stages of replacement teeth is thus not pointed, but rounded. Their profile corresponds to the course of the boundary between orthodentine and modified dentine in ground thin-sections. Young tooth anlagen show the great extent of the inner enamel epithelium which covers the forming modified dentine as a thick cap. Between the apical portion of the orthodentine and the inner enamel epithelium there is, prior to the deposition of modified dentine, a space that is conical in section and that was probably filled with fluid in life and becomes filled, at least in part, with modified dentine.

Among the teleosts modified dentine is very widely distributed. Its development is always the same, at least in principle. I could determine this in section preparations for the following genera: *Salmo, Thymallus, Dussumeria, Cyprinus, Tinca, Silurus, Anguilla, Conger, Esox, Belone, Exocoetus, Parascopelopsis, Labrus, Crenilabrus, Sparus, Sargus, Dentex, Chaetodon, Balistes, Priacanthus, Tetraodon, Siganus, Pomadasys, Epinephelus, Lepidopus, Trichiurus, Blennius, Gadus, Merluccius, Lota, Solea, Podas, Trigla, Zeus, Lophius.*

The connective tissue that surrounds the tooth anlage contains numerous small blood vessels whose arrangement and topographic relations to the outer enamel epithelium require particular note. Very small vessels approach the tooth anlage closely, and it may be indisputably demonstrated in many instances that mesodermal papillae containing capillaries enter between protruding portions of the outer enamel epithelium (Pls. 37-b and 38-a). Particularly excellent examples for this are the labrids and sparids

(Pl. 38-b). J. H. Mummery first described such structures under the designation of "tubular enamel." [1]

Our investigations of *Sparus auratus, Dentex dentex, Sargus, Labrus,* and *Crenilabrus* confirm and augment Mummery's observations. These suggest that the tooth anlage at a certain stage of its development receives materials necessary for its formation not only from the blood stream through the pulp cavity, but also from the outside through small vessels that approach it from the surrounding connective tissue. Plate 39-a shows a stage of development of a tooth anlage of *Pomadasys* where the two blood supplies are approximately in balance.

In contrast to *Lepisosteus,* usually neither the nuclei nor the walls of the cells of the enamel epithelium are clearly visible in certain teleosts at early developmental stages of the teeth of adult specimens. Mummery calls "stromata" those derivatives of the enamel epithelium in which the cell boundaries and the nuclei are no longer clearly recognizable.

From the wealth of forms of such stromata our illustrations (Pls. 37-b and 40-a) give a few examples of their appearance in horizontal and vertical section. Further investigations will be necessary to achieve a closer morphological understanding of their origin from normal histological relations, as well as clarification of the physiological processes that take place in these stromata.

Plicidentine

Although *Lepisosteus* among the holosteans offers an excellent example of dentine folding, we find this but rarely among teleosts and then only in modest development restricted to the base of the teeth.

Trabecular dentine

The best-known example of trabecular dentine in teeth of teleosts is the pike (*Esox*) (Pl. 40-b). *Esox* teeth in process of formation show, however, a very different picture from the mode of development of trabecular dentine in elasmobranchs, as clearly seen by comparison of Plate 41-a and Plate 17-a. The vertical course of the canals in the "osteodentine" of the pike appears to be determined not only by the arrangement of the blood vessels, but equally by the primarily vertical orientation of the prominent connective tissue strands that contribute mainly to the formation of the hard tissue (Pls. 41-b and 42-a). In the illustrated examples of elasmobranch

---

[1] That this is not enamel, but modified dentine is evident from the fact that true enamel is beautifully developed around the tooth base in labrids and sparids. That Mummery's interpretation of this hard substance is no longer tenable is irrelevant compared to the fact that Mummery clearly recognized the physiological significance of the observed morphological relations.

teeth the course of the dentine trabecules is not obviously everywhere determined by the distribution and arrangement of the blood vessels (Pls. 17-a and b) of the pulp cavity. In view of published statements (for example by Ørvig, 1951) that there is a close structural (and implied functional) relation between the dentine trabecules and the differentiation of the vascular knot in the pulp cavity, this matter should be studied in modern forms by special methods.

Osteal dentine

A tooth hard substance in which dentinal tubules and osteocytes (or cell spaces, in fossil condition) occur together was described in *Amia* (Pl. 33-b) and *Lepisosteus;* among teleost fishes I could find no typical examples of such a formation.

Vasodentine

Vasodentine in Tomes' sense is characterized by the presence of canals that contain capillaries only and have no histogenetic relations to dentinal tubules. The lumen of the canals of this vasodentine is usually larger than that of dentinal tubules. Vasodentine occurs primarily among the cods of which we illustrate the hake *Merluccius* as an example (Pl. 42-b) .

The terminology of the dentine

Orthodentine: To designate the type of dentine that does not fundamentally differ in its mode of formation from that hard substance in man, the long-familiar name "orthodentine" suffices. The mixed composition of this name from Greek and Latin components is no adequate reason to sacrifice it for the term "normodentine" which has not become established.

Modified dentine: This designation, proposed in the present work, should be used only for a number of ganoid and teleost tooth hard substances that have been described and illustrated in the preceding chapters.

The term "durodentine," proposed by Schmidt, emphasizes merely the great hardness of the dentine layer, a characteristic not adequate to distinguish modified dentine from the likewise very hard outermost layer of the elasmobranch dentine. The latter is called by many authors by the familiar term "vitrodentine." There is no need to change this name.

Trabecular dentine (osteodentine, vasodentine) : The following may be repeated from the discussion on elasmobranchs (p. 61) .

1. Trabecular dentine (in the sense of Röse, 1897) is that type of dentine usually form an irregular spongework in the internal space. Trabecular dentine lacking cell spaces in the innermost material of the dentinal tra-

beculi can be distinguished from the tissue that contains such when the character of this difference is better understood.

2. To avoid misunderstanding, we ought to abandon the term "osteo-dentine," because it has been used in a variety of senses.

3. We recommend the term "vasodentine" (in Tomes' 1879 sense) exclusively to describe a dentine that is being penetrated by relatively wide tubes containing capillaries.

4. We propose to call "osteal dentine" that hard substance in which dentinal tubules and bone cells (or their cell spaces) occur together, and which Röse called "osteodentine" (a term already used in a different sense) by slightly altering the term.

Plicidentine is characterized by the radial folding of the basal portion of the tooth wall. It is well developed in *Lepisosteus* and some other ganoid fishes, but occurs only rarely and then only in very modest development in teleosts. A fuller discussion of plicidentine is given in the section on amphibian teeth (p. 124).

Irregular dentine as well as the so-called protective dentine or replacement dentine play a role in connection with the long period of functioning of the teeth in mammals (p. 213).

There is presently no unanimity about the terminology of types of dentine (and tooth hard substances in general). This unanimity might be achieved by international agreement.

Bone of attachment

The bone tissue which holds the teeth on the jawbone, and which is eroded during tooth replacement and then newly formed for the successor, was called "bone of attachment" by Tomes.

As in the ganoid fishes, space for the young tooth anlagen has to be created by resorption of the bone of attachment of older teeth. The appearance in the section of continuous destruction and rebuilding is the same as that already described for *Lepisosteus* (Pl. 30-b).

Tooth replacement

To characterize enamel and dentine adequately, the mode of formation of the teeth had to be considered. To these observations the following may be added. Replacement-tooth anlagen of the teleosts originate generally in broad connection with the ectoderm of the mucous membrane of mouth and throat. As seen in microtome sections, the eruption of the teeth is simple, since only a very thin epithelial layer has to be pierced. In many cases, however, the young anlagen, must change their location considerably to reach their final position of function.

Tooth development always begins apically and ends with the completion of the basal tooth portion and its attachment to the jaw, whether by connective tissue or by bone of attachment. In early developmental stages, the enamel epithelium that surrounds the mesodermal tooth papilla is basally very extensive.

Survey of the forms of the actinopterygians

Because of the tremendous number of fossil and Recent genera and species of Osteichthyes, and because of the variety of structure of their teeth, it should be mentioned by way of introduction that even an approximately complete treatment of the topic is not possible in the available space. In some cases, furthermore, I was not able to procure material. As a result the different groups are not equally well represented.

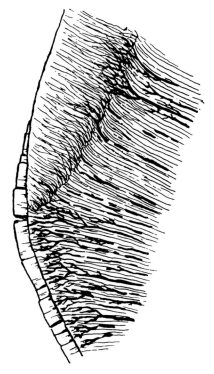

Fig. 55.—Portion of a vertical section through a tooth of the fossil ganoid fish *Birgeria mougeoti*. In the upper left, the basal end of the modified dentine cap; below left, the true enamel; right side, orthodentine. Note the large number of dentinal tubules that enter the modified dentine. About 60:1. Compare Color Plate II, C, and Fig. 3. From Guttormsen (1937).

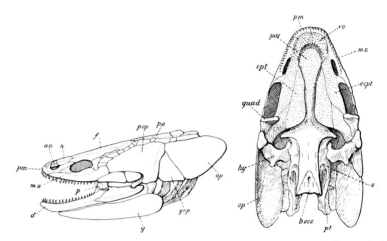

FIG. 56.—*Polypterus bichir;* skull in lateral and ventral views. After Müller and Allis, from Goodrich, *A Treatise on Zoology, Part 9: Vetebrata Craniata* (London: Adam and Charles Black, 1909) , by permission.

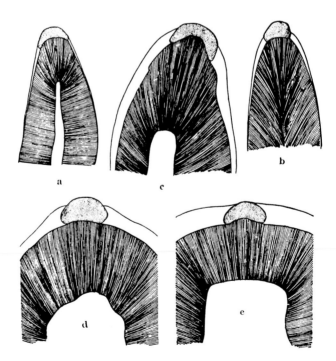

FIG. 57.—Pointed teeth and pavement teeth of *Colobodus* in vertical section, showing the differing extent of the modified dentine. Much enlarged. From Guttormsen (1937) .

among the teleosts. Many extinct forms from the latest Jurassic and the Cretaceous are closely related to it (for the histology of the teeth, see p. 93).

Lepisosteus and *Amia* are the last living representatives of the Holostei that had a great evolutionary radiation in the Mesozoic era; of them only a very few representatives will be mentioned. The genus *Lepidotes* occurs in Jurassic and Cretaceous deposits. The largest species, *L. maximus,* reached a length of nearly two meters. The dentition, for crushing shells (Pl. 43-c), consists of a pavement of strong cylindrical teeth with globular crowns. The marginal teeth are pointed and conical. The replacement teeth are formed in cavities of the bone beneath the functional teeth; their histology (Pl. 27-c) was described by Peyer (1954). The dentition of *Dapedius* is also durophagously specialized (Color Plate II, a). The anterior marginal teeth may be multicuspid; for the histology see Guttormsen (1937).

Sargodon tomicus was described by Plieninger from the Rhaetic of Württemberg and has since been identified in numerous Rhaetic bone beds. It is characteristic of this age. So far, only the globular pavement teeth and

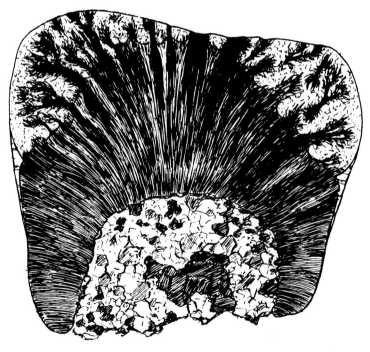

Fɪɢ. 59.—Vertical section through a badly worn pavement tooth of the ganoid fish *Sargodon tomicus* from the Rhaetic. Because of wear the dentinal tubules have been cut into, so that they are visible on the chewing surface. The complicated course of the boundary between ortho-dentine and modified dentine is noteworthy, as is the thin enamel layer that surrounds the tooth base. Much enlarged. From Guttormsen (1937).

the marginal incisor-like teeth are known (Fig. 59, Pl. 44-a) (Peyer, 1919, 1937).

The structure of all well-preserved pycnodont teeth, consisting of enamel, modified dentine and orthodentine, is clearly apparent in thin-sections. The basal enamel layer, however, is easily lost. In abraded specimens only the modified dentine appears to have been retained. Sections through pycnodont teeth from the North American Cretaceous show the basal coat of enamel particularly well (Pl. 44-b). In the durophagously specialized dentition of the genus *Microdon* (Fig. 50) the unpaired vomer dentition opposes paired lower plates in front of which there are on each side two basally united incisor-shaped teeth. The pavement teeth have particular shapes in the different genera; many show a characteristic sculpture. *Pachycormus* from the upper Lias should be mentioned because the structure of its conical teeth has not yet been fully clarified. The bone of its jaw seems to reach far into the pulp cavity. *Aspidorhynchus,* common in the lithographic limestone of Solnhofen, has a rostrum that reaches far beyond the mandible (Fig. 44).

The youngest, but by far the most numerous, group of the Osteichthyes are the Teleostei, the bony fishes *sensu stricto.* They differ from more primitive forms not only in a simplified, lighter construction of the scales, but in numerous additional characters of their organization, that need not be enumerated here. The transition is a gradual one.

The earliest teleosts are known from the Lias. But even in the uppermost Jurassic, for example in the lithographic limestones of Solnhofen, they are represented by but few genera. The segregation into the different large, modern groups took place primarily during Cretaceous time. Despite many rich fossil fish occurrences from this period, the evolution of the teleosts cannot yet be clearly surveyed. In the Eocene most of the ancient forms became extinct, and in the middle and younger Tertiary the fish fauna, aside from species and sometimes generic differences, is essentially modern.

The Clupeiformes or herring-like fishes are a very diversified group of teleosts that originated in the Jurassic and still exist. Their dentition generally shows no particular differentiation. We mention only *Xiphactinus molossus* and *Saurodon,* both large predators of the Cretaceous seas. *Xiphactinus* reached a length of nearly four meters. The knife-sharp, large fang teeth sit in deep pits.

The salmonoid fishes are closely related to the herring-like fishes. In breeding males the lower jaw becomes hook-shaped, a change that involves only the bone of the jaw and not the teeth.

Among the osteoglossids that are primarily distributed in the older Tertiary, *Plethodus* is interesting because a plate of denticles rides on the parasphenoid and interacts with the dentition of the glossohyal.

In the Mormyridae the narrow mouth opening is often directed ventrad; the premaxillae are fused, the maxillae and the bones of the palate are toothless.

Among the Stomiatoidei and Iniomi are deep sea fishes, for example, *Chauliodus, Malacosteus* and *Idiacanthus,* characterized by an extremely wide mouth cleft (Fig. 43).

The catfishes (Siluroidea), carp-like fishes (Cyprinoidea) and the South American and African Characinoidea are grouped together under the term Ostariophysi (*ostarion,* "little bone"; *physe,* pertaining to the swim bladder) because they are all equipped with a Weberian apparatus, a device that consists of a series of four little ossicles on each side of the body midline, which have been derived from parts of vertebrae, and which extend from the swim bladder to the membraneous closure of the perilymphatic space of the inner ear. They register changes in the level of gas content of the swim bladder.

The mouth of the cyprinids is protrusible and toothless, but the lower throat denticles are powerfully developed. They act against a horny pad that lies on a ventral projection of the basioccipital. The differences in form of the throat teeth of the different cyprinid fishes is so characteristic that they can be used to identify genera and species (Pl. 45-a).

Among the Siluroidea, the European catfish *Silurus glanis* has a much reduced toothless maxilla whose sole function it is to carry a large barble. In spite of the fact that this catfish is a voracious predator reaching maximally four meters in length, it has only brush teeth distributed on the premaxillae, vomers, dental bones and the upper and lower throat bones. The number of teeth for a specimen with a skull-base length of 24 cm was estimated to be about 9,000.

The South American Loricarioidea or armored catfishes that generally are included among the Siluroidea, represent, in my opinion, a separate suborder, because they have on their scales and lepidotrichia movably attached skin denticles. The dentition teeth of *Loricaria* and of *Hypostoma* are curved in an S-shaped way, and in *Loricaria* (Pl. 27-a) their cutting edges are bicuspid. In *Ancistrus* (*Chaetostomus*) long, bent skin denticles, laterally slightly behind the mouth opening, form a kind of mustache that is said to be more pronounced in males than in females.

The Charcinoidea are a greatly varied group distributed in South America and Africa, of which two genera will be mentioned because of their dentitions. *Serrasalmus,* the awesome piranhas of South American rivers, are relatively small fishes which, when occurring in large numbers, are known to have skeletonized large mammals and men in minutes. *Myletes* [1]

---

[1] The genus *Myeletes* has been replaced by three genera: *Colosoma, Metynnis* and *Mylosoma.*

(Pl. 45-b) has a durophagously specialized dentition whose replacement teeth are formed in caverns of the jaw bones.

In the Apodes or eels the premaxillae are either lost or fused to the vomers. A few deep sea forms such as *Labichthys, Saccopharynx* and *Macropharynx* are notable for the amazing width of the mouth opening among the Lyomeri. Plate 45-c shows the mode of attachment of the teeth in the marine eel *Conger.*

Numerous very different fish families are grouped around the pike-like fishes, in the broadest sense, the Esociformes, of whose dentitions only a few examples can be mentioned. *Esox lucius,* the pike, is interesting in that the large fang teeth of this predator's dentition may be inclined backward. The gill arches are covered with teeth that sit on special bony platelets (Pl. 46-a).

In contrast to the Cyprinidae, the small, largely viviparous tooth carps Cyprinodontiformes have toothed jaws.

The seahorse, *Hippocampus,* the pipefish, *Syngnathus* and some related forms are toothless, and their mouth opening is extremely narrow (Figs. 41, 42).

Concerning the delimitation of the largest group of the modern teleosts, the spiny-rayed fishes or acanthopterygians (from *acanthos,* "spine" and *pteryx,* "wing" or "fin") opinions are divided. The boundary may be drawn broadly or more narrowly. In the interest of simplicity I shall follow Romer (1945), who considers the group in its very broadest sense. Acanthopterygians have a supporting skeleton of the unpaired fins consisting of unjointed spiny rays and jointed, dichotomously dividing soft rays, among many other peculiarities that cannot be mentioned here.

Typical spiny rayed fishes are the perches of which *Perca,* the perch, may be mentioned. Figure 52 shows the characteristic exclusion of the maxilla from the rim of the mouth opening, common among acanthopterygians, and the loss of its teeth.

From the almost boundless wealth of genera of Perciformes the *Pharyngognathi* (from *pharynx,* "throat" and *gnathos,* "jaw") are mentioned because in these forms the throat dentition is especially well developed (Pl. 46-b) (for the histology of the teeth in the family Labridae, see p. 95). In *Pseudoscarus* replacement teeth, protected from mechanical injury, form in a cavity of the jaw bone.

From the group of the Zeoidea, *Zeus faber,* the "John Dory" of the English, may be mentioned as an example of a very protrusible snout.

The trichiurids, belonging to the scombroids, are characterized by particularly powerful teeth that have sharp cutting edges. *Lepidopus,* related to *Trichiurus* (Fig. 47), which still lives today, for example in the Adriatic, is by far the most common fish in the Oligocene fish shales of the Sernf valley (Glarus, Switzerland) .

Istiophorus has a rostrum that extends far beyond the lower jaw; the same is true of *Xiphias,* the swordfish, of which adults are toothless, while the young possess teeth.

Among the blennoids *Blennius* has a protractile mouth. The seawolf, *Anarhichas lupus,* is notable for its unusually strong dentition. *Toxotes,* the archerfish, is capable of directing a stream of water toward an insect to capture it.

Among the cods and their relatives (Anacanthini) , the large teeth of the hake *Merluccius* are depressable backwards (for the histology of the teeth of the Gadidae, see p. 99) .

Diodon, Tetraodon and related forms are grouped together as Gymno-dontes (naked-teeth fishes) . This designation is not always pertinent, since the so-called tooth plates of *Tetraodon* are, as already pointed out by Ludwig (in Leunis, 1883), not ordinary teeth, but curious dermal hard substances. There are also normal dentine teeth, which contain in addition to orthodentine modified dentine (Pl. 39-b) . In *Diodon* and *Chiromycterus* the large, stacked plates are true dentine teeth consisting only of ortho-dentine (see footnote, p. 62).

The maxilla of the Plectognathi is usually fused with the premaxilla; the upper jaw articulates with the ethmoid. *Ostracion* has long, narrow teeth. The sparse, stout, incisor-shaped teeth of *Balistes* stand in deep alveoli at the bottom of which there are replacement tooth anlagen.

The boxfishes (*Ostracion* and relatives) have also been called Ostraco-dermi, a designation that is now used for fossil Agnatha.

In contrast to the rays and skates, whose bodies are flattened dorso-ventrally, the Heterosomata are laterally compressed fishes. They have become bottom dwellers; that is, they lie on the bottom with one side of the body, so that both sides have changed accordingly. The eye that belongs to the side of the body facing the bottom has been displaced to the other side. In many genera, as in *Solea* and *Pleuronectes,* the right body side always faces upward; in other genera it is always the left side. In the genus *Psettodes* there are species in which the right side faces upward, others where it is the left side. These changes of body form brought about asym-metries in the skull that also affected the jaws.

The name of the angler fish *Lophius piscatorius* (Pediculati) refers to the fact that a movable illicium ending in a frayed flag extends from the middle of the anterior edge of the broad head. By the movements of this lure smaller fishes are attracted, and if they get close enough, they are sucked into the extraordinarily large mouth armed with strong teeth; the large fang teeth can be tilted backward, but not as perfectly as in *Merluccius*.

CHOANICHTHYES

1. *Crossopterygia*

The skull of the geologically early crossopterygians is unusual in many ways. Only recently has it become possible to relate its structure to that of the actinopterygians and the tetrapods satisfactorily. The dentition of the edges of the jaws, the palate and the lower jaws, however (Fig. 60), is readily understood.

Eusthenopteron has rather large fang teeth, set some distance apart, and between them smaller conical teeth. The larger teeth do not stand at the edge of the mouth, which in the upper jaw is formed by the premaxillae and the maxillae, but rather more inward on a series of bones that form the roof of the mouth: the vomer, palatine and the ectopterygoid; in the lower jaw the fang teeth are on the coronoids.

According to the morphology of the supporting skeleton of the unpaired fins, two groups of crossopterygians are distinguished: the Rhipidistia that gave rise to the tetrapods at the end of the Devonian, and the Coelacanthida that were thought to have become extinct in the Cretaceous period until a living representative, *Latimeria*, was discovered in 1938.

Modified dentine does not occur in Choanichthyes. Their teeth consist only of orthodentine and true enamel. In many rhipidistians the basal portion of the wall of the pulp cavity is corrugated by radial folds. In a few genera, such as *Rhizodus* and *Holoptychius* (Fig. 61) the intensity of this folding has increased to such an extent that it has led to a labyrinthodont tooth structure, comparable in its complication to that of the stereospondylous stegocephalians (see p. 124).

The dentition of *Latimeria* has been described in detail in the large work on the anatomy of *Latimeria* by Millot and Anthony (1958). From the wealth of illustrations only little is reproduced because of limitations of space (Pl. 47; Fig. 62).

2. *Dipnoi*

In the structure of the visceral skeleton and in the differentiation of the dentition, the Dipnoi have become a very specialized group. They are holostylic; that is, the upper portion of the jaw arch, the palatoquadrate, is fused to the neurocranium. This is thought to be related to the character of the dentition. The latter typically consists of tough plates whose functioning requires a powerful musculature, which in turn is thought to have made

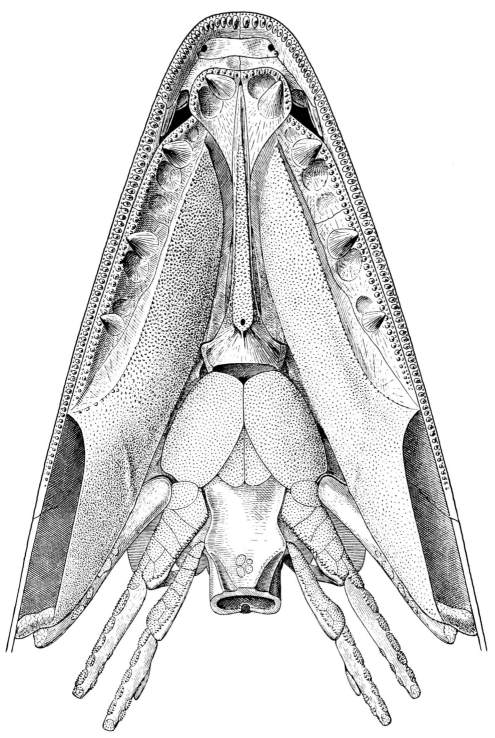

Fig. 60.—Skull of the Devonian crossopterygian *Eusthenopteron foordi* in ventral view, without lower jaw. 1.7:1. From Jarvik (1954).

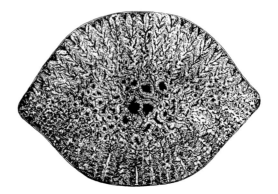

FIG. 61.—Horizontal ground thin-section through a tooth of the Devonian crossopterygian *Holoptychius biporcatus*. Labyrinthine tooth structure. After C. H. Pander, from Peyer (1937), in Bolk-Göppert-Kallius-Lubosch, *Handbuch der Vergleichenden Anatomie der Wirbeltiere* (Vienna and Berlin: Verlag Urban & Schwarzenberg, (1931–39), by permission.

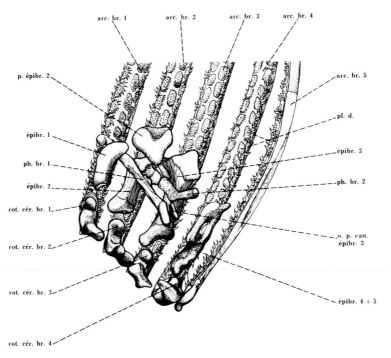

FIG. 62.—Denticulate bone platelets of the gill arches of *Latimeria chalumnae*. *arc. br.* 1–5, branchial arches; *epibr.*, epibranchials; *ph. br.*, pharyngobranchials. From Millot and Anthony, *Anatomie de* Latimeria chalumnae, vol. 1 (Paris: Centre National de la Recherche Scientifique, 1958), by permission.

necessary a particularly massive construction of the skull. The same probably applies to the holostyly of the holocephalians (see p. 78).

The modern dipnoans are the Australian *Neoceratodus forsteri* living in a few small rivers of Queensland, the African *Protopterus*, and *Lepidosiren* which inhabits the region of the Amazon River. In all three the dentition is restricted to the palate and the medial portion of the lower jaw. Related to this is the loss of the premaxillae and maxillae. In one of the oldest dipnoans, *Dipterus*, a vestige of those bones is present.

The dentition of *Ceratodus*, similar to that of the modern *Neoceratodus*, consists of large tooth plates. Altogether there are six plates: a pair of larger plates above, usually designated as pterygopalatine plates, and in front of them two very much smaller vomer teeth. There is only a single pair of plates below, the splenial teeth. The shape of the large tooth plates is illustrated in Plate 48-b. Their inner edges form a convex curve medially; the outer edge forms, in *Neoceratodus*, six projections whose size decreases from front to back. The formation of these projections is related to the divergence outward of the radical ridges on the surface of the tooth plates. These may become less conspicuous by wear. The small, chisel-shaped vomer teeth are obliquely posed. Their anterior ends touch at the mid-line.

Notable finds of *Ceratodus* skeletons are not available from the Mesozoic. But finds of isolated tooth plates are locally common in certain horizons, as for example in the Cenomanian of Egypt, *Ceratodus africanus*; in the Rhaetic of Hallau (Switzerland) and Württemberg, *Ceratodus parvus;* and in the Rhaetic of Aust Cliff (England), *Ceratodus polymorphus*. Recently, Jain, Robinson and Chowdhury (1964) discovered in the Maleri formation of India more *Ceratodus* material. The species name *polymorphus* concerns the variety in shape of the specimens, which is partly due to age differences, but mainly to the different degrees of wear. To describe specimens from a single locality, the proposal of different species is not indicated, even in the face of very notable differences of form. We may assume that the *Ceratodus* finds that extend throughout the Mesozoic might have represented not only different species, but perhaps also different genera. As long, however, as only tooth plates are known, multiplication of genera is unjustified.

Particularly large, massive tooth plates occur in the Keuper of Württemberg; for example, those of *Ceratodus runcinatus* and *C. kaupi*. *Ceratodus polymorphus*, from Aust Cliff, likewise may reach considerable size. In many instances, it was not only the vomer teeth that were in contact with one another, as in *Neoceratodus*, but also the large palatal plates along a more or less extensive contact surface.

When the first fossil teeth of *Ceratodus* were described by Louis Agassiz, modern comparative material was still totally lacking. Thus there was no other course than to place them tentatively among the elasmobranchs. The correct assignment in the system did not come about until, toward the end of the sixties of the last century, the living representative was discovered in Australia.

Histology and tooth development in the Choanichthyes

Crossopterygians and dipnoans correspond notably also in that the teeth of both possess true enamel. The enamel character of the outermost layer of the teeth of dipnoans appears sharply in thin-sections of tooth plates of *Ceratodus parvus,* if viewed in polarized light (Fig. 63; Color Plate VI, e). On the teeth of the modern *Neoceratodus forsteri* the enamel is retained only at the vertically dropping side faces of the tooth plates; elsewhere it is soon removed by wear (Peyer, 1959a).

Of *Latimeria chalumnae* I could investigate teeth thanks to Prof. J. Millot and Prof. J. Anthony of the Institut scientifique de Madagascar. Ground thin-sections in polarized light showed the presence of a thin layer of enamel. In microtome sections stained with azan a difference in the staining quality similar to that between enamel and orthodentine in *Crenilabrus* (Pl. 34-b) and in labrids and sparids generally occurred at the corresponding places. Prior to these investigations, Schweizer (personal communication) had determined the presence of enamel in teeth of coelacanthids from the uppermost Jurassic of Nusplingen and the Rhaetic bone bed of Hallau.

The investigations of Gross (1956) suggest that *Onychodus* probably belongs to the crossopterygians. This is a genus of great geologic age whose oldest examples are found in the Devonian. In the teeth of this fish Gross described and illustrated a layer of enamel. I received material of *Onychodus sigmoides* from the middle Devonian of Delaware, Ohio through the courtesy of the Field Museum of Natural History. Thin-sections through a large symphyseal tooth (Color Plate VI, d) show an enamel layer of great thickness. It is composed of tiny, short, and relatively thick columns that stand at right angles to the surface. In a cross section through the symphyseal teeth, the little columns that lie side by side show a regular alternation of the optical orientation in polarized light (Pl. 48-a).

The little tooth described by Rohon as *Palaeodus* from the Ordovician of Petersberg, a much older find, may be mentioned in connection with *Onychodus.* Its nature has not yet been satisfactorily clarified (Fig. 64).

The dentine in *Latimeria* is a regularly structured orthodentine of interest in connection with the transition from crossopterygians to tetrapods. In contrast, the interior space of the teeth of *Ceratodus* is taken up by a dense spongework of trabecular dentine. This type of construction is probably related, for mechanical reasons, to the size and overall shape of the

Ceratodus tooth plates. The juvenile stage of a *Ceratodus* tooth (Fig. 65) illustrated by Semon still shows an open pulp cavity, while the filling-in of the youthful stages of the teeth of the Rhaetic *C. parvus* is not nearly as dense as in the tooth plates of older individuals. We owe a closer knowledge of the developmental history of *Neoceratodus* to Richard Semon who, on his famous expedition to Australia, reared material for histological study. Unfortunately, the series of developmental stages is incomplete. It terminates presumably at the time the yolk material was exhausted. At this stage, most of the organs had essentially completed their development; but not, however, the teeth. In the oldest stage described by Semon (Fig. 65) there are still separate, individual tooth anlagen instead of large tooth plates. Even if it has not yet been possible to observe how these individual tooth anlagen become united, there can be no reasonable doubt that this represents a definite instance of concrescence. The mode of construction of the tooth plates of *Dipterus* (Fig. 66) corresponds with this view in principle (Semon and O. Jaekel). *Dipterus* is one of the oldest dipnoans from the Devonian. In this genus the radial crests of the tooth plates are not uniform structures; they consist of many single, conical denticles that are separated from each other (Fig. 66).

In the Carboniferous genus *Ctenodus* ("crest tooth," from *kten*, "crest") the radial crests do not show a composition of discrete denticles; it is, however, probable that the different points of these crests (Fig. 67) have originated from individual denticles. In the Carboniferous genus *Sagenodus* there occurs, perhaps partly by wear, an approach of the tooth form to that of *Ceratodus*. Many finds of very small tooth plates of *C. parvus* from the Rhaetic of Hallau that belong to juvenile specimens (Pl. 49-a) show clearly that the tooth plates of the genus *Ceratodus* went through a youth stage in the Rhaetic comparable to the stage of differentiation of *Ctenodus* of Carboniferous age. We may expect that the tooth development of the modern *Neoceratodus* when completely known will show corresponding conditions.

Vomer teeth of fossil ceratodontids have not been known until recently. The locality of Hallau has now furnished also juvenile stages of unquestionable vomer teeth. That these are not merely isolated radial crests may be seen from the oval circumference of the intact bases. The cutting edge, as in the radial crests, consists of pronounced cusps (Pl. 49-b).

Ground thin-sections of the youngest available stages, both of larger tooth plates and of vomer teeth, show that near the surface each of the protruding points corresponds to a tooth-like structure that is separate from its neighbor (Fig. 63). Basally, these individual toothlets gradually grade into a common hard tissue consisting of dentine, which in turn is underlain

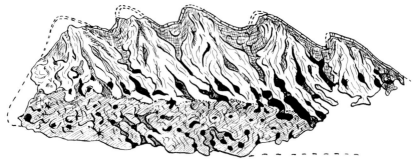

FIG. 63.—Juvenile stage of a tooth plate of the fossil lungfish *Ceratodus parvus* from the Rhaetic. Vertical longitudinal ground section through one of the serrated radial crests of the tooth plate. Beneath the dentine the bony substrate. In the depressions between the serrations the enamel layer has been preserved. Enlarged. See also Color Plate VI and Fig. 5. From Peyer (1959).

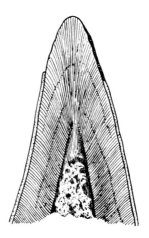

FIG. 64.—*Palaeodus brevis*, a tiny tooth from the Russian Lower Silurian, described by Rohon, that has been differently interpreted. Much enlarged. After Stromer v. Reichenbach, from Peyer (1937), in Bolk-Göppert-Kallius-Lubosch, *Handbuch der Vergleichenden Anatomie der Wirbeltiere* (Vienna and Berlin: Verlag Urban & Schwarzenberg, (1931–39), by permission.

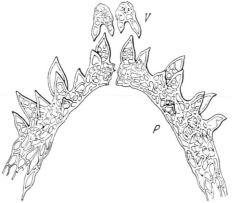

FIG. 65.—Developmental stage of the tooth plates of the modern lungfish *Neoceratodus forsteri*: *P*, palatal tooth plates; *V*, vomerine teeth. After R. Semon, from Peyer (1959).

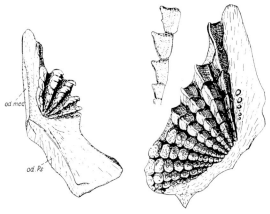

FIG. 66.—On the right side, lower; on the left side, upper tooth plate of the Devonian lungfish *Rhinodipterus secans* showing the composition of the radial crests of individual single denticles: *od. med.*, medan suture; *od. ps.*, sutural surface for the parasphenoid. 3:1. After Gross (1956), from Peyer (1959).

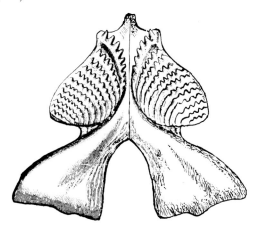

FIG. 67.—Palatal tooth plates and pterygoids of the carboniferous lungfish *Ctenodus cristatus*. About 1:2. After Athey and Hancock from Zittel, *Grundzüge der Paläontologie* (Munich and Berlin: Verlag R. Oldenbourg, 1923), by permission.

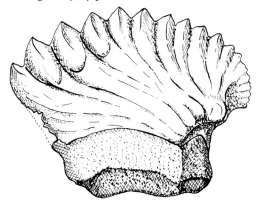

FIG. 68.—Juvenile stage of a right vomer tooth of *Ceratodus parvus*. View of the lingual surface, to illustrate the mode of growth of the tooth plate. 15.5:1. From Peyer (1959).

by bone. Each of the protruding points has a cover of enamel which was soon lost by wear.

In an upper or lower tooth plate, the medial portion apparently is formed first; the diverting crests originate from it. Young developmental stages show that the different protruding points of a radial crest increase in size laterad in the same way that individual denticles of a tooth plate of *Dipterus* do (Fig. 68). Apparently, the most lateral largest point was formed last. Along the edge of this point a shallow furrow runs approximately parallel to the lower edge of the particular radial crest, giving the impression that this line, prior to the formation of the last point, corresponded to the lower edge of the radial crest, and that in connection with the anlage of the last lateral point a further reinforcing layer of dentine was formed beneath the radial crest and (by similar processes in the other radial crests) the entire tooth plate.

Such relations between the anlagen of individual points and the growth in thickness of the entire tooth plate are recognizable in *Ceratodus parvus* only in the stages of early youth. The original sawtooth edge of the crests is soon completely removed by wear.

The radial crests in the Carboniferous genera *Ctenodus* and *Sagenodus* are denticulate even in the adult stage. Faintly similar conditions occur in *Ceratodus runcinatus* in the Keuper and in Jaekel's genus *Hemictenodus*.

Structure and development of the teeth of *Protopterus* have been described by Lison (1941). A note concerning the conditions of occlusion of the tooth plates of *Lepidosiren* may be found in Tomes (1923).

AMPHIBIA

The class Amphibia includes the frogs and toads, the Salientia (or Anura), the salamanders and their relatives, the Caudata (or Urodela) and the tropical, burrowing Caecilia; and a host of fossil forms that have been grouped together under the name Stegocephalia.

Since the content of the concept "Amphibia" has changed in the course of time and since the amphibians in the modern sense are gathered in a variety of ways into larger groups, a few notes may here be inserted that exceed the absolutely necessary for an understanding of the odontological relations.

In Linnaeus' *Systema Naturae* and still at the beginning of the nineteenth century, the reptiles were included among the amphibians. The division, first proposed by B. Merrem and by F. S. Leuckart into two independent animal classes signified great progress, because the differences between amphibians and reptiles turned out to be rather considerable.

Concerning the relations of the amphibians to the fishes, it was assumed already in the second half of the nineteenth century for comparative-developmental reasons, that the tetrapods or four-footed animals, that is, the lung-breathing vertebrates with their two pairs of extremities, were derived from tetrapterygians (four-finned animals), that is, from gill-breathing vertebrates, whose pectoral and pelvic fins are built, however, according to another ground plan. Special comparisons of modern amphibians with modern fishes yielded at first only unsatisfactory results. Even the investigation of the extinct amphibians of the Upper Triassic—first among the fossil forms to have become better known—led not much further. A clarification was not achieved until a few decades ago when tetrapterygians of Devonian age could be compared to ancient amphibians. These investigations led to the conclusion that only representatives of the crossopterygians (in particular the rhipidistians) could be considered as ancestors for the tetrapods. Confidence in this conclusion is great because it rests on the corresponding results of the interpretation of several organ systems. It could be shown that, among the paired fins of fishes, only those of certain rhipidistians (*Eusthenopteron, Sauripterus*) exhibit a structure that may be compared in a special way with that of the tetrapods. Even more impressive are the correspondences in the structure of the skull. These may be demonstrated with great accuracy because of a particularly fortunate circumstance: the lateral line system, a system of sense organs generally restricted to the fishes, has been retained in the head region of the ancient amphibians with its complicated pattern of branching. This provided a possibility of discerning homologies among the skull bones of crossopterygians and stegocephalians; it was possible to demonstrate that the topographic relations of the skull bones to the branches of the lateral line are of particular significance in the area of the head.

The correspondence of the earliest amphibians of the order Ichthyostegalia with the crossopterygians is so great in this respect that in certain fossil finds, as long as no remains of the appendicular skeleton were available, it could not be decided whether they belonged to a crossopterygian or to a tetrapod.

In traditional usage we designate in the following the extinct amphibians, with the exception of the relatively few forms that belong to the Salientia or to the Caudata (fossil Caecilia have not become known so far), *in toto* as stegocephalians. The name implies that in these animals the temporal region of the skull has no fenestrations but is instead roofed over entirely by bone.

The term "Stegocephalia" no longer denotes a group of closely related, early amphibians, and the forms once included under this term are now considered as representatives of several orders. To describe the teeth and the dentition we prefer, however, to use the term "Stegocephalia" in its traditional sense, especially since odontological information is rather sparse in most of the fossil groups.

Application of the principles of a so-called vertical classification, in which the probable or proved phyletic relations are more strongly emphasized, has recently enabled a new grouping of the fossil and modern amphibians. Thus, agreeing with Watson, Romer classifies, in the systematic section of his *Vertebrate Paleontology,* the Labyrinthodontia (which include most of the stegocephalia) with the Salientia as Aspidospondyli on the basis of the vertebrae, opposing them to the Lepospondyli, which include the lepospondylous stegocephalians, the Caudata and the Caecilia.

Stegocephalians

The fossil Amphibia traditionally included under the name Stegocephalia extend from the Upper Devonian to the end of the Triassic. During this long time they changed and segregated into differently organized branches. The stegocephalians of the Keuper, of which well-preserved skulls were first discovered, were at first thought to be very primitive forms. Only gradually was it realized that they represent end members of a long phyletic line.

Reptiles evolved rather soon from the early tetrapods, but the further evolution of the stegocephalians remained amphibian, that is, it did not lead to forms that would have differed significantly from the modern amphibians. In particular, there was, as could be demonstrated for a number of instances, a gill-breathing stage in youth when the gill arches were covered with denticles. Bystrow (1938b) could even show that *Dwinosaurus* is a neotenic stegocephalian; that is, a form in which a metamorphosis and thereby a transition to life on land failed to take place (Fig. 69).

The mode of locomotion of the stegocephalians on land was often a clumsy, salamander-like crawling and shoving. A few late forms were probably no longer able to live outside the water.

To describe the dentition, we need not, except for a difference in the structure of the teeth, discuss the systematic grouping of the stegocephalians, because the differentiation of the dentition is either relatively uniform or not adequately known. The jaw joint is a hinge joint, and jaw movement thus ginglymic. Conceivably this restriction to a single kind of jaw movement might be related to the formation of the temporal region of the skull. It might be argued that its complete bony cover did not permit a further differentiation of the cranio-mandibular musculature; compare Bluntschli (1911).

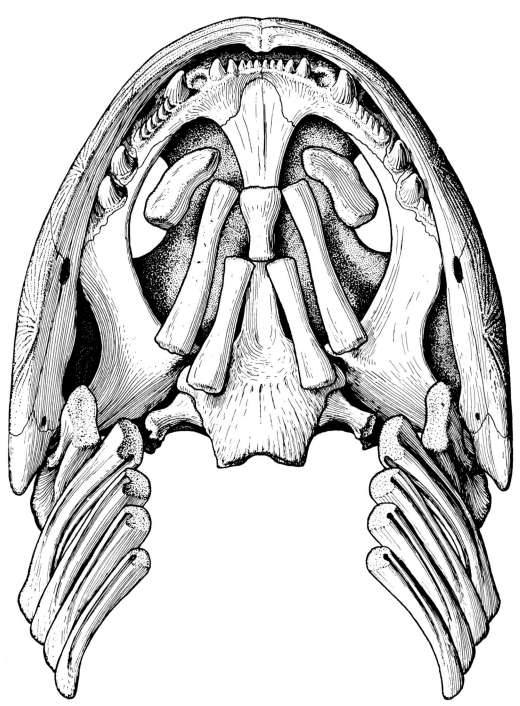

Fig. 69.—Reconstruction of the skull and the visceral skeleton of the Permian stegocephalian *Dwinosaurus*, as seen from below. Well developed ceratobranchials permit the assumption of gill breathing. Note enlarged teeth of the inner row (formed by the vomer, palatine and ecto-pterygoid); the smaller teeth of the outer row (on premaxilla and maxilla) are hidden by the lower jaw. From Bystrow (1938).

The teeth almost always show a simple conical form; they differ primarily in size. Often large, widely spaced fang teeth alternate with smaller teeth. In *Mastodonsaurus* an anterior pair of fang teeth of the lower jaw reaches such size that to close the mouth completely would have been impossible had not the premaxillae been penetrated by holes to receive these fang teeth (Fig. 70). These fang teeth are carried by bones slightly more medial, —mainly the vomers and the palatines (Fig. 71)—than in many reptiles in which the edges of the jaws bear them. Some of the palatal bones may carry small half-spherical shagreen denticles or they may be toothless. The size of the bone surface of the palate that determines the extent of the dentition varies with the size of the space between the two pterygoids.

The large cone-shaped teeth sit in thecodont fashion in alveoli of variable depth. The smaller teeth may be rigidly connected to the jaw or palatal bones by bone of attachment.

From the type of the dentition we assume that there were no vegetarians among the stegocephalians. The large forms were carnivorous; for the smaller ones the expression "animalivorous" may be more applicable. Durophagous specialization of the dentition appears not to occur among any amphibians.

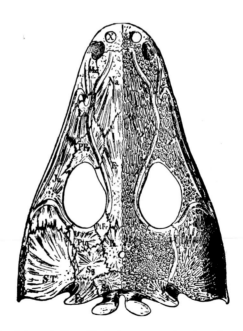

FIG. 70.—Skull of the stegocephalian *Mastodonsaurus giganteus* from the Upper Triassic of Württemberg. On either side, in front of the external nasal opening there is in the premaxillae an opening labeled *x*, which accommodates a large fang tooth of the mandible when the mouth is closed. Much reduced. After E. Fraas, from Zittel, *Grundzüge der Paläontologie* (Munich and Berlin: Verlag R. Oldenbourg, 1923), by permission.

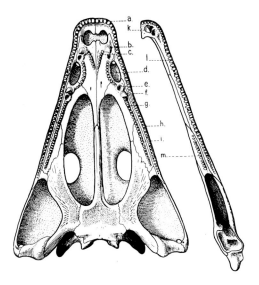

FIG. 71.—Skull and mandible of the stegocephalian *Benthosuchus sushkini* from the Triassic of Russia. Teeth (*a*) of the premaxilla; (*b, c, d*) of the vomer; (*e, f, g*) of the palatine; (*h*) of the maxilla; (*i*) of the ectopterygoid; *l*, dental bone; *m*, the coronoid. 1:29. From Bystrow (1938).

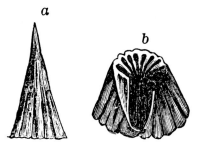

FIG. 72.—Tooth of the Permian stegocephalian *Archegosaurus: a*, outer view; *b*, lower half broken open to show the simple radial folding. From Zittel, *Grundzüge der Paläontologie* (Munich and Berlin: Verlag R. Oldenbourg, 1923), by permission.

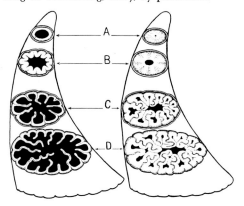

FIG. 73.—Horizontal ground thin-sections. *Left,* through a relatively young; *right,* through an older tooth of *Benthosuchus*. 8:1. From Bystrow (1938).

According to the structure of the teeth, two groups may be distinguished among the stegocephalians: forms in which the tooth wall is not folded basally and has a circular or oval cross-section, and forms with teeth in which the wall of the basal portion is more or less intricately radially folded. A simple folding occurs, for example, in *Archegosaurus* (Fig. 72). Radial folding of the tooth base occurs here and there among other groups of vertebrates: for example, in the holostean *Lepisosteus* (Pl. 28); in the crossopterygians *Rhizodus* and *Holoptychius* (Fig. 61); among the reptiles in ichthyosaurs (Fig. 89), *Squamata* (Pl. 65-a), and in *Champsosaurus* (Fig. 100). Radial folding of the tooth base seems to occur always where—for reasons that need not be the same—the tooth base has an extraordinarily large circumference. This type of formation, like corrugated sheet metal construction, guarantees much greater strength without significant increase in the material used. Folding of the tooth wall is always restricted to the lower portion of the tooth. Even where the folding is very intensive, the pulp cavity in the apical part of the tooth shows a simple circular cross-section. Where the folding has become very complex, it is called labyrinthine. The cross-section of the teeth of the Stereospondyli, a group that appears geologically relatively late, is truly labyrinthine. We now generally designate as Labyrinthodontia all those stegocephalians whose teeth show radial folding, because these forms also show some common features in the construction of the vertebrae.

Bystrow (1938a) devoted a detailed study to the tooth replacement of the labyrinthodont *Benthosuchus;* we offer a few illustrations from this paper (Figs. 73, 74, 75). The dentine wall of the young teeth, including the radial folds, has not yet attained its final thickness, a condition reached by further apposition of dentine. When the teeth are fully differentiated, a process of destruction sets in that ultimately leads to the shedding of the tooth. This process is detectable by characteristic phenomena of resorption. With the tooth, the surrounding bone of attachment is also resorbed.

Palatal teeth of *Benthosuchus* may become covered by a new layer of bone before the destruction has been completed. Resorption then takes place, as may be seen on sections, in the depth of the bone (Fig. 76). A similar overgrowth of partly resorbed teeth by a sheet of bone was noted by Bullet (1942) on jaws of *Varanus salvator* (p. 157). Both instances may reflect periods of rapid growth in the individuals concerned.

The labyrinthine construction of the teeth of *Mastodonsaurus,* an animal known from the Keuper of southern Germany, was illustrated by Owen (1840-45, Pl. 64A and B). The tooth that furnished the thin-section shown here (Pl. 50-a) originates from the Rhaetic bone bed of Hallau, Switzerland. Because the possibility of sedimentary redeposition of this material

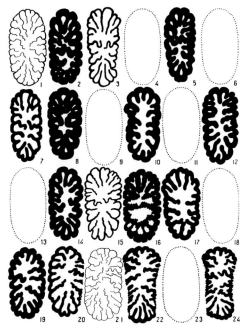

FIG. 74.—Succeeding basal horizontal ground sections from a tooth row of the mandible of *Benthosuchus:* 21, a young, 8, a fully developed tooth; 16, 22 and 24 are partially resorbed; dotted ovals are places where teeth have dropped out. 5:1. From Bystrow (1938).

may almost certainly be excluded, these finds may belong to the very latest stegocephalians. The last known stegocephalian was found in the Lias. The teeth used for thin-sectioning were small; possibly they belonged to juvenile animals. Thus, the spaces between the dental lamellae that protrude into the interior of the pulp cavity are relatively wider than in larger teeth. Plate 50-a shows, moreover, that the coat of dentine is surrounded by a layer of enamel that does not extend into the interior of the tooth. The first-formed dental lamella that penetrates the interior differs by lighter coloration from the dentine layers that were later deposited on it (Pl. 50-a). Plate 50-b, taken from the work of A. Fritsch, *Fauna der Gaskohle und der Kalksteine der Permformation Böhmens* (1883-1901), shows that the teeth of the Lepospondyli differ from those of the labyrinthodonts in the absence of a distinct radial folding of the basal portion. The contrast in tooth structure is, however, not absolute. Plate 51-a and b show that in *Euryodus*, a microsaur, the tooth wall is basally differentiated into radial struts of dentine and bone of attachment, which simulates radial folding; Plate 51-b shows that no folding of the dentine has taken place (see also Gregory *et al.*, 1956). Functionally this structure appears to be an alternative to radial folding of the dentine. The crown of *Euryodus* is covered with a fairly thick layer of enamel (Pl. 52-a).

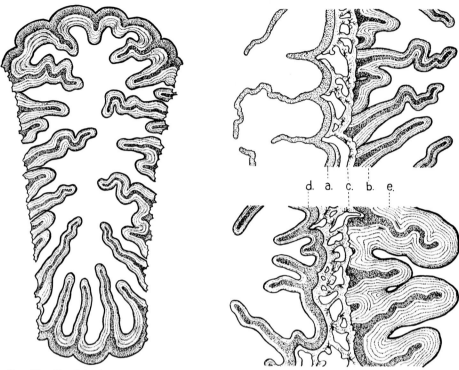

FIG. 75.—Basal horizontal ground sections through teeth of *Benthosuchus: Left,* tooth with resorbed walls; *right,* side walls of neighboring teeth of different ages; between them cementum effecting secondary closure of the resorbed side walls of the teeth on the right side. *A,* 28:1; *B,* 38:1. From Bystrow (1938).

Possibly the intensity of labyrinthine folding is a function of tooth size, and thus follows the rules of allometric growth.

Salientia

The name Salientia (jumpers)—or Anura (tailless amphibian), as they are also called—applies only to the post-metamorphic state of its representatives. The larval forms, the tadpoles, have tails. In the structure of the skeleton, the form of locomotion of the adult animals is reflected in the elongated posterior limbs, the elongation of the proximal tarsals, and the small number of vertebrae. The differences between larvae and adults are especially great in this group, because the tadpole breathes through gills and feeds on vegetation using tiny horny denticles—restricted to the larval life—that have nothing in common with dentine teeth (except the function) and are purely epidermal formations (Fig. 77). These denticles change in rapid succession and have no genetic relations whatever with the horny teeth of cyclostomes.

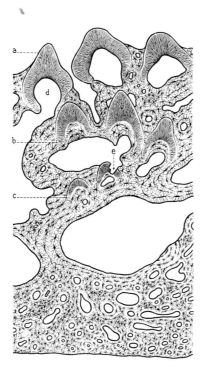

Fig. 76.—Vertical ground section through a portion of the roof of the mouth cavity (ptery-goid with shagreen teeth) of *Benthosuchus: a,* functioning tooth; *d,* its pulp cavity; *b* and *c,* teeth of two earlier tooth generations, which have been covered by bone; at *e,* resorption of such a tooth in the interior of the bone. 98:1. From Bystrow (1938).

During metamorphosis, the visceral skeleton undergoes a notable reconstruction which affects particularly the hyoid and branchial arches. The dentine teeth of the adult animals are restricted above to the premaxillae, the maxillae and the vomers; below to the dentaries. The genus *Rana* has teeth only in the upper jaw.

The tooth crown in *Rana* usually has two tiny points covered by a layer of enamel (Fig. 81 and Color Plate VII, a). The teeth in the upper jaw of the frog, despite their smallness and their lack of antagonists in the lower jaw, seem nevertheless to fulfill a significant task, as suggested by the very intensive tooth replacement in *Rana* (Fig. 78). Teeth are continuously replaced by new ones, and even the pedestal, on which the tooth is fastened, is destroyed and rebuilt. This activity suggests that a dentition restricted to the upper jaw need not be functionally insignificant.

In non-mammals precise occlusion of upper and lower tooth crowns occurs only extremely rarely. The type of action of the dentition is different from that of mammals. Even in mammals, for instance in ruminants, the anterior lower teeth do not act against upper ones, but against a strongly cornified, tough, cutaneous plate. The cornified inner surface of the toothless lower jaw of frogs probably enables pressing small prey against the sharp, backward-pointing tips of the upper teeth. The many simultaneously functioning teeth and replacement teeth of different ages are illustrated in Figure 78.

The mouth opening of the Salientia is generally very wide. Only in the family Engystomatidae is it usually narrow. Differences in distribution of the dentition among the modern Salientia are used in classification. Teeth are only very rarely present in both jaws, as in *Amphignathodon;* the toads are toothless.

The teeth of frogs consist primarily of orthodentine, covered by a cap of enamel. The tooth sits on a high, tubular, bony pedestal. Krause (1923) and Parsons and Williams (1962) note that the bone of the pedestal in *Rana,* close to the tooth, has no bone cells (or cell spaces).

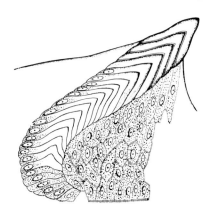

Fig. 77.—Horny denticles of a 20-mm larva of *Rana esculenta* in vertical section. After Schulze (1888) from Peyer (1937), in Bolk-Göppert-Kallius-Lubosch, *Handbuch der Vergleichenden Anatomie der Wirbeltiere* (Vienna and Berlin: Verlag Urban & Schwarzenberg, 1931–39), by permission.

Fig. 78.—Tooth replacement of *Rana esculenta*. Slightly schematic drawing from a cleared preparation that shows the functional teeth and the replacement tooth anlagen in lingual view. Curvature of the maxilla exaggerated by warping. 11:1. From P. Meyer, *Normale Histologie und Entwicklungsgeschichte der Zähne des Menschen*. (Munich: Carl Hanser Verlag, 1944), by permission.

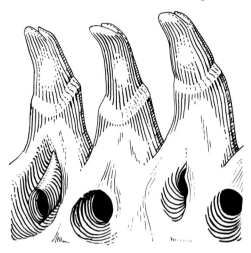

FIG. 79.—Tooth replacement in *Rana esculenta*. Entrance of the replacement tooth anlage into the hollow, bony pedestal of the predecessor. Maceration preparation in lingual view. From P. Meyer, *Normale Histologie und Entwicklungsgeschichte der Zähne des Menschen* (Munich: Carl Hanser Verlag, 1944), by permission.

The replacement tooth is at first lingual with respect to its predecessor. It then migrates labiad through a portal in the wall into the interior of the hollow pedestal and thus comes to be beneath its predecessor. It then moves vertically toward the apex of the functional tooth. Intensive resorption now plays the major role in shedding the functional tooth (Fig. 79). With the reconstruction of a new bony pedestal, the new tooth attains a firm basis and itself becomes functional.

The structures of enamel, dentine, and bony pedestal, as well as the different stages of development of the teeth, will be discussed below.

Salientia have long been known from rocks of Tertiary age, for example, *Latonia,* from the freshwater limestone of Oeningen. For some time, *Montsechobatrachus* from the upper Jurassic of Montsech in Spain figured as the earliest batrachian, until Piveteau (1937) described a small batrachian, *Protobatrachus* from the early Triassic of Madagascar. The skull of this form resembles closely that of the modern frogs and toads, but in the post-cranial skeleton most of the features of the modern Salientia are not yet evident.

Caudata

The tailed amphibians or Caudata (from *cauda,* "tail"), sometimes also referred to as Urodela (from *delos,* "distinct" and *ura,* "tail"), are distinguished from the Salientia by the body form and by anatomical characters of the adult form, and by their less striking metamorphosis.

In the neotenic forms, in which metamorphosis fails to materialize, the larval form becomes sexually mature, as in the axolotl, the juvenile form of

Amblystoma tigrinum. Study of these relationships has shown that the so-called Perennibranchiata are by no means especially primitive Caudata, but are merely neotenic forms. In the so-called Derotremata, for example in the giant salamanders *Megalobatrachus* and *Cryptobranchus*, metamorphosis appears to have only been partially suppressed.

In the development of the dentition, horny teeth do not precede dentine teeth as in the Salientia. The teeth are usually conical, often slightly curved backward, sometimes double-pointed. The crown portion is generally separated from the pedestal. Parsons and Williams (1962) surveyed these relations among modern Amphibia.

The distribution of the denticulate area varies. Most numerous are the teeth in the Plethodontidae in which the parasphenoid also bears teeth. The palato-vomerine teeth may be arranged either in two posteriorly diverging longitudinal rows, or in a cross row. According to this different arrangement Mecodonta and Lechriodonta were formerly distinguished. Ground thin-sections of teeth show in polarized light a thin cap of enamel. Sections through jaws of the fire salamander and the axolotl suggest that tooth replacement is very intensive.

The ontogenetic development of the teeth and the bones surrounding the mouth cavity of the Caudata has been carefully investigated by Hertwig (1874) and used in a theory about the phyogenetic origin of the bones of the mouth cavity. These theoretical postulates are, however, no longer tenable; at least not in the formulation proposed by Hertwig. Since Stensiö could demonstrate beyond doubt that bone already occurs in certain Agnatha, namely in the Osteostraci, one can hardly expect to learn anything about the phylogenetic mode of origin of the bones of the mouth cavity in forms as advanced as the Amphibia. Against Hertwig's concept speaks also the circumstance that the individual tooth anlagen occur well separated from the bones.

Gymnophiona

The name Gymnophiona (from *gymnos*, "naked" and *ophis*, "snake") is, in addition to the fact that they are amphibians, not applicable since a number of forms have hidden scales in the neck region. Of other terms used for this group, Caecilia (from *caecus*, "blind") emphasizes the reduction of the power of sight, which may go so far that the eyes may be covered by the maxillary bones; and Apoda signifies the loss of the limbs. Both reductions are probably related to the burrowing mode of life of these animals, as is the massiveness of the skull in which many bones, ordinarily separate, have become fused.

The dentition of the Gymnophiona consists exclusively of uniform,

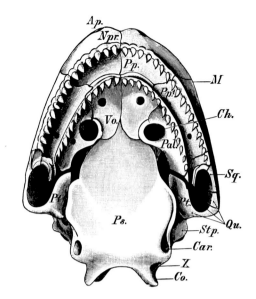

Fig. 80.—Roof of the mouth of the caecilian *Siphonops annulatus*. From R. Wiedersheim, *Vergleichende Anatomie der Wirbeltiere* (Jena: Gustav Fischer Verlag, 1909), by permission.

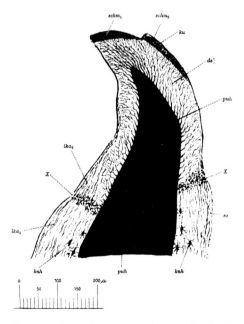

Fig. 81.—Vertical ground section through a premaxillary tooth of a frog: *schm₁*, enamel cap of the main point; *schm₂*, enamel cap of the side point; *ku*, cuticle; *de*, dentine; *puh*, pulp cavity; *x*, tooth pedestal boundary; *so*, pedestal; *knh*, bone cell spaces of the pedestal; *lka₁*, longitudinal canals of the dentine. From R. Krause, *Mikroskopische Anatomie der Wirbeltiere III*, Vereinigung Wissenschaftlicher Verleger, Berlin and Leipzig: Walter de Gruyter & Co., 1923, by permission.

powerful, conical teeth, whose point is usually curved slightly backwards. The entire lower surface of the tongue is connected to the floor of the mouth cavity and cannot be protruded. In the upper jaw (Fig. 80) there are two rows of teeth arranged in an arc. In the lower jaw one or two rows may occur: an outer one is always on the dental bone, and an inner, weaker one.

Food varies and consists of small animals, in some instances even of small snakes.

The Gymnophiona are distributed in tropical Africa, in Central and South America, in India and in the Malayan area in about 40 species distributed among 17 genera. They are absent in Australia, New Guinea and Madagascar; but they do occur in the Seychelles. This disjunct distribution speaks for a high geologic age. That no fossil representatives have so far been found is probably because the chances of preservation as fossils are very small for animals that live in moist holes in the soil.

Histology and developmental history of the teeth in modern Amphibia

For Anura and Urodela (I had no material of Gymnophiona available for first-hand investigation) it may be noted by way of introduction that the cells of young developmental stages (those of the inner and outer enamel epithelium, and those of the pulp cavity) have a relatively large size and are, compared to conditions in fishes and reptiles, relatively less numerous (Pl. 52-b).

In an investigation of tooth chimeras produced experimentally by implanting material from the neural crest of *Bombina pachypus* into approximately equally well-developed larvae of *Triton alpestris*, Wagner (1955) determined that the young tooth anlagen of *Bombina* contain a larger number of odontoblasts than those of *Triton*. The unfortunately short-lived chimerical tooth anlagen are similar in shape to those of *Bombina* (Pl. 3-c).

In the approximately horizontal section across a tooth anlage of *Salamandra* (Pl. 53-a) the ring of cells of the inner enamel epithelium that surround the predentine, consists of about 20 cells. The notably smaller cells of the outer enamel epithelium (which is partly multilayered) are more numerous. In the pulp cavity about 5 mesodermal cells appear in the section. In somewhat younger stages, in which predentine has not begun to be deposited, the cells of the inner enamel epithelium border on the mesodermal cells of the pulp papilla from which they are separated only by the basal membrane (Pls. 52-b and 53-a). With the beginning of predentine formation, the two cell territories are separated by a cell-free zone.

Only very exceptionally can one find an isolated cell nucleus in the predentine; but its provenience cannot be determined. Such dislocated cells appear to originate more probably from the pulp cavity than from the inner enamel epithelium. Many sections show that the ectodermal portion of the tooth anlage is broadly connected with the epithelium of the mouth cavity (Pl. 55-a).

The boundary of the cells of the inner enamel epithelium against the predentine is often emphasized if there is a cleavage space between them and the predentine; such a space probably originated from shrinking during fixation of the object. The large nuclei do not lie in the middle of the ameloblasts, but on the side away from the tooth. An extensive portion of cytoplasm faces the predentine. The cell walls appear very clearly in this zone as more or less parallel lines.

As seen in preparations of *Rana esculenta* and *Salamandra maculosa*, the enamel is totally dissolved during decalcification which is necessary for sectioning the material; nothing remains even of its organic ground substance. Despite this, much as in mammalian teeth, the original presence of enamel is evident even in such sections, because the space that was occupied by enamel prior to decalcification is very sharply outlined, and corresponds accurately with observations on ground thin-sections. In the latter, the enamel is readily differentiated from the dentine by its strong negative birefringence. In the preparations of the axolotl I could detect no enamel layer; compare also Kerr (1960).

At the beginning of dentine deposition, the forms investigated for this study (frog, fire salamander, axolotl) all show a noteworthy peculiarity: in developmental stages in which there is only a thin layer of predentine between odontoblasts and ameloblasts, there are fibers within the predentine that are clearly emphasized against the background (Pl. 53-b and Color Plate VII, d).

Such fibers appear to originate in part from the basal membrane and to end in the predentine layer; others cross the entire thickness of the predentine layer, and still others seem to be attached to the odontoblasts. In slightly older stages in which the layer of predentine has increased in thickness and has already been changed to dentine peripherally, the fibers form only a narrow seam of radially arranged structures that extend only a little way into the interior of the dentine (Pl. 54-a). These fibers are most obvious in early stages of tooth development in *Rana* and in *Salamandra*, as seen in specimens stained with Tuchechtgelb or Goldnerstain. Most likely these are reticular fibers; but proof would require additional selective stains. As already mentioned in the section on Osteichthyes (p. 96) similar, probably also reticular, fibers occur early in the tooth development of the angler fish *Lophius piscatorius* and penetrate almost the entire thickness of the predentine layer. The same fibers in later stages of development represent only a narrow, peripheral, radially striated edge of the dentine that has meanwhile become much thicker. The change in proportion that takes place in the course of dentine formation is the same in both cases.

The dentine of the Anura and the Urodela is characterized (compared to that of the reptiles, the mammals and of many Osteichthyes) by a particular feature that is probably related to the relatively large size of the odontoblasts and their relatively small number. Several cell processes of odontoblasts enter the predentine forming a strand, which soon divides into branches that are further divided peripherally.

The appearance of the pulp cavity changes during the development of the tooth anlage into the fully formed tooth. In the earliest stages of development, the space of the future pulp cavity is filled densely and uniformly by relatively few cells. Then occurs the differentiation of the odontoblasts. In horizontal section there appears a ring surrounding the inner pulp cells. Vertical sections show impressively the filling, even after the deposition of the first layer of predentine, of the pulp cavity by a small number of large mesodermal cells and their arrangement (Pl. 54-b). In later stages, the fabric of the inner pulp cells becomes looser (Pl. 55-a). A histological and cytological characterization of the content of the pulp cavity cannot be given here since no further study of this content has been possible. The pulp cavity of the fully formed tooth appears to contain fewer cells than that of the developing anlage. With the destruction of the tooth by resorption there goes hand in hand a depletion of the content of the pulp cavity. Plates 55-a and b show the bony pedestals of the teeth of *Rana* and the axolotl.

REPTILIA

The reptiles still alive today, that is, the turtles, the crocodiles, the snakes and lizards, and the tuatara *Spenodon* (restricted to a few small islands near New Zealand), do not give us an adequate picture of the diversity of organization that existed in this class of animals during the Mesozoic era. At that time, there existed, in addition to the lizard-like crawling and walking animals, erect predators that ran on their hind limbs, and fleeing peaceful herbivores; giants that walked on four-limb columns and belonged to the largest land vertebrates of all time; fliers of considerable agility, and, finally, a large number of forms that had become adapted more or less perfectly to life in the sea. The Mesozoic era is thus properly called the age of reptiles.

The first four-footed vertebrates originated at the end of the Devonian period. In the following period forms of amphibian organization, the stegocephalians, predominated at first. But already toward the end of the Carboniferous period a differentiation in Amphibia and Reptilia had taken place, and in the Permian the reptiles were the dominant land vertebrates.

In the Amphibia the adaptation to the life on land has been arrested midway, so to speak. In the Reptilia it has taken place with all consequences. Thus, the reptiles became the superior competitors of the amphibians. This competition, however, did not bring about the complete elimination of the amphibians. The latter survived in certain environments that suited them, and they managed to evolve further. This phyletic differentiation remained true to the amphibian type and led to the modern representatives: the frogs, the salamanders, and the Gymnophiona.

The evolution that led from the earliest, probably poorly land-adapted tetrapods to the reptiles may be studied directly only by comparison of modern Amphibia with modern Reptilia. The structures primarily involved were soft parts that have little chance of fossil preservation. The integument must have achieved resistance against radiation and drying by cornification. Even more important was the phyletic development that led to the emancipation from having to deposit eggs in the water. This development was brought about by the differentiation of particular embryonic structures that are absent in lower vertebrates. The embryo completes its development in a fluid-filled sac, the amnion. Thus surrounded by fluid the embryo lives basically in water. Simultaneous with the development of the amnion another sac, the allantois, arose from the primary gut behind the yolk sac. The allantois permits the gas exchange in the land-locked egg. Amnion and allantois are present not only in reptiles, but also in birds and mammals. These three classes are therefore called "amniotes."

The fossil remains naturally can give us no clues as to how these structures came into being. On the other hand, it may be concluded with certainty from the construction of the visceral skeleton that the fossil reptiles—in contrast to the amphibians—had no gill-breathing youth stages. Comparative anatomical investigations have shown that the amniotes correspond not only in the possession of the embryonic structures mentioned, but also in many other significant characteristics of their organization. Thus, despite the great variety of external form, the vertebrae of all amniotes are constructed on the same fundamental plan, whereas among amphibians several structural types occur. In the excretory system, in the metameric structure of the head, and in many other features the amniotes also correspond closely to one another. It can hardly be doubted that they had a common ancestry, although contrary views have been voiced recently.

A few general remarks about the reptile skull are necessary because there are close relations between the dentition and the construction of the skull, and because the systematic grouping of the reptiles is mainly based on skull characteristics.

For a comparison of the skull construction of fishes and amphibians the topographic relations of the skull bones to the branches of the lateral line in the head region are significant. The lateral line is, however, an organ that is characteristic of the gill breathing vertebrates. In the transition to life on land it was abolished but, fortunately, not all at once. The stegocephalians still had it. The correspondence in the arrangement of the bones of the skull roof in the oldest reptiles and the oldest stegocephalians is so close that the genus *Seymouria* from the Permian of Texas is sometimes placed among the amphibians and sometimes among the reptiles. Because of this great similarity, it was possible to establish the homology of the skull elements of the reptiles with those of the amphibians and, indirectly, with those of the fishes as well.

In reptile classification, differentiation of the temporal region of the skull is particularly significant. In the oldest reptiles the temporal region is, as in stegocephalians, fully covered by bone. This condition is called anapsid. In most of the younger forms fenestration of the region occurs. In the diapsid (from *di*, "two"; and *apsis*, "arch," in this case, jugular arch) condition two penetrations, an upper and a lower temporal opening, are present; correspondingly, there are two arches, an upper and a lower one. When only a single opening is present, a parapsid, euryapsid, or a synapsid condition may be recognized, depending on the position of the opening with regard to the surrounding bones (Pl. 56-a). The expression "synapsid" goes back linguistically and conceptually to an idea, no longer tenable, that a single lower jugular arch has arisen from the fusion of an upper and lower arch. The single temporal opening of the lizards is usually assumed to have originated from the diapsid type by reduction of the lower arch.

Among the factors that influence differentiation of the skull, the sense organs and the central nervous system are of prime importance. The reptiles are predominantly sight animals. With the size of the eyes is connected the development of an extensive interorbital septum. In many fossil forms and some modern ones a foramen parietale indicates the original presence of an unpaired parietal eye; in modern forms this organ is more or less reduced.

Reptile skulls in which the quadrate bone is immovably attached to the rest of the skull are called monimostylic; skulls with movable quadrates, as in lizards and snakes are streptostylic. In a broadened sense, the movabil-

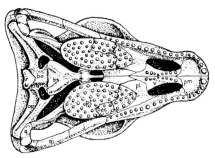

FIG. 82.—Roof of the mouth of the pelycosaur *Edaphosaurus*. From A. S. Romer (1945).

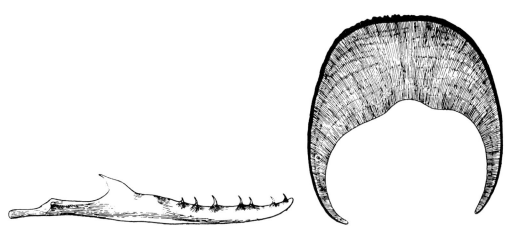

FIG. 83.—*Varanus niloticus. Left,* mandible of juvenile specimen (length of skull basis 22 mm) with pointed teeth; *right,* a replacement tooth in process of development of an old specimen with blunt dentition; enamel black. Lower jaw about 1:3.5; replacement tooth 13:1. From Peyer (1929).

ity of entire skull portions against each other is called streptostyly. Details of the kinetics of the skull, although unquestionably significant in the mode of feeding, cannot be adequately discussed here.

The different routing of the air passages has an influence on the structural differentiation of the skull and thus on the dentition. In mammals, with their increased respiratory requirements, the route along which the food passage and the air passage cross one another is reduced to a minimum by the presence of a secondary palate. A secondary palate is also present in the late synapsid reptiles, in the crocodiles, and in the modern cheloniid sea turtles. In all these reptiles acquisition of a secondary palate has undoubtedly happened independently.

The extent of the tooth-covered area of the mouth is greatest among the most ancient reptiles. Nearly all bones that form the wall of the mouth cavity may carry teeth (Fig. 82). In the younger groups the dentition is often restricted to the edges of the jaws. Total toothlessness, as it occurs, for example, among all fossil and modern turtles (except one), is a secondary phenomenon, as it is in all gnathostomous vertebrates.

The tooth form of the reptiles is generally that of a straight or curved cone. Its cross section is circular, or the teeth are laterally flattened and provided with anterior and posterior cutting edges. These edges often show a more or less pronounced serration which, particularly in fossil forms, may be emphasized to form accessory points. Very small, flattish, granular teeth sometimes form tooth pavements on certain bones, and are called "shagreen denticles."

In adaptation to eating hard-shelled prey, blunt cylindrical teeth or flat tooth plates evolved from conical teeth. Sometimes this process may be observed ontogenetically: in *Varanus niloticus,* for example, juvenile individuals still have pointed, conical teeth (Fig. 83). In extinct forms, unless a large amount of material is available, it would be difficult to decide whether the condition is due to differences in individual age or to specific differences.

Although no cases of typical herbivory are known among amphibians, disregarding larvae of anura, segregation according to food consumed had occurred among reptiles even in Permian time. It led to the evolution of plant eaters and of carnivores that preyed on them. Differentiation in the dentition to cope with plant food remained rather modest however, compared to that in the mammals.

The form of certain teeth in snakes became very highly specialized with the evolution of poison glands (p. 158).

Fixation of the teeth on the jaws usually takes place by bone of attachment (see p. 142). The bony tooth base may be formed differently, for which particular designations are in use: "Pleurodont" is that type of attachment in which the tooth base adheres to the lingual face of the jaw and is fused to it by bone. The rather inefficient oblique position of the attachment surface of the tooth may, under more intense functional requirements, be complemented by special devices. "Acrodont" attachment means that the teeth sit on the edges of the jaws. Teeth that sit in a pit are designated as "thecodont"—"prothecodont," if the pit is very shallow.

Reptiles are generally polyphyodont. Our sections through jaws of crocodiles and *Varanus* show in favorable cases the simultaneous presence of three different age stages.

The mode of tooth replacement has recently been studied in great detail by Edmund (1960) in a large number of reptile groups as well as in some amphibians and fishes. Almost universally tooth replacement is not a response to wear on the functional tooth; instead the replacement process

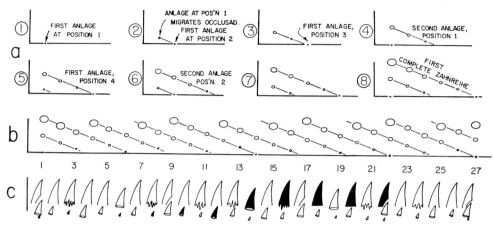

FIG. 84.—Stages in the production of the dentition of a typical lower vertebrate. In each case anterior is to the left: *a*, the sequence of production of tooth buds to form the Zahnreihen; *b*, the completed dentition consisting of numerous Zahnreihen; *c*, the diagrammatic appearance of the above dentition; one replacement wave is shown in black. From Edmund (1960).

is a continuous one as in elasmobranchs (see p. 47). It may be recalled that in sharks the teeth of adjacent cross rows are alternately in a slightly more labial or more lingual position. In tetrapods the principle of this scheme is the same, but because of modifications probably related to the fact that the dental lamina has become enclosed within the jaw bone, the replacement pattern is far from evident on casual inspection. Thus, along the edge of the jaw mature teeth, empty alveoli, teeth about to be shed, and young teeth are arranged in a seemingly irregular order. Close analysis shows, however, that this is not true. Over limited sections of a jaw "odd" and "even" numbered tooth positions show similarities that reflect the relative age of tooth anlagen on the dental lamina of adjacent "cross rows" or tooth families (see p. 185). Over the entire extent of a jaw this replacement pattern forms waves usually directed from back to front (Fig. 84).

Histology and developmental history of the reptile teeth

A. Investigation of ground thin-sections

Enamel:—The enamel layer is generally well developed. When viewed under polarized light, it is sharply set off from the dentine (Pl. 57-a). On ground thin-sections through modern and fossil crocodile teeth there is often a clear layering visible, the result of irregularities in the deposition during growth (Pl. 57-a). These contour lines correspond to the "lines of Retzius" of mammalian teeth (see p. 202). As in the mammals, these thin-sections show that the last-formed layer of enamel lies outermost.

Thin-sections of reptile teeth often show dark lines, usually standing at about right angles to the tooth surface; these lines are the result of cracks that penetrate the enamel (Pl. 57-a and b). Such cracks probably developed already during the drying of the tooth material, partly perhaps during the preparation of the sections. In relatively thin sections there are, in addition to these more pronounced lines, others that are much fainter. The others also stand at a right angle to the surface and might represent the boundaries of enamel prisms; microtome sections also show indications of a prismatic structure of the enamel (see below).

A survey of ground sections of fossil teeth seen under polarized light, and representing different reptile groups, revealed some differences in detail, but the sections were essentially corresponding. Based on these observations it may be assumed that a regular alternation occurs in the optical orientation of neighboring prism groups (Color Plate VII, e). But since we deal with fossil forms, we must assume that diagenetic changes may play a role also. Comparison of ground thin-sections through modern and fossil crocodile teeth shows, however, that diagenetic changes were not able to change fundamentally the original structure.

Plate 57-a shows that the minute projections of the relief of the tooth surface is without effect on the course of the dentine-enamel boundary, whereas the named boundary in cases of more pronounced sculpturing— for example the denticulation of the cutting edges of a carnosaur tooth— follows the differentiation of the tooth surface (Pl. 57-b). This little detail is of some theoretical interest in connection with the investigation of the formational processes.

Dentine:—The dentinal tubules show up more clearly in ground thin-sections than in microtome sections. In any single tooth the tubules in the apical portion of the tooth may be differently constituted than those in the basal portion. In a small replacement tooth of a crocodilian the dentinal tubules run straight and undivided in the apical region almost out to the point, whereas in the region of the tooth base they divide much sooner. Among Permian genera, *Labidosaurus* is of interest because of the development of true interglobular areas; a thick section of *Captorhinus* shows a vascular canal that leads into the pulp cavity as well as the mode of attachment of the tooth to the bone. The delicate dentinal tubules of *Diadectes* are crossed by contour lines.

Under low magnification the dentine of the reptiles, from the Permian to the Present and in the most varied reptile orders, gives the impression of uniform structure. To learn whether there are taxonomically useful differences that may show up only under higher magnification, would require additional study.

Tooth cementum:—Tooth cementum is discussed elsewhere (see p. 142).

B. Investigation of microtome sections

The dentitions of a small crocodile about 20 cm long and of a *Varanus* 50 cm long were studied with the aid of stained microtome sections. Both animals were anaesthetized, decapitated, and immediately fixed in Formalin. Azan and iron hematoxylin were the chief stains used, but occasionally also Tuchechtgelb was used. In both species the tooth development could be followed from the earliest stages to the fully formed tooth, because of the polyphyodont character of the reptile dentition. As introduction to the following section pictures, Plate 56-b shows the macroscopic development of the crocodile teeth (after Owen). Plates 57-c and 58-a show the histological relations between the elements of a tooth replacement series (cross row or tooth family). The sections depict the entrance of a replacement tooth into the interior of the functional tooth via a resorption portal.

Enamel:—Early in development the cells of the inner enamel epithelium, of an intermediate more or less reticular layer, and of the outer enamel epithelium appear clearly. Before initial deposition of enamel the cells of the inner enamel epithelium become cylindrical ameloblasts separated from one another (in the sections) by considerable interstitial spaces (Pl. 58-b). These spaces are perhaps artifacts, due to shrinkage during the fixation of the objects, but the picture is almost too regular for such an interpretation.

Following the course of enamel formation in the sections is difficult because the fully formed reptile enamel is dissolved in the decalcification necessary for the preparation of the sections. One exception is, however, the very early stages of amelogenesis, in which mineralization has not yet reached an advanced state and in which even after decalcification a formed structure remains. Such stages show a material produced by the ameloblasts that is vividly stainable by a variety of dyes, for example, black in iron-hematoxylin preparations and dark red in azan slides. The more intensive the staining, the younger are the stages of amelogenesis shown. The substance thus stained shows no structure, however, except for a narrow zone that lies next to the already mineralized enamel, no longer present in the preparations (Pls. 58-b and 59-a). In this boundary zone, one may observe in favorable places, that the deposition of the enamel takes place in layers. Somewhat less obvious although determinable with certainty, are rod-shaped structures that stand more or less at right angles to the enamel layers and are usually slightly curved (Pl. 58-b). Comparison to the corresponding relations in mammal teeth (p. 205) shows that these very probably are the organic pre-stages of enamel prisms.

The substance that is being formed by the ameloblasts at the beginning of enamel deposition is stained intensively in iron hematoxylin preparations; it forms a homogenous, optically opaque, black mass. Unexpectedly, however, it was this apparently unfavorable staining behavior that led to a valuable observation in preparations from *Crocodylus*. The iron hematoxylin not only stained the substance already secreted by the ameloblasts, but also selectively stained droplets of a substance still contained within the ameloblasts (Pl. 59-b). A microchemical analysis would be desirable of both the substance already deposited by the ameloblasts and the selectively stained material still within the ameloblast bodies.

Observations on section preparations of teeth of the crocodile confirm that generally the mineralization of the tooth begins at the apex; thus, apically there is a space that reflects the enamel that was removed during decalcification, whereas near the base the beginning of enamel deposition may still be encountered.

Dentine:—Plate 60-a shows the course of the odontoblast processes within the dentinal tubules.

Bone of attachment:—In most reptiles the teeth are fastened to the jaws by bone of attachment, which is resorbed each time a tooth is replaced and is rebuilt for the new tooth (for the special conditions seen in *Varanus salvator*, see p. 157).

Tooth cementum:—Tooth cementum corresponding to that in the mammal teeth occurs only rarely in reptiles. Topographically and functionally it differs from bone of attachment with which the basal portion of the tooth wall is rigidly attached to the jaw bone in such manner that the layer of cementum adheres only to the outside face of the dentine wall, whereas the connection with the jaw bone of the alveolar wall is brought about by the alveolar-dental membrane (Pl. 60-b) that permits a slight springiness to the connection. Among modern reptiles tooth cementum is present in the crocodiles (Pls. 58-a and 61-a); among the fossil ones, in many ichthyosaurs (see p. 146).

Survey of forms

Cotylosauria

Among the anapsid reptiles belong the cotylosaurs widely distributed in the Permian whose last representatives died out in the Upper Triassic and the turtles, whose representatives include modern species.

Even though there are, among the oldest known reptiles, not only cotylosaurs, but also relatives of another order, the former are nevertheless a stem group from which the other orders originated.

Of the two main divisions of the cotylosaurs, the Captorhinomorpha were probably mostly carnivorous, to judge from the character of their dentition. The other group, the Diadectomorpha, probably ate plant material. The Diadectomorpha appear to be the first plant eaters among the tetrapods, since the amphibians apparently fed almost exclusively on animals.

The dentition of the cotylosaurs is of interest in a number of respects. They differ from labyrinthodonts, as pointed out by Romer, first in that the teeth on the bones inside of premaxilla and maxilla remained generally small, whereas in the fossil amphibians large fang teeth sometimes developed in the corresponding places (Fig. 60). The dentition was generally not restricted to the edges of the jaws; other bones such as vomer, palatine, and pterygoid may bear teeth. The evolution of plant-eating tetrapods probably led relatively soon to the evolution of large reptilian predators, capable of subduing the herbivores. Among the herbivores defensive structures evolved, partly in the form of armor, partly in the acquisition of a faster mode of locomotion. The phyletic increase in the body size likewise may have proved favorable in the defense against aggressors. Beginnings of a relationship between the perfection of means of offense in the carnivores and of defense in the herbivores, which is dramatically apparent among the dinosaurs, can already be seen among the primitive reptiles.

In lateral views of the skulls of *Limnoscelis, Labidosaurus* and *Captorhinus* (Fig. 85) the carnivorous character of the dentition is clearly apparent. The ventrally curved premaxilla in *Labidosaurus* is peculiar. Their

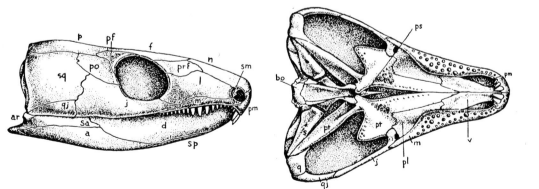

Fig. 85.—Skull in lateral and palatal views of the Permian cotylosaur *Captorhinus: pm*, premaxilla; *m*, maxilla; *pt*, pterygoid; *d*, dental bone. Almost natural size. From Romer (1945).

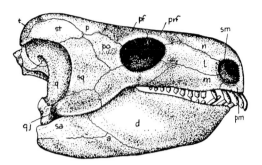

FIG. 86.—Skull of the Permian cotylosaur *Diadectes* in lateral view. About ⅓ natural size. After S. W. Williston, from Romer (1945).

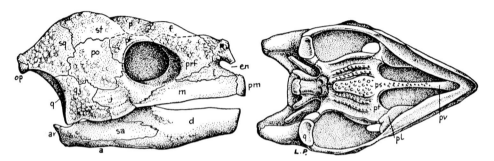

FIG. 87.—Side view of skull and tooth-bearing palate of the turtle *Triassochelys* from the uppermost Triassic of Germany: *pv*, vomer; *ps*, parasphenoid; *pl*, palatine; *pt*, pterygoid. About ½ natural size. From Romer (1945).

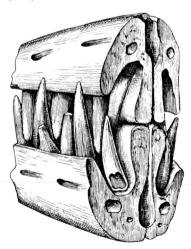

FIG. 88.—Snout fragment of an ichthyosaur from the upper Jurassic, seen obliquely from the back. After Quenstedt from Peyer (1937), in Bolk-Göppert-Kallius-Lubosch, *Handbuch der Vergleichenden Anatomie der Wirbeltiere* (Vienna and Berlin: Verlag Urban & Schwarzenberg, 1931–39), by permission.

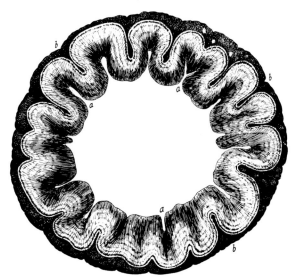

FIG. 89.—Horizontal ground thin-section through the basal portion of an ichthyosaur tooth: *a*, folded dentine wall; *b*, the tooth cementum that surrounds it. After Owen, from Peyer (1937), in Bolk-Göppert-Kallius-Lubosch, *Handbuch der Vergleichenden Anatomie der Wirbeltiere* (Vienna and Berlin: Verlag Urban & Schwarzenberg, 1931–39) by permission.

anterior teeth, as a consequence of this flexion, faced obliquely backwards. A similar curvature in the premaxilla is found among the reptiles in certain rhynchocephalians, in *Chasmatosaurus* an archosaurian from the Lower Triassic of South Africa, and among the fishes in *Lepisosteus* (Fig. 46).

The adaptations of the Diadectomorpha to a herbivorous diet are clear, but they had not evolved very far. The posterior teeth are transversally broadened and tuberculated. The chisel-shaped, oliquely implanted anterior teeth of *Diadectes* (Fig. 86; Pl. 61-b), according to Romer, served the purpose of tearing off fodder.

Thin-sections through teeth of *Labidosaurus* and *Captorhinus* (Pl. 62-a) show no essential differences in the structure of dentine and enamel from those of later reptiles.

Testudinata

The reason for including the turtles (Chelonia, Testudinata) among the anapsids lies in the probability that their temporal region, although it may display a variety of forms, never experienced true fenestration.

Modern turtles and the majority of the fossil turtles are toothless. Their jaws bear strong, horny beaks, provided with sharp edges. These beaks are suitable to procure animal as well as plant food.

The earliest chelonians so far known occur in the Keuper (Late Triassic) of southern Germany. They differ from all post-Triassic turtles in several ways, including the presence of teeth on the palate. But the shape of the bones of the edge of the mouth indicates that these early turtles already possessed horny beaks. Such a tooth-bearing turtle is *Triassochelys,* described by Jaekel from the Keuper of Halberstadt (Fig. 87). The turtles confirm the rule for all gnathostomous vertebrates: a toothless condition is preceded by a tooth-bearing condition.

Ichthyosauria

The ichthyosaurs have long been among the most popular fossil verte-brates, especially in Europe. In the seas of the Mesozoic era their role corresponded to that of the whales (Cetacea), that is, they were lung-breathing, originally terrestrial animals that adapted to a life in the sea. Propulsion of their torpedo-shaped body took place by lateral excursions of a vertical tail fin.

The ichthyosaurs possess an upper temporal opening. This opening is different, however, from the upper temporal opening of other reptiles in that its lateral boundary is not formed by the postorbital and squamosal bones but by the postfrontal and supratemporal bones (Pl. 56-a). Thereby the ichthyosaurs assume a particular systematic position. It has not been possible to determine from which group of terrestrial reptiles they evolved, since fossil finds reach back no farther than the Middle Triassic. In the oldest known genera the transition to permanent life in the sea had already been completed in all essential respects. In many details of their organiza-tion, however, we may observe the increasingly perfect adaptation to the marine environment during Upper Jurassic and Cretaceous time. Here we shall mention only those changes that pertain to the dentition.

In the Triassic ichthyosaurs (Pl. 62-b), whose various genera are included under the designation "mixosaurs," the teeth stand singly in pits on the premaxillae, maxillae, and the dentaries. In the Jurassic forms and in those of the Cretaceous, the teeth are crowded together in deep grooves that run lengthwise along the jaw bones (Fig 88). In the mixosaurs the pulp cavity of the teeth is either smooth-walled or the base of the tooth wall shows only a weak radial folding; there is little or no tooth cementum. In the later ichthyosaurs the basal tooth wall is intensively radially folded and the tooth base is surrounded by a coat of cementum (Fig. 89, Pl. 63-a). These differences probably are related to changes in the mode of attachment. If, indeed, the teeth are merely fastened by connective tissue in their position of function, it would seem highly advantageous for the tooth base to be much enlarged to offer the connective tissue fibers an adequate surface for attachment. The radial folding of the tooth wall and the occurrence of cementum serve the strengthening of the enlarged tooth base. In the *schisti bituminosi* of the Triassic of the Monte San Giorgio (Tessin, Switzerland) there occur two mixosaurs belonging to two genera of which one possesses none or only a slight folding of the basal portion of the tooth wall and virtually no cementum, and the other shows considerable radial folding and notable amounts of cementum (Pl. 63-a).

The teeth that lie in the front part of the jaws are generally slender and shaped like pointed cones. Toward the jaw joint they often become somewhat flattened and are more robust as, for example, among the mixosaurs of the Triassic of the Tessin. In *Omphalosaurus* from the middle Triassic of Nevada and in *Pessopteryx* from the middle Triassic of Spitzbergen there are even hemispherical teeth that probably served for crushing hard-shelled prey. Besides snails and clams, dibranchiate cephalopods were important animals of prey; in the well preserved skeletons of ichthyosaurs from the Lias of Württemberg heaps of belemnite rostra and arm hooks have been observed. For this reason the *"Belemnitenschlachten"* ("belemnite battle-fields") —accumulations of belemnite rostra in criss-cross array—are interpreted as gastric regurgitates (comparable to the owl pellets) of ichthyosaurs.

Ophthalmosaurus, an ichthyosaur of the Upper Jurassic, must be mentioned because its dentition has become vestigial or has been totally reduced. In *Eurhinosaurus*, a genus from the Lias of Württemberg, the upper jaw is much longer than the mandible, much as in *Eurhinodelphis* among the whales.

It may finally be mentioned that Kiprijanoff (1881) described peculiar tubules in thin-sections of ichthyosaur teeth, which he did not interpret correctly. These structures turned out to be bore holes, produced by a plant organism, the so-called *"Mycelites ossifragus"* Roux (see Pl. 63-b, and Peyer, 1945 and 1946). That the tubules in the ichthyosaur enter the tooth from the outside through the enamel layer indicates that the mining took place *intra vitam*. In postmortem *Myelites* infection the softer dentine layer serves as the place of entry. The ichthyosaurs died out before the end of the Cretaceous period.

Mesosauria

Only two genera are recognized as mesosaurs: *Mesosaurus* from the Permian of South Africa and *Stereosternum* from the Lowest Permian of South America. According to the most recent studies they possess a lower temporal opening. Since they show no other affinities to the synapsids, their affinities among the reptiles cannot be determined with certainty. The mesosaurs are aquatic reptiles. The elongated skull whose jaws are lined with slender teeth (Fig. 90) suggests that they preyed on fishes.

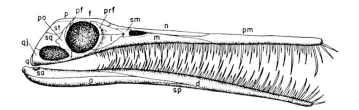

FIG. 90.—Skull of the Permian reptile *Meso-saurus* in lateral view. About natural size. After v. Huene, from Romer (1945).

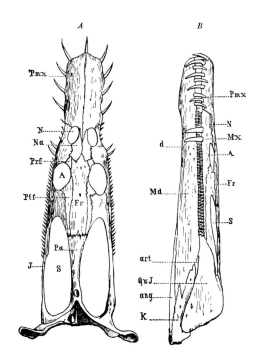

FIG. 91.—Skull in dorsal and lateral views of the Triassic sauropterygian *Nothosaurus mirabilis: n,* nasal opening; *A,* orbit; *S,* temporal fenestra. 1:4. After H. v. Meyer, from Zittel-Eastman, *Text-Book of Palaeontology* (London: Mac-millan and Co., 1902), by permission.

FIG. 92.—Lower jaw of three plesio-saurs: *A, Plesiosaurus dolichodeirus; B, Thaumatosaurus indicus; C, Peloneustes philarchus.* After *Guide Foss. Rept. Brit. Mus. (Nat. Hist.)* (1910), from Abel, *Die Stämme der Wirbeltiere,* Vereinigung Wissenschaftlicher Verleger (Berlin and Leipzig: Walter de Gruyter & Co., 1919), by permission.

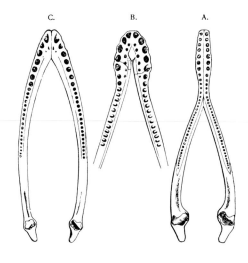

Sauropterygia

Like the ichthyosaurs, the plesiosaurs are well known fossils of the Jurassic and Cretaceous periods. They are included with related forms of the Triassic, the Nothosauria, within the order Sauropterygia. The plesiosaurs also inhabited the sea. Their mode of locomotion, however, differed from that of the ichthyosaurs: in the latter the tail fin is the propeller; in the plesiosaurs the anterior and posterior pairs of limbs became paddles.

The sauropterygians have an upper temporal opening whose lateral rim is formed by the postorbital and the squamosal bones. The plesiosaurs are geologically younger than the nothosaurs, but they cannot have originated from them because the palate of the older forms is already more specialized than in the plesiosaurs, of which, so far, only a single genus has been found in the Triassic.

The nothosaurs and, in a much more pronounced way, the plesiosaurs show all kinds of aquatic specializations in the construction of their skeletons. The dentition is restricted to the edges of the jaws (Fig. 91). The teeth sit in alveoli. The size of the teeth generally decreases steadily from front to back although, for example, in *Nothosaurus,* two fang teeth may be situated anterior to the orbit, which surpass their neighbors in height (Fig. 91). Many teeth of sauropterygians are slightly curved backwards. Quite often they show a more or less pronounced vertical ribbing. The cross section of the teeth is often circular as in *Nothosaurus.* The length of the symphysis of the mandible varies greatly; it is especially long in *Peloneustes* (Fig. 92).

Two evolutionary directions may be discerned in the plesiosaurs: one of these led to the evolution of a long neck (with up to 76 vertebrae in *Elasmosaurus*) and a relatively small skull; the other led to a relatively short neck and large skull which in *Pliosaurus* may reach a length of 1.5 meters. The teeth of this form reach a length (or height) of 20 cm (Fig. 93).

The enamel layer of the teeth of the sauropterygians is usually quite thick. The dentinal tubules are tightly crowded, and branches are visible only near the enamel boundary.

Placodontia

The placodonts (flat-toothed reptiles, from *plax, plakos,* "plate" and *odus, odontos,* "tooth") were in the past usually included as a suborder among the sauropterygians. Considerable differences justify, however, their treatment as a separate order.

At the beginning of the nineteenth century almost the only specimens known of *Placodus* were the large tooth plates and tooth-bearing jawbones. Since certain elasmobranchs possess similarly funtioning dentitions for

FIG. 93.—Tooth of a plesiosaur, *Pliosaurus grandis*, from the uppermost Jurassic. 1:2. After Owen, from Zittel, *Grundzüge der Paläontologie* (Munich and Berlin: Verlag R. Oldenbourg, 1923), by permission.

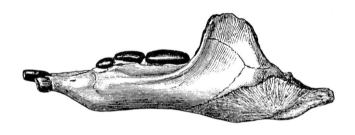

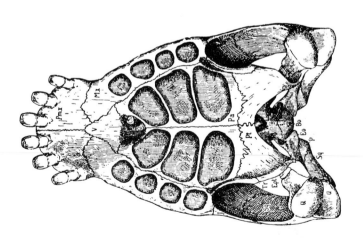

FIG. 94.—Palate of the placodont *Placodus gigas*. After Broili, from Zittel (1923). Lower jaw of *Placodus gigas*. 1:2. After Meyer from Zittel, *Grundzüge der Paläontologie* (Munich and Berlin: Verlag R. Oldenbourg, 1923), by permission.

cracking hard-shelled prey, both Agassiz and Owen placed the placodonts among the elasmobranchs. But it was Owen himself who assigned the placodonts a place among the reptiles when better specimens of skulls became known. For a long time our knowledge was restricted to the skull. The first find in which nearly the entire skeleton was associated, was a specialized form, *Placochelys,* from the Upper Triassic of Hungary; it is armored, and its habitus superficially resembles that of a sea turtle. It was not until much later that a well preserved skeleton of *Placodus* was found in the Muschelkalk of southern Germany; it was subsequently described by Drevermann.

Other genera of placodonts are *Henodus, Paraplacodus,* and *Helveticosaurus;* furthermore, there exist as yet undescribed finds from the Triassic of the Jordan Valley.

The placodonts are, so far as known, aquatic animals. In the geologically late forms the body was propelled by the paired limbs in much the same way as it is in sea turtles. In the geologically older genera a long tail was present that probably contributed significantly to their locomotion.

The skull of the placodonts possesses an upper temporal opening and a large parietal foramen. Its structure is massive, which probably is related mainly to the great functional requirements that were placed on the dentition. The unusually strong development (for a reptile) of the coronoid process of the lower jaw unquestionably is an indication that the adductor muscles that insert on this process must have been greatly developed.

In *Placodus* (Fig. 94) the palate, aside from the choanae, is an unperforated plate. The unpaired vomer is toothless. The largest tooth plates, three on each side, lie on the palatines. Their opposing structures were three likewise broadly enlarged tooth plates on the mandible. In each maxilla there are four much smaller, somewhat flattened teeth. A form with five teeth in the maxilla has been described as *Placodus quinquemolaris;* it seems doubtful, however, that it is indeed a separate species. In each premaxilla there are three chisel-shaped teeth, corresponding to similar teeth in the lower jaw. These teeth are implanted in the extensive symphyseal portion of the mandible in a more or less horizontal position. Of the enlarged plate-shaped teeth the most anterior are separated by a wide cleft. That these tooth plates served to crack hard-shelled prey cannot be doubted. It is assumed that the anterior teeth were used to break loose the shells of sessile invertebrates. Signs of wear are evident on the anterior teeth of the Senckenberg Museum specimen of *Placodus gigas.*

Among modern reptiles there are forms with similar tooth shapes, for example, *Dracaena guianensis* (Fig. 101) and *Varanus niloticus* (Fig. 83). In the latter species ontogenetic development shows that dentition types that deviate greatly from the normal conical form of the dentition teeth have been derived from the normal form; very young specimens of *Varanus niloticus* still possess normal pointed teeth. The blunted form of the teeth of older specimens is not brought about by wear, rather the later tooth generations assume progressively blunter shape in their anlagen (Fig 83). It is, therefore, also assumed that the dentition of the extinct *Placodus*, as a durophagous specialization, had evolved from a reptile dentition consisting of pointed teeth. This interpretation has been confirmed by more recent finds. *Paraplacodus* from the Triassic of the Tessin possesses more numerous teeth than does *Placodus*, which are, moreover, much less notably flattened (Fig. 95). Still another genus from the same deposit, which to judge from the structure of its skeleton must be placed among the placodonts, *Helveticosaurus zollingeri,* has only pointed teeth (Pl. 64-a).

For a long time another placodont has been known from the Germanic Muschelkalk, but only from skulls. H. V. Meyer called it "*Cyamodus*" (beantooth, from *kyamos,* "bean"). This form too is represented in the Tessin (Fig. 96). In contrast to *Placodus* it is heavily armored much as is the genus *Placochelys*. The teeth of the premaxilla are weak in *Cyamodus;* in *Placochelys* they are entirely absent. It is thus assumed that this genus and other

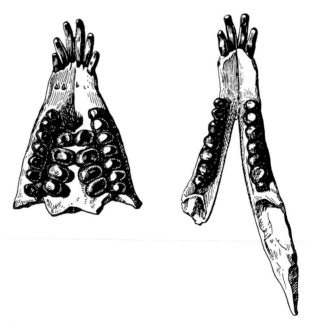

Fig. 95.—Palate and lower jaw of the placodont *Paraplacodus* from the Triassic of Monte San Giorgio, Tessin. 1.6:1. From Peyer, *Geschichte der Tierwelt* (Zürich: Büchergilde Gutenberg, 1950), by permission.

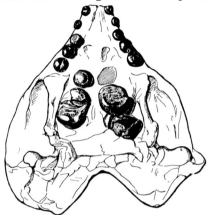

Fig. 96.—Palate of the placodont *Cyamodus hildegardis*, from the Triassic of Monte San Giorgio, Tessin. 1.6:1. From Peyer, *Geschichte der Tierwelt* (Zürich: Büchergilde Gutenberg, 1950), by permission.

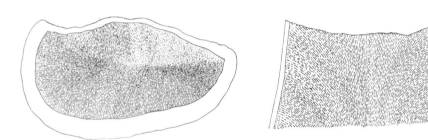

Fig. 97.—Ground thin-sections through teeth of the placodont *Helveticosaurus*. *Left*, horizontal (15:1); *right*, vertical (21:1). Enamel layer very much thicker on the outer side than on the inner side of tooth. From Peyer (1955).

closely related forms possessed horny beaks in the anterior region of the mouth. Even further reduction of the dentition is seen in the "one tooth" *Henodus* from the Suabian Keuper (Huene, 1936). In *Henodus* only a single tooth in each quadrant of the dentition has been retained.

Although the genus *Placodus* probably did not survive beyond the Muschelkalk, *Placochelys* and related forms reach up into the Rhaetic—in the southern Tessin possibly into the Lias, if the fossils there are not redeposited. A further increase in our knowledge of the dentition of the placodonts is to be expected from the study of new finds from the Triassic of the Jordan Valley.

Histologically the placodont teeth are of interest because they possess an enamel layer of considerable thickness. In the curved teeth of *Helveticosaurus* the enamel coat is thicker on the convex labial face than on the lingual face (Fig. 97).

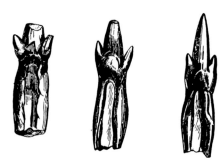

Fig. 98.—Tri-cusped teeth of a small specimen of the long-necked reptile *Tanystropheus*. 7.4:1. From Peyer (1944).

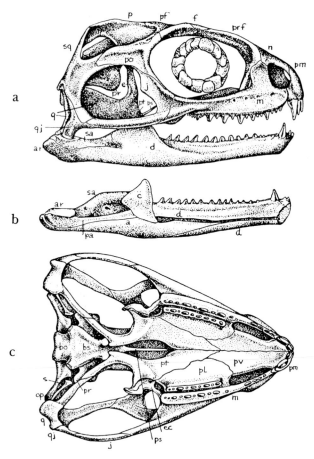

Fig. 99.—Skull of the tuatara *Sphenodon: a,* in side view; *b,* lingual view of the lower jaw; *c,* palatal view; *pm,* premaxilla; *m,* maxilla; *pv,* vomer; *pl,* palatine; *pt,* pterygoid; *d,* dental. Natural size. From Romer (1945).

Lepidosauria

Among the Lepidosauria (from *lepis, lepidos,* "scale," and *sauros,* "reptile") Romer (1945) grouped the lizard-like reptiles in the broadest sense: the extinct earliest lizard-like reptiles, the Eosuchia; the Rhynchocephalia, which today are represented only by the tuatara, *Sphenodon* (restricted to some small islands near New Zealand) which were much more numerous in ancient times, and, finally, the Squamata (from *squama,* "scale"), under which name, the closely related lizards (Lacertilia) and the snakes (Ophidia or Serpentes) are gathered.

To discuss the structural relations of the skull of the Lepidosauria we shall start with that of the tuatara, *Sphenodon. Sphenodon* is diapsid; it has an upper and a lateral temporal opening and an upper and lower jugular arch (Fig. 99). The Lacertilia have only an upper jugular arch. Important reasons suggest that in these forms a formerly present lower arch has been lost by reduction. In the snakes the upper arch is also missing. For this reason, they are said to be gymnokrotaphous (from *gymnos,* "naked," and *krotaphos,* "temple"). In connection with the loss of a lower jugular arch, the quadrate achieved notable movability already in the lizards. Their skull has become streptostylic (see p. 136). This movability is even greater in snakes, which have none of the jugular arch structures.

Among the Eosuchia, *Youngina* of the Permian of South Africa has two closed jugular arches. In *Prolacerta* from the lower Triassic of that area the lower arch is incomplete. Among the old lizard-like reptiles we also include the three genera *Askeptosaurus* (E. Kuhn-Schnyder, 1952), *Macrocnemus,* and *Tanystropheus* (Peyer, 1937, 1931) from the Triassic of the Tessin. The dentition of the long-necked reptile *Tanystropheus* is noteworthy because in all of the small specimens the middle and posterior teeth are tricuspid (Fig. 98), whereas in all larger specimens the teeth are single-pointed. Very probably, these differences do indicate age differences rather than presence of two different species. Similar age variations are observed in modern lizards. In *Tupinambis,* for example, the juvenile specimens have, according to Brehm, tricuspid teeth, whereas in the adult animals the middle teeth of the dental bones and the maxillae have a simple conical form.

At the anterior end of the dentary of *Tanystropheus* there is a ventral projection of the bone (Pl. 64-b). This projection did not serve to protect the upper fang teeth, as in the saber-toothed cats (Fig. 144), rather it appears to have been merely a strengthening of the bone for the support of the very large lower fang teeth.

The name "Rhynchocephalia" (beak heads) indicates that the premaxilla of *Sphenodon* (Fig. 99) is slightly curved ventrad, but it was very much

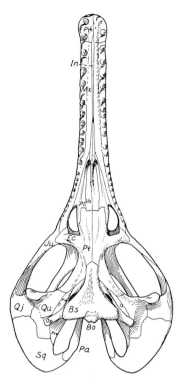

Fig. 100.—Skull of *Champsosaurus natator;* the teeth of this genus are radially folded. 1:5.2. From Russell (1956).

more so in some extinct relatives, for example in *Rhynchosaurus* and in *Hyperodapedon.* Specialized form relationships are also present in the rhynchocephalians *Hescheleria* and *Clarazia* from the Tessin Triassic.

The jaw movement of *Sphenodon* is propalinal. The tooth row of the lower jaw moves in a forward and backward gliding motion in a longitudinal groove that is formed by the parallel tooth rows of the maxilla and the palate. The attachment of the teeth is acrodont.

In contrast to the crocodiles and the turtles, which possess only an "egg tubercle" to shred the egg shell, the rhynchocephalians, lizards, and snakes are provided with an egg tooth that is connected to the premaxilla and is shed after fullfillment of its function.

The teeth of *Champsosaurus* (Fig. 100), a rhynchocephalian from the Cretaceous and the Early Tertiary, possess basally a radially folded tooth wall.

The Squamata—the lizards and snakes—show many corresponding features in addition to primarily adaptive differences. Loss of the limbs is not a feature that would exclude the snakes from this group since there are a number of limbless lizards, for example *Anguis fragilis.* A comparison with the geologically oldest Lepidosauria shows that the modern Lacertilia

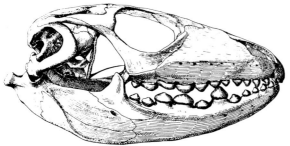

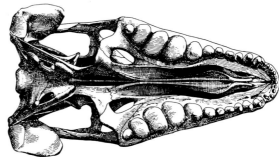

Fig. 101.—Lateral and palatal views of the skull of the lizard *Dracaena guianensis*. Slightly reduced. From Peyer (1929).

have not deviated much in the differentiation of the palate from the conditions of the Permian forms. In addition to the bones that form the edges of the jaws, the pterygoid, palatine, and vomer may also bear teeth. The mode of tooth attachment is used, although in only a subsidiary manner, to classify them. Thus, for example, the varanids and the lacertids are pleurodont, whereas the agamids and *Chamaeleon* are acrodont.

The oblique position of the attachment plane on the jaw bone in the pleurodont mode of tooth attachment is evidently unsatisfactory under intense use of the dentition. Bullet (1942) described complications of the tooth structure in *Varanus salvator* that may be interpreted as compensation for the disadvantages of the pleurodont type of attachment: a basal closure of the pulp cavity brought about by folding of the dentine wall, the development of special attachment devices at the basal surface, and a generous amount of bone of attachment, which is destroyed and rebuilt in each cycle of tooth replacement (Pls. 65-a and 66-a). Before the shedding of a tooth, resorption sets in from within and without. Bullet could show that sometimes teeth break off, and their bases, before total resorption has been accomplished, are overwhelmed by a layer of bone. The tooth ruins thus enclosed are gradually resorbed in the depth of the bone (Pl. 65-b). The process recalls the relations described in the stegocephalian *Benthosuchus* by Bystrow (1938) (p. 124).

Predominantly plant diet, as it occurs, for example in iguanids, is not very prevalent. Generally lizards feed on all manner of small animals.

Adaptation to a diet of hard-shelled prey occurs primarily in *Dracaena guianensis* (Fig. 101) and *Varanus niloticus* (Fig. 83). A radiograph of the stomach content of an alcohol specimen of *Dracaena* shows the remains of snail shells, probably of ampullarians. Noteworthy conditions pertaining to the feeding mechanism are seen in the mosasaurs, an extinct group of varanoid lizards (restricted to the Cretaceous period) that became adapted to life in the sea, where some of them reached enormous size. They were fast-swimming predators. Their large mouth, generally with pointed teeth, permitted swallowing large prey. A peculiar structure of the mandible is thought to be related to this feeding on large prey: between its anterior and posterior bony components a joint developed (Fig. 102). This mechanism was, as was the merely ligamentous connection of the two rami of the lower jaw at the symphysis, apparently significant in the handling of large prey.

The large teeth of the mosasaurs sit in shallow alveoli. They are either smooth or vertically ribbed and, in general, are provided with anterior and posterior cutting edges. The teeth of *Globidens,* in adaptation to a diet of hard-shelled prey, are not conical and pointed but globular.

A pronounced heterodonty is observed in *Heloderma.* In this American lizard the poison tooth shows special structural features suitable for the passage of venom (Pl. 66-b).

In the snakes the mobility of the mouth parts, because of the absence of jugular arches, is even further enhanced than that observable in lizards. The prey, often of tremendous size in comparison with the snake, is killed by the action of venom, is crushed by constriction of loops of the body, or, as in the Ringelnatter, is eaten alive.

In the vipers the fangs, borne on shortened maxillae, are automatically erected when the mouth is opened, by the pterygoids acting as levers. In resting position the fangs are flatly aligned with the roof of the mouth (Fig. 103). Although the maxilla in vipers bears only the functioning fang and its replacement teeth, it carries additional teeth in other venomous snakes.

In the opisthoglyphous snakes the poison fangs are located in the posterior part of the maxilla, whereas in the proteroglyphous forms the fangs are in front. In both a groove extends along the anterior (mesial) edge of the fang for the transmission of the venom from the tooth to the wound inflicted on the prey. In the vipers there is a closed canal instead of a mere groove (Fig. 104), for which reason they are called Solenoglypha (from *solen,* "tube" or "pipe"). The canal has come about by the fusion of the edges of the notably deepened groove. As a result of the formation of the canal, the pulp cavity has become distorted so that it is the shape of a half-moon in cross section (Fig. 104, A, B). During the warm season of the year the re-

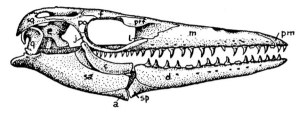

FIG. 102.—Skull of the mosasaur *Clidastes* from the Cretaceous in side view showing movable connection between anterior and posterior portions of the lower jaw. From Romer (1945).

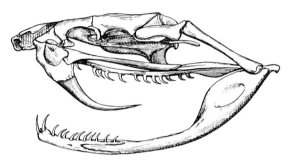

FIG. 103.—Skull of a pit viper in lateral view. After Boas, from Peyer (1937), in Bolk-Göppert-Kallius-Lubosch, *Handbuch der Vergleichenden Anatomie der Wirbeltiere* (Vienna and Berlin: Verlag Urban & Schwarzenberg, 1931–39), by permission.

placement of the fang teeth in vipers is rather rapid; it is estimated to take place about once a month.

Some cobras (spitting cobras) have evolved the behavior of ejecting dual jets of venom under pressure at potential enemies. This behavior is reflected in the structure of the venom canal of the fangs (Fig. 104, C). The dentition of these snakes has been studied in great detail by Bogart (1943).

Nonpoisonous snakes, such as the pythonids, possess in the upper jaw two parallel rows of backward curved teeth of which the outer one is borne by the maxilla, the inner one by the palatine and pterygoid (Fig. 105). In the tree snake *Dasypeltis* the teeth are reduced; the snake feeds on bird eggs. Presumably to prevent loss of the contents of the eggs, these are not crushed until they reach the esophagus, where they are pressed against pointed hypapophyses of the vertebrae that reach into the esophagus.

In two insectivorous snake families the mouth is not capable of being extended. These families are the Typhlopidae, in which teeth are present only in the upper jaw, and the Glauconiidae, in which only the lower jaw bears teeth.

Geologically, the snakes are a relatively young group. The oldest forms known so far occur in the Lower Cretaceous.

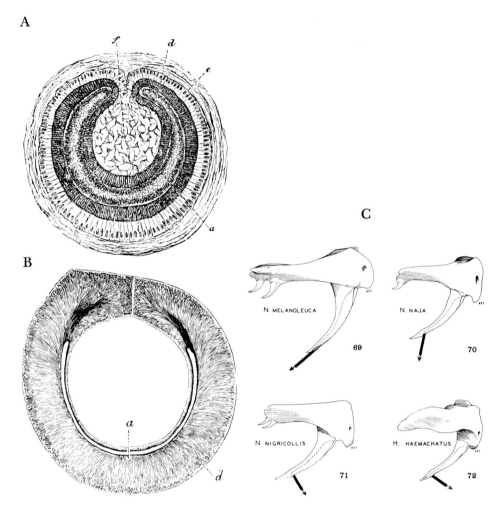

Fig. 104.—Cross-sections through venom fangs of snakes: *A*, viper fang, prior to closure of the venom groove to form a tube; *B*, fully developed fang of the rattlesnake; *a*, pulp cavity; *d*, dentine; *e*, ameloblasts; *f*, ectodermal tissue that later disappears. From Tomes, *A Manual of Dental Anatomy, Human and Comparative* (London: J. and A. Churchill, 1923) ; *C*, lateral views of four types of fangs in the cobra genera *Naja* and *Hemachatus*: 69, a non-spitter from Africa; 70, a Chinese cobra partly adapted to spitting, but not reported as a spitter; 71, the most widely distributed spitting cobra in Africa; 72, the most perfectly adapted of all spitting cobras. Dotted lines indicate extent of venom canal; arrows indicate direction of liquid ejected, as determined by experiment with removed fangs. From Bogert (1943) .

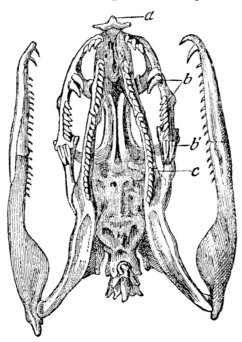

Fɪɢ. 105.—Skull of *Python molurus* in ventral view: *a*, premaxilla; *b*, maxilla; *c*, palatal teeth. From Leunis and Ludwig, *Synopsis der Tierkunde* (Hanover: Hahnsche Buchhandlung, 1883), by permission.

Archosauria

The name "Archosauria" means "ruling reptiles" (from *archos*, "ruler"). Several reptile orders are grouped together under the term "Archosauria" because, based on the structure of the skeleton, it must be assumed that they are more closely related to one another than to any other reptiles. The only Archosauria still extant are the crocodiles. Among extinct groups are the Thecodontia, many extinct crocodilians, the pterosaurs (flying reptiles), and the dinosaurs. The last are not a natural group; they belong to two distinct orders, the saurischians and the ornithischians, that have in the past wrongly been interpreted as very closely related archosaurs.

Thecodontia

To the thecodonts belong ancient forms from the Triassic, in which the osteological peculiarities of the archosaurs had not yet been clearly expressed, and the phytosaurs, also of Triassic age, reptiles of crocodilian appearance although not of crocodilian affinity. The name "Thecodontia" means simply that the teeth are set in alveoli, which is also characteristic of a few other reptiles of Triassic age that do not belong in this group.

Euparkeria from the Triassic of South Africa is a primitive thecodont genus in structure of the palate and dentition. Besides this primitive structure, the skull shows a feature characteristic of many archosaurs: antorbital openings located in front of the eye cavities. In *Chasmatosaurus* (Fig. 106), which also has a tooth-bearing palate, the orbit and the antorbital opening are united. The peculiar form of the premaxilla in *Chasmatosaurus* has already been mentioned (p. 145).

Of the phytosaurs the genera *Phytosaurus* and *Mystriosuchus* from the Keuper of Württemberg and the closely related *Machaeroprosopus* (Fig. 107) from the Upper Triassic of North America may be mentioned.

The numerous pointed teeth are borne only on the edges of the jaw bones; the mode of attachment is thecodont. The anterior-most teeth may be greatly enlarged.

Crocodilia

One of the most obvious features of the crocodile skull is easily visible by external inspection. The bony outer nasal opening lies at the tip of the snout; the choanae, however, lie in the vicinity of the occiptal condyle. Between these two points the respiratory air is confined to a canal separated from the mouth cavity. Its bony floor is formed by horizontal lamellae of the premaxillae, the maxillae, the palatines, and the pterygoids that have joined in the midline and thus form a secondary palate (Fig. 108).

In the geologically oldest crocodiles the pterygoid lamellae are not yet united. The choana thus lies farther forward. These old forms are grouped togther as Mesosuchia, a few particularly early genera as Protosuchia, and the crocodiles with choanae behind the pterygoids as Eusuchia. *Sebecus*, an Eocene crocodile from South America does not fit into any of these suborders.

Long-snouted and short and broad-snouted forms occur in the most different groups of modern and extinct crocodilians. The alligator is short-snouted. In the genus *Crocodylus* there are relatively short-snouted as well a long- and narrow-snouted species. The snouts of the East Asian gavials and *Tomistoma* are very long and narrow. Among the extinct forms *Libycosuchus* is especially short-snouted; the marine mesosuchian *Teleosaurus* is very long-snouted (Fig. 109). These differences are probably related to different modes of feeding; the long-snouted marine forms were piscivorous.

In the alligators the teeth of the lower jaw lie inside of the tooth row of the upper jaw. The first and the fifth tooth are provided with pits in the upper jaw. In *Crocodylus* upper and lower teeth interlock. The first tooth of the lower jaw fits into a pit or a hole in the skull, and the fourth tooth of the mandible occupies a notch in the lateral edge of the snout. The teeth of

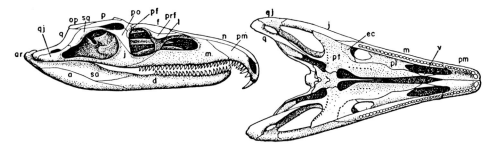

FIG. 106.—Skull of the thecodont *Chasmatosaurus*, from the Triassic of South Africa, in lateral and ventral views. About 1/7 natural size. After Broili and Schroeder, from Romer (1945).

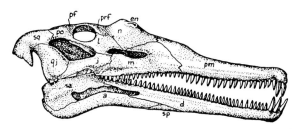

FIG. 107.—Skull of the phytosaur *Machaeroprosopus*, from the Triassic, in lateral view. About 1/3 natural size. After Camp, from Romer (1945).

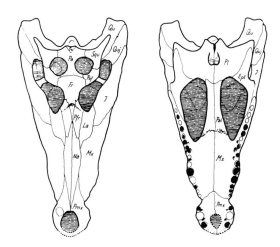

FIG. 108.—Skull of a crocodile, *Brachyuranochampsa eversolei*, from the Eocene of Wyoming. 1:7.5. From Zangerl (1944).

crocodilians are lodged in deep alveoli. Sometimes, the edges of the alveoli are elevated above the level of the surrounding jaw surface as in the late Cretaceous *Hypsosaurus natator*. In the extremely long-snouted *Euthecodon* (Pliocene, Egypt) the alveoli form protruding, bony tubes all along the snout.

Even if the number of teeth on the different jaw bones has not yet reached the same degree of constancy as in mammals, tooth numbers nevertheless begin to play a certain role in the detailed systematics of the crocodilia.

For histological study I had available selectively stained microtome sections, ground thin-sections through teeth of the modern crocodile, and thin-sections of crocodile teeth from the Lower Cretaceous of Texas. This circumstance permitted a comparison of the microscopic structure of modern and more or less closely related fossil forms, which revealed, except for the loss of birefringence of the collagenous fibers, no significant postmortem, diagenetic changes.

Pterosauria

It may be determined from the structure of the skull that the pterosaurs, which flew by means of a flight membrane after the fashion of the bats, also belong to the archosaurs. Acquisition of the facility to fly probably took place in the late Triassic, because in the Lower Jurassic there are genera that do not represent transitional forms, but, as did *Dimorphodon* from the Lower Lias of Dorsetshire, possessed a respectable flight capacity. All these old pterosaurs had long tails. They are so different from the later, short-tailed pterodactyls, that they have been grouped together in a separate suborder, the Rhamphorhynchoidea. In the lithographic limestone of Solnhofen *Rhamphorhynchus,* one of the last long-tailed forms, and *Pterodactylus,* one of the earliest of the short-tailed ones, occur together. The pterosaurs of the Cretaceous all have short tails.

Corresponding to the requirements of flight, the skull of the flying reptiles is extremely lightly built. The sutures between bones fused early in ontogeny. The mandibular rami are connected by bone at the symphysis. The usually slender, pointed teeth are arranged on the edges of the jaws in single rows, and they sit in alveoli. The dentition is more robust and more extensive in the long-tailed forms than in the pterodactyls, in which it is sometimes restricted to the anterior parts of the jaws or is entirely absent.

The generic name *"Dimorphodon"* indicates that the anterior teeth are much larger and more broadly spaced than the posterior ones. The points of the robust anterior teeth of *Rhamphorhynchus* are obliquely directed forward and outward (Fig. 110). The weaker dentition of *Pterodactylus* does

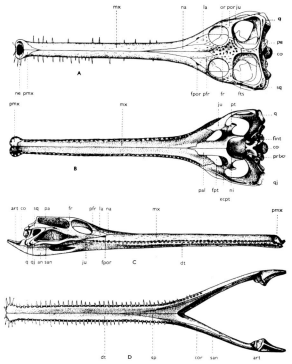

FIG. 109.—Skull of the long-snouted crocodilian *Teleosaurus* from the Lias. About 1:5.3. After Deslongchamps from Kälin, *Traité de Paléontologie*, vol. V (Paris: Masson et Cie, 1955), by permission.

not extend as far backward as in *Rhamphorhynchus. Ctenochasma* (Fig. 111) possesses extremely delicate, slender, tightly crowded teeth, of which it is assumed that they formed a wier; *Pteranodon* is toothless, as indicated by the name. With a wing span of over 8 meters *Pteranodon* was not only the largest flying reptile, but also the largest flying animal of all time. It is assumed that its jaws, like those of other toothless pterosaurs, were covered by horny sheaths after the fashion of birds. Most remains of pterosaurs have been found in unmistakably marine deposits. It is, therefore, assumed that they swept over the surface of the sea preying on fishes. The pterosaurs died out before the end of the Cretaceous. The superior competition of the birds may have been the reason for their extinction.

Dinosaurs

The dinosaurs were not closely enough related to form a unified order of reptiles; rather they represent, from the very beginning, two sharply circumscribed groups that are now generally regarded as orders: the Saurischia and the Ornithischia. The Saurischia include the suborders Theropoda and

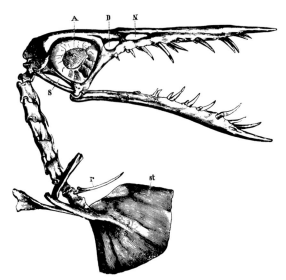

FIG. 110.—Skull of the pterosaur *Rhamphorhynchus* from the late Jurassic of Bavaria, in lateral view. From Zittel-Eastman, *Text-Book of Palaeontology* (London: Macmillan and Co., 1902), by permission.

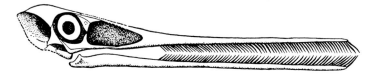

FIG. 111.—Skull of the pterosaur *Ctenochasma* from the Upper Jurassic. About ⅔ natural size. After Broili, from Romer (1945).

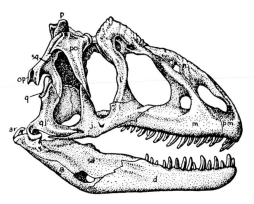

Fig. 112.—Skull of the saurischian *Allosaurus* from the late Jurassic. About 11 × natural size. After Gilmore, from Romer (1945).

Sauropoda; the Ornithischia, the Ornithopoda, the Stegosauria, the Ancylo-sauria, and the Ceratopsida.

In contrast to the Ornithischia, the jaws of the Saurischia bear teeth al-most for their entire length. In both orders the geologically old representa-tives are bipedal, that is, they walked more or less erect on their hind limbs. In both orders there are, however, also representatives that, apparently sec-ondarily, have assumed a quadrupedal gait. Carnivores and herbivores may be distinguished according to the dentition. Although the dentition as a whole may have been equally effective, herbivorous diet did not bring about comparably complicated tooth forms in reptiles as it did in herbivorous mammals. Among the Saurischia the theropods are predominantly carnivo-rous; the sauropods, herbivorous. All suborders of the Ornithischia were herbivorous.

Saurischia

The first of the two suborders of the saurischians, the theropods, includes coelurosaurs, the carnosaurs, and the prosauropods. The early history of the saurischians has not yet been satisfactorily clarified because the forms from the Triassic and the Lower Jurassic, unlike later genera, are relatively rare finds. Usually, they are of smallish size. Here and there they show charac-teristics that point toward a relationship to the thecodonts. But in addition to these characteristics they have typical features of the saurischians. The coelurosaurs were all exclusively bipedal and probably predominantly car-nivorous. The skeleton of *Compsognathus*, a genus that has so far become known only from a single skeleton in the lithographic limestones of Soln-hofen, contains remnants of a smaller skeleton in its abdominal region, which Marsh (1897) interpreted as an embryo, and v. Nopcsa (1903) as the remains of eaten prey. A number of late forms, such as *Struthiomimus*, resemble the ratites in the habitus of their skeletons. *Oviraptor* from the Cretaceous of the Mongoly is suspected of having eaten the eggs of other dinosaurs.

The predatory nature of the carnosaurs is clearly evident from the differ-entiation of their dentition (Fig 112). Such forms existed from the upper Triassic to the end of the Cretaceous. *Gresslyosaurus*, an incompletely known form from the Upper Keuper and the Rhaetic of Württemberg and Switzerland, was named by Rütimeyer for the geologist and early paleoecolo-gist, Amanz Gressley. The North American genera *Allosaurus* (Fig. 112) as well as *Tyrannosaurus* and *Gorgosaurus* are represented by exceptionally well preserved skeletons. *Tyrannosaurus* was nearly 16 meters long and when it stood erect to walk, was about 6 meters tall. Thus, it is thought to have been the largest land-living carnivore of all time.

Thin-sections through teeth of carnosaurs from the lower Cretaceous of Texas show a relatively thin layer of enamel.

A few bipedal forms, such as *Zaleosaurus (Anchisaurus)* and *Plateosaurus,* are thought to be ancestors of the sauropods because of certain skeletal characters and the not typically carnivorous character of the dentition. The temporal relations suggest such a possibility. The sauropods do not occur dominantly until the latest Jurassic (in the Morrison formation of North America and in the approximately contemporaneous deposits of the Tendaguru area in Africa).

The best known representatives of the sauropods are *Diplodocus* (Fig. 113) (length up to 29 meters), *Brachiosaurus* (somewhat shorter, but otherwise of even more giant dimensions than *Diplodocus*), *Brontosaurus,* and the somewhat smaller *Camarosaurus.* The jaws of *Diplodocus* were short and delicate. The teeth were relatively small and slender, bulbous, or spoon-shaped. In each jaw half there were rarely more than about a dozen teeth. It seems almost unbelievable that this dentition and jaw apparatus was capable of harvesting enough food to support such an enormous body. But it should be remembered that the food plants were probably soft aquatic forms whose consumption did not require great effort, and *Diplodocus* probably spent most waking hours feeding.

The question of their food requirements is not the only puzzle presented by the large sauropods. Because of the position of the external nasal opening, high on the roof of the skull, it is assumed that they spent most of their time on the bottom of shallow lakes and slow flowing rivers and only raised the nasal opening out of water from time to time.

Ornithischia

In the Ornithischia there is, in front of the dentary, a separate bone, the predentary. The ornithischians grouped in the suborder Ornithopoda are bipedal; all others are secondarily quadrupedal. A well known ornithopode is *Iguanodon* (Fig. 114) of which, at the beginning of the 1880's, well preserved skeletons were obtained from late Cretaceous deposits of Bernissart in Belgium. Figure 114 shows the predental bone anterior to the dental, the toothless premaxilla, and the row of cheek teeth that follow one another in closed sequence. The teeth form a simple row and are located in shallow pits on the jaws. The name *Iguanodon* alludes to the fact that the cutting edges of the unworn spatula-shaped teeth are denticulate, as in the modern lizard *Iguana.*

In the more or less aquatic *Anatosaurus* several rows of spatula-shaped teeth are present in which the anterior and the posterior cutting edges are denticulate. In the middle of the lingual face there extends a vertical strut

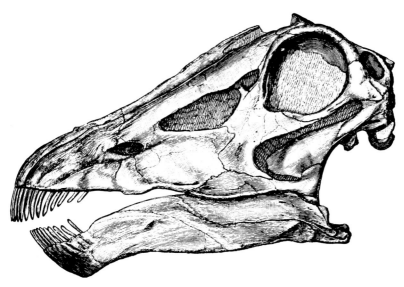

Fig. 113.—Skull of the saurischian *Diplodocus,* from the late Jurassic. 1:5.5. From Marsh (1896).

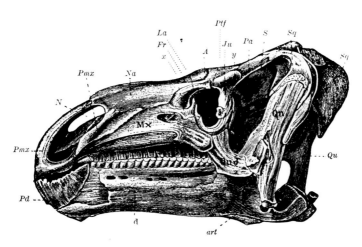

Fig. 114.—Skull of the ornithischian *Iguanodon* from the lower Cretaceous: *pd,* predental. 1:8.7. From Zittel, *Grundzüge der Paläontologie,* (Munich and Berlin: Verlag R. Oldenbourg, 1923), by permission.

(Fig. 115). In spite of this relatively simple tooth form, the dentition was highly efficient because many teeth functioned simultaneously. A. S. Romer estimates their number in each jaw quadrant as about 500, hence a total of some 2,000 teeth. It may be assumed that the water plants that served as food for these duckbilled dinosaurs required a higher degree of masticatory efficiency than did the aquatic vegetation that formed the staple diet of the large sauropods. The hadrosaurs are generally considered to have been fairly aquatic in their habits, and the amazing modifications of the nose-throat passages in some genera have been thought to be related to feeding under water. Ostrum (1962), however, has suggested that these structures may be specialized olfactory organs.

While the iguanodonts and the hadrosaurs belong to the bipedal forms, the following three groups, the stegosaurs, the ankylosaurs, and the ceratopsians, have become secondarily quadrupedal. All are land forms equipped with defensive weapons.

In the stegosaurs the back was armored with large bony plates and the tail with long bony spikes. The ankylosaurs were armored after the fashion of armadillos. The horn-bearing ceratopsians possessed a bony shield, formed by the parietals and the squamosals, that protected the neck.

In the stegosaurs and ankylosaurs the teeth were relatively small. Only a single row was simultaneously functional. The dentition of the ceratopsians (Fig 116) shows a number of specializations not yet present in their immediate predecessors, the protoceratopsians; for example, in the ceratopsians there is a toothless rostral element in front of the toothless premaxilla, which is not present in *Protoceratops*. The premaxilla of the latter carries a few teeth. In the protoceratopsians the functional teeth stand in one or two rows. In the ceratopsids they are always in several rows. The tooth replacement in ceratopsids was probably intensive, as suggested by the considerable number of replacement teeth in readiness (Fig. 116).

The shape of the tooth base (often called "root") is probably related to tooth replacement. The base consists of two branches between which the apex of the following replacement tooth fits. In *Protoceratops* the tooth base is still uniform.

No dinosaurs survived the Cretaceous. The cause of their extinction has been much debated, but a satisfactory explanation has not yet been given.

Synapsida

Synapsid reptiles are those whose skull possesses only a single lower temporal opening, bordered medially by the postorbital and the squamosal bones. Corresponding to this arrangement there is only a single lower jugular arch.

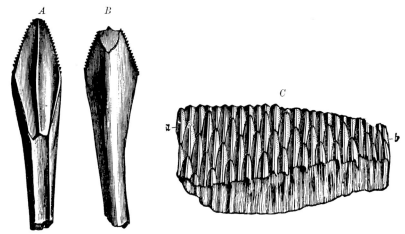

FIG. 115.—Teeth of the ornithischian *Anatosaurus (Trachodon)* from the late Cretaceous: *A*, a tooth in lingual view, *B*, in labial; *C*, dentition of the dental bone, lingual view. *A* and *B* slightly enlarged. After Leidy and Marsh, from Zittel-Eastman, *Text-Book of Palaeontology*, (London: Macmillan and Co., 1902, by permission.

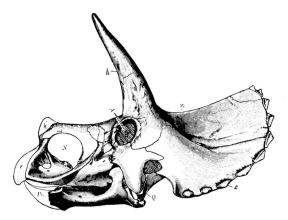

FIG. 116.—Skull of the ornithischian *Triceratops* from the uppermost Cretaceous: *r*, rostral bone in front of the premaxilla; *pd*, predental. 1:25. After Marsh, from Zittel-Eastman, *Text-Book of Palaeontology* (London: Macmillan and Co., 1902), by permission.

Even if the differentiation of the temporal region (see p. 136), despite its unquestionably great significance, does not by itself represent an absolute criterion for the interpretation of the systematic position of a reptile, experience has nevertheless shown that the synapsid reptiles, except for a few of doubtful affinity, form a large natural group of closely related forms. This conclusion is suggested by important features of their organization. A brief note concerning the phylogeny of the synapsids is necessary because the relations between the reptiles and the mammals involve also a discussion of odontological features.

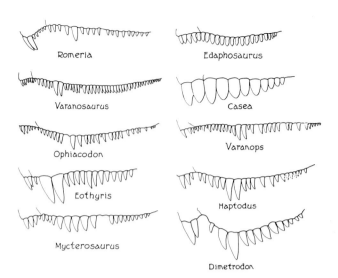

FIG. 117.—The upper left tooth row in a captorhinomorph *(Romeria)* and representative pelycosaurs. After Romer and Price (1940), from Romer (1961).

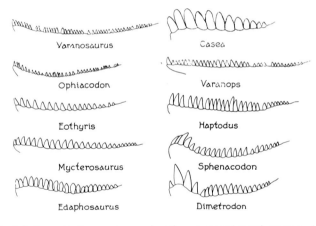

FIG. 118.—The left lower tooth row in a series of representative pelycosaurs. After Romer and Price (1940), from Romer (1961).

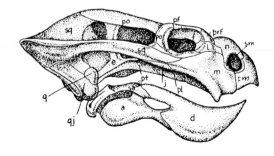

FIG. 119.—Skull of the Permian dicynodont *Dicynodon*. About ⅕ natural size. From Romer (1945).

The transition from gill-breathing ichthyopterygians to lung-breathing tetrapods took place toward the end of the Devonian period. In early tetrapods emancipation from life in the water was not completely carried through. In the Carboniferous, an admittedly long period, a segregation took place into forms whose evolution, even in the following periods, did not lead beyond amphibian levels of organization and forms whose evolution brought about adaptations to life on land involving the last consequences of such a transition. The earliest records of such animals are found in the late Pennsylvanian. They correspond to the stegocephalians in that they also possess a bony roof over the temporal region. This condition was retained for an extended geological time only in two reptile groups, the Cotylosaurs and the turtles. From the anapsid ancestral stock other reptiles originated relatively soon in which the bony cover of the temporal region was pierced in a variety of ways. Among the oldest of these forms are the synapsid pelycosaurs that reach back into the latest Pennsylvanian.

Pelycosauria

Pelycosaurs show clear evidence of a beginning heterodonty (Figs. 117, 118). *Varanosaurus,* an animal about 1½ meters long and of generalized lizard-like habitus, has an elongated skull whose numerous teeth are of about equal size. Only two teeth, at the anterior end of the maxilla, were notably larger than their neighbors. Romer (1961) suggested that these enlarged anterior teeth may functionally represent the beginning of the formation of canine teeth. According to the same author *Varanosaurus* was probably a fish eater that spent most of its time in the water. *Dimetrodon* and *Edaphosaurus* are characterized by an extraordinary elongation of the spinal processes of the dorsal vertebrae, but in their mode of life they differed appreciably since, according to the dentition, *Edaphosaurus* was a herbivore (Figs. 117, 118) and *Dimetrodon* a predaceous carnivore. The herbivorous pelycosaurs were the competitors of the likewise herbivorous diadectomorphs. The carnivorous pelycosaurs surpassed the ancient carnivorous cotylosaurs in efficiency and gave rise themselves to more modern synapsids, the therapsids in late Permian time. The latter evolved great variety in form but became extinct toward the end of the Triassic except for the lines that led to the mammals.

Therapsida

One of the subgroups of the therapsids, the dinocephalians—so called because of the generally notable size of the skull—encompasses several families that are partly carnivorous, partly herbivorous, among them the Dicynodontidae. In *Dicynodon* (Fig. 119) there is only a single tooth on each side of the upper jaw. *Ouenodon* was entirely toothless. It is probable that this was the toothless female of *Dicynodon*. According to Romer (1945), the dicynodonts were herbivorous marsh inhabitants. They probably had horny beaks like those of turtles.

A second subgroup of the therapsids are the theriodonts, so called because of the mammal-like heterodonty of their dentition. The gorgonopsians, the cynodonts, and the therocephalians belong to this group.

In the pelycosaurs there are beginnings of a segregation of the dentition into pre-canine, canine, and post-canine tooth series. In the more advanced synapsids the differentiation of the tooth form in the different regions of the dentition becomes progressively more pronounced.

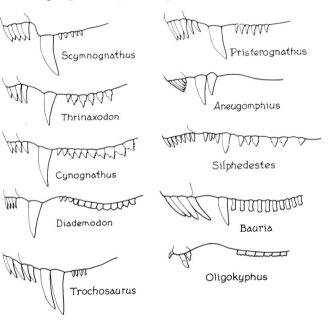

FIG. 120.—Left upper dentitions of typical theriodont therapsids. After Boonstra, Watson, Brink, Kühne and Broom, from Romer (1961).

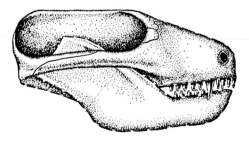

FIG. 121.—Skull of a little ictidosaur from the Triassic of South Africa. After Broom, from Romer (1945).

The most generalized theriodonts are found among the gorgonopsians, of which *Scymnognathus* (Fig. 120) may be mentioned. The cynodonts are more highly differentiated, as for example *Cynognathus* (Fig. 120). Even further differentiated are the therocephalians, of which *Lycosuchus* and *Bauria* (Fig. 120) may be noted as examples.

The phyletic relations are difficult to discern because the evolutionary progression apparently did not proceed along a single line but along several parallel phyletic lines. Certain especially mammal-like characteristics occur in the different lines at different levels of progression.

Accompanying the evolution of the dentition there are changes in the skull and in the post-cranial skeleton that likewise lead toward mammal-like conditions. Only a few aspects of this problem will be mentioned here; for greater detail I may refer the reader to the textbooks of paleontology, particularly the account that Romer rendered in his *Vertebrate Paleontology* (1945). I have taken the following from his work.

Of the numerous skull bones of the labyrinthodonts and the early reptiles many were lost as was the parietal foramen. Because, finally, the posterior bony border of the orbit was also reduced, the orbit became broadly united with the temporal fossa as in primitive mammals (Fig. 121). In the lower jaw the dental bone became by far the most prominent element. The bones lying behind it decreased in relative size, as did the quadrate. Finally, the dental bone entered into an articular connection with the squamosal bone. These two bones characteristically form the jaw joint in the mammals, whereas the quadrate and articular bones assume the function of sound transmission under the names "incus" and "malleus."

To draw a practical boundary between reptiles and mammals it is necessary to rely on these osteological relations. If the lower jaw consists of only a single bone, the animal is classified as a mammal; if there are additional very small ossifications behind the dental, the animal is considered a reptile.

It should be emphasized, however, that there are also mammal-like forms among the theriodonts, which cannot be considered as direct predecessors of the mammals. Nearly all of the extremely varied synapsid reptiles died out toward the end of the Triassic, without leaving successors.

The mammals probably originated from small, still incompletely known synapsids that are grouped under the name Ictidosauria (from *iktis*, "marten").

Ictidosauria

In addition to the South African ictidosaurs there are associated with this group forms that have mammal-like teeth but that by present definition,

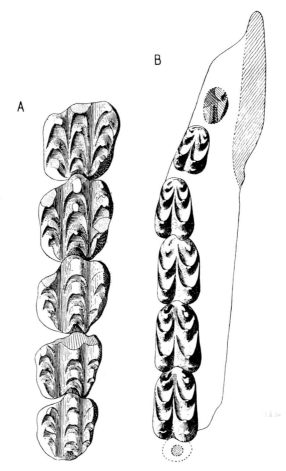

FIG. 122.—Dentition of the therapsid *Oligokyphus major* from the Lias. The "half-moons" in the upper jaw (*A*) concave forward, in the lower jaw (*B*) concave backwards. Much enlarged. From Kühne (1956).

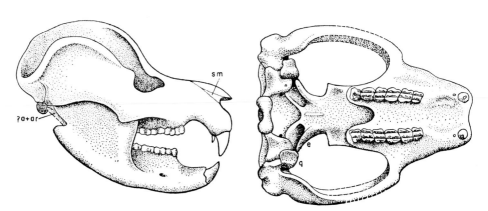

FIG. 123.—Skull in lateral and palatal aspects of the therapsid *Bienotherium* from the upper Triassic of China. About ½ natural size. After Joung and Watson, from Romer (1945).

belong to the reptiles, for example the widely distributed genus *Tritylodon*, the closely related genus *Oligokyphus* from the Rhaetic of Württemberg and from the Rhaeto-Lias of England (Fig. 122), and *Bienotherium* from the uppermost Triassic of China (Fig. 123). Still uncertain is the systematic position of forms such as the Haramyidae (microlestids), of which only teeth have been found so far. Nonetheless, in view of recent discoveries, it may no longer be doubted that the mammals reach back to the Rhaetic.

I cannot close the section on the synapsids without pointing out again that a consideration of the results of paleontology is necessary also for the study of odontological relations and may occasionally even provide the guidelines. As Romer (1945) pointed out, the varied organization of the therapsids bridges the chasm between the reptiles and the primitive mammals. The mammals have evolved from synapsids, which suggests the necessity of further studies of the tooth relations in this group of reptiles. Since they are extinct without exception and, moreover, are largely rare finds, the circumstances of the study material are not particularly favorable. Still it is hoped that additional investigations will bring a solution to many presently open questions.

AVES

Because all modern birds are toothless, and there are no birds with teeth known from Tertiary deposits, the description of the dentition of the birds is restricted to the meager knowledge we have concerning the dentition of the primeval bird *Archaeopteryx* from the lithographic limestones of Solnhofen and of a few birds of Cretaceous age.

Probably the specimens from Solnhofen, the London and the Berlin specimens, and a third, more recent discovery, all belong to the same genus, *Archaeopteryx*, since there are no significant differences between them other than a minor one of size. In the upper jaw of the Berlin specimen there are 13 pointed, conical teeth that sit in alveoli (Fig. 124). Nothing is known concerning the dentition of the mandible.

Although it is taken for certain that the segregation of the birds into the different subdivisions must have occurred largely during the Cretaceous period, only a few finds of fossil birds are known from this time. Except for a number of incompletely known European genera, there are primarily the genera *Ichthyornis* and *Hesperornis* from the Niobrara formation (Late Cretaceous) of Kansas.

In contrast to *Archaeopteryx*, whose reptile-like, long tail was bi-serially feathered, the two Cretaceous birds had short tails whose most posterior vertebrae were fused to form a pygostyle in *Ichthyornis*, as in modern birds.

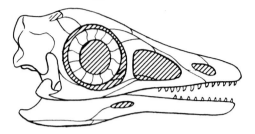

Archaeopteryx

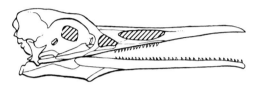

Hesperornis

FIG. 124.—Skulls of the ancient bird *Archaeopteryx* from the uppermost Jurassic and of the toothed bird *Hesperornis* from the Cretaceous. From Stirton, *Life, Time and Man* (New York: John Wiley and Sons, 1959), by permission.

Judging by the structure of the forelimbs of *Hesperornis* it seems evident that this bird had become incapable of flight.

The premaxilla had become toothless; it was probably already equipped with a horny beak, whereas the maxilla bore teeth. The dental bone (Fig. 124) was provided with teeth along its entire length. The teeth are not located in separate alveoli but rather in continuous grooves.

In contrast to *Hesperornis, Ichthyornis* was a good flyer. Nothing is known regarding its dentition, since J. T. Gregory (1951) could show that the tooth-bearing jaws that had been found with remains of *Ichthyornis,* and had been ascribed to it, are instead the jaws of a young mosasaur. The discoverer of *Ichthyornis,* O. Marsh, had originally identified them as such, but he later assigned them to *Ichthyornis.*

MAMMALIA

The teeth of man and the mammals were understandably the first objects of investigation of odontology. Only much later were the teeth of other classes of vertebrates also investigated. This historical origin is evident today in the fact that the odontological terminology describes, first of all, mammalian conditions; thus certain difficulties arise in its use among non-mammalia. In our account we reverse the sequence because the results of comparative anatomy and paleontology clearly suggest that mammals, in a phylogenetic progression clearly documented by fossils, have evolved from synapsid reptiles. How this transition affected the teeth is the subject of two opposed theories, the concrescence theory and the differentiation theory, that shall be discussed in the following.

The concrescence theory assumes that mammalian teeth originated by fusion of the anlagen of originally discrete reptile teeth.

In this connection it should be noted that the same question, this special case apart, arises for all classes of vertebrates: whether the dentine teeth of the mouth cavity represent morphologically simple structures, or are complex formations consisting of aggregated primary form elements. With respect to the Chondrichthyes, especially the sharks, this question has become current in connection with Ørvig's (1951) theoretical views, which represent a further development of Weidenreich's idea concerning the morphological nature of the selachian tooth. The results of my own investigations led me to the following conclusions about this question.

Among the tooth structures of the mouth cavity of sharks the mucous membrane denticles are unquestionably the most primitive, as evidenced by their structural correspondence with the dermal denticles.[1] For this reason, comparison of the dentine teeth of the mouth cavity of the sharks with the bone tissue of other classes of vertebrates should always be initiated with the mucous membrane denticles as the most generalized structures, not with dentition teeth that have become specialized in particular ways, such as those that have trabecular dentine beneath a coat of orthodentine. With their structurally simple pulp cavity, the mucous membrane denticles do not show any particular similarity to bone beyond the fact that both tissues are hard substances formed by similar mesodermal cells.

Because of the emphasis on corresponding features of trabecular dentine and bone, the important differences were unfortunately not given their proper weight. It is to be noted (as Ørvig, 1951, has done) that the distribution of trabecular dentine, as of any dentine, is restricted to the vicinity of the ectoderm; this restriction might be connected with an organizing influence emanating from it. For bone there are no such topographic restrictions. It may occur at any distance from the ectoderm. The mode of formation differs in that many of the bone-producing cells, the osteoblasts, become entirely enclosed by the hard substance they produce; and cells that produce dentine, the odontoblasts, generally retreat from the newly produced hard substance, leaving behind only a single cytoplasmatic process. Intermediate

---

[1] According to the lepidomorial theory of Stensiö-Ørvig (Stensiö, 1961, 1962), the dermal denticle of modern sharks is not considered a primary morphological element; for a discussion of this matter, see p. 59.

tissues are known, however, and the question of what histogenetic factors determine the differentiation of bone or dentine in the immediate vicinity of the ectodermal body cover begs an answer.

Among the hundreds of thousands of mucous membrane denticles that may be observed in the mucous membrane of *Carcharodon carcharias*, I could not find a single fusion of adjacent denticles. Furthermore, among dentition teeth of elasmobranchs, I have learned of not a single proved case of true fusion of adjacent teeth. Pathological fusions in the form of odontomas in teleosts are naturally not impossible. The view offered by A. S. Woodward (1889), that the large tooth plates of cochliodonts (Fig. 24) have originated from the fusion of smaller elements, is a mere assumption which appears not very plausible in view of the ontogenetic investigation of the tooth plates of *Myliobatis aquila* (see p. 73), revealing in this instance that the large plates are not formed by fusion of smaller ones, but by allometric growth.

It is questionable whether fusions of neighboring elements occur among dermal denticles of modern sharks, rays and skates. But among fossil forms several examples are known in the family Edestidae, where fusion of denticles occurs in all degrees of complexity (Fig. 32). Furthermore, among the dermal denticles on the dorsal spines of *Asteracanthus* and *Ctenacanthus* (see p. 72), there are unquestionably fusions. Among the actinopterygians the dentition teeth with their generally simple pulp cavity surrounded by orthodentine show no signs of a composition of different components.

In contrast to the Chondrichthyes, there is among the Osteichthyes at least one instance of fusion of different tooth anlagen to form a tooth plate, namely in the teeth of *Neoceratodus*, even though the actual process of fusion has not yet been observed.

The teeth of fossil and living amphibians, both with respect to their form relationships and to their behavior during otogeny, present a picture of structural simplicity. The teeth of reptiles and the few birds in which teeth are known are also structurally simple. Almost without exception they are regarded as morphologically uniform structures.

In this survey we emphasize particularly the relations of the pulp cavities, which seem to suggest that the teeth of non-mammals, with a very few especially noted exceptions, correspond in their morphological uniformity.

In the usually strongly heterodont dentition of the mammals only the incisor and the canine teeth are generally simply formed; but the molars and some premolars may assume very complicated forms. Thus, for example, the most posterior molar of the rodent *Hydrochoerus* consists of many antero-posteriorly arranged transverse lamellae. Except for such cases of maximal molar complication, even more simply constructed cheek teeth, such as those of man, show considerable differences from the simple conical reptile teeth. These differences led, about the turn of the century, to extensive investigations of the morphological relations between the teeth of the different classes of vertebrates, and consequently to hypotheses about the mode of origin of the mammal molar from more simple tooth forms, more particularly to the two opposed theories of concrescence and differentiation.

Concrescence theory

According to the concrescence theory, a multicuspid mammal molar is formed in such a way that a number of simple conical teeth fuse to form an entity of a higher order. Origin by concrescence was particularly assumed for the molar teeth of the extinct multituberculates that consist of a greater or lesser number of discrete cusps (Fig. 125). It was thereby assumed first of all that each cusp represented originally a separate tooth. Some difficulties with this assumption were encountered in the fact that the late multituberculates show a higher number of cusps than the geologically older forms. A close comparison with the reptiles suggested a distinction between two kinds of fusion: of teeth located along the edges of the jaws in anteroposterior rows or generally of teeth belonging to the same tooth generation; and in a labiolingual direction, that is of a functional tooth with one or

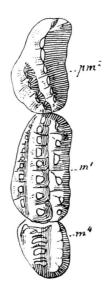

FIG. 125.—Multicusped cheek teeth of the multituberlate *Ptilodus* from the Lower Eocene. After Osborn, from Weber, *Die Säugetiere* (Jena: Gustav Fischer Verlag, 1928), by permission.

several of the following replacement teeth. Consideration of this sort led Louis Bolk to change the original concrescence theory into a concentration theory. The principle remained, however, the same. The concentration theory also assumes that the mammalian molar originated from several structures that are morphologically equivalent to the tooth anlagen of reptiles. With respect to the topographic relations of these tooth anlagen to one another, Bolk does not assume any fusion of tooth anlagen located one behind the other on the edge of the jaw, but only a fusion in the labiolingual direction; that is, of tooth anlagen located in a cross row.

The teeth of such a cross row, that is, a functional tooth and all the replacement teeth that follow it in a polyphyodont dentition, Bolk calls "tooth family." With respect to the number of tooth anlagen from which a molar tooth of a mammal is supposed to have originated, the terms "concentration theory" and "dimer theory" do not seem to correspond exactly, in so far as "dimer" implies origin from "two parts"; and following the idea of concentration, the whole anlage material of a polyphyodont reptile dentition is supposed to enter into the formation of a single molar. In contrast to earlier theories of concentration, it is not anlagen of simple conical teeth that become fused, according to Bolk's theory, but anlagen of teeth that have become triconodont by differentiation: from the combination of two such triconodont anlagen a six-cuspid molar is supposed to have originated.

Bolk's (1913–1919) theoretical concepts are based on the arrangement of individual teeth and replacement teeth of a polyphyodont dentition as it occurs most clearly in sharks, but which may also be recognized in amphibians and reptiles.

If in sharks there is only one longitudinal row of functional teeth, this row does not follow perfectly the edge of the jaw; the teeth are arranged in a zig-zag line in which the functional teeth alternately assume a more lingual and more labial position. Correspondingly, the replacement teeth of neighboring cross rows alternate with one another. Those functional teeth that lie slightly further buccally or labially are called "exostichos" in Bolk's terminology, the somewhat more lingual teeth "endostichos." The whole of the "exostichos" comprises, according to Bolk, the slightly labial functional teeth and all of their replacement teeth, and the whole of the "endostichos" the alternating cross rows. Bolk's concentration theory assumes that the anlage material, from which in non-mammals all succeeding teeth of a cross row or a tooth family originate, enters into the formation of a single tooth in mammals. Since, according to Bolk, the cross rows of teeth and tooth anlagen are distinguished by the fact that some belong to the exostichos and others to the endostichos, there must also be a difference in the products of concentration: the whole of the exostichos produces all the teeth of the

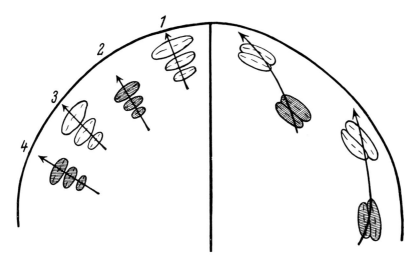

FIG. 126.—Diagram of Bolk's theory. Left the shark dentition whose exostichal and endostichal cross rows consist of independent tooth individuals; right the mammalian dentition in which all tooth anlagen in each cross-row are thought to be assimilated into the formation of a single tooth, whereby the exostichal cross rows are said to produce the milk teeth, the endostichal cross rows the permanent teeth. According to Bolk the total endostichos replaces the total exostichos in the tooth replacement of mammals. From W. Meyer, *Normale Histologie und Entwicklungsgeschichte der Zähne des Menschen* (Munich: Carl Hanser Verlag, 1951), by permission.

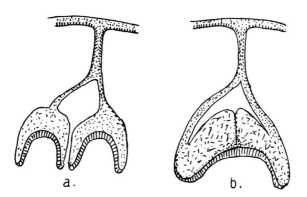

FIG. 127.—Semi-diagrammatic presentations of (*a*) two tooth generations of *Varanus* and (*b*) an anlage of a tooth of a primate to explain the origin of the enamel septum. After Bolk, from W. Meyer, *Normale Histologie und Entwicklungsgeschichte der Zähne des Menschen* (Munich: Carl Hanser Verlag, 1951), by permission.

lactating tooth generation of the mammals, the whole of the endostichos all the teeth of the permanent generation. Tooth replacement in mammals would thus be, according to this view, a process principally different from that of non-mammals. If, in mammals, the teeth of the permanent generation assume the position of the teeth of the lactating generation, then, if the concentration theory is correct, morphologically uniform teeth do not replace equally uniform predecessors, but the whole of the exostichos replaces the whole of the endostichos (Fig. 126). According to the terminology of Bolk's theory, the dentition of non-mammals is hamastichous, its tooth replacement merobolic, the dentition of the mammals choristichous, and its tooth replacement stichobolic. To this short description of the essential content of Bolk's theory there may be added that the molars of the multituberculates and the proboscidians are supposed to differ from the molars of the remaining mammals, in that their construction is to be regarded not as dimer but as polymer.

Bolk's bold theory was, at any rate, heuristically valuable, in that it stimulated many odontological investigations. His theory has adherents even today, but it is highly controversial. Even the embryological arguments, on which the theory is mainly based—the presence of a so-called enamel septum (Fig. 127), and a so-called enamel nook and a double connection of the enamel organ with the dental lamina—have received different interpretations. In one instance, however, Bolk's theory is based on observations that are not disputed by anyone. As has been mentioned above, Bolk distinguished as exostichos and endostichos adjacent cross rows of teeth which stand slightly more lingually or slightly more labially to one another in the dentitions of many selachians, and in such reptiles as *Sphenodon*. The significance of these positional relations is severely impaired, however, by the fact that their determination requires the arbitrary designation of a phase in the tooth replacement process of non-mammals. From the schematic presentation of a selachian dentition, it is perfectly evident that, among the functional teeth in their zig-zag longitudinal row, the more labial ones (Bolk's "exostichos") are shed first. Once removed, the endostichos teeth assume an exostichos position on the edge of the jaw; in other words, all rows are alternately in endostichal and exostichal positions in the course of tooth replacement (Fig. 128). The distinction of exostichos and endostichos thus seems pointless. Quite apart from this objection, it seems highly doubtful that there are any important differences between teeth of adjacent cross rows in the selachian dentition.

For the dentition of mammals, Bolk believed he had found a criterion for distinguishing between exostichos and endostichos, in that the topographic relations of the tooth anlagen of the exostichos are supposed to differ from

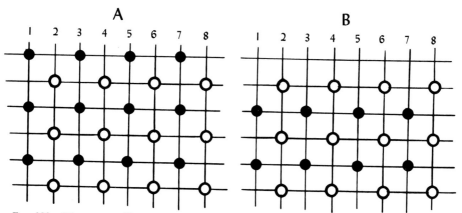

Fig. 128.—Diagram to illustrate justification of my opposition to Bolk's theory. Whether a cross-row must be regarded as exo- or endostichos in the selachian dentition depends merely on the time of observation. At the time *A* the most labial teeth of the cross rows 1, 3, 5 and 7 occupy an exostichal position; at the time *B*, however, the most labial teeth of these cross-rows have dropped out; the same cross-rows now occupy an endostichal position.

those of the endostichos. The exostichal anlagen were said to be in a parietal position, the endostichal ones in a terminal position in the development of the dental lamina. This proposition also has been proved wrong (Woerdeman, 1920).

The insights provided by paleontology have been too little considered by Bolk, as is evident in his view of the genesis of the elephant molars. According to Bolk, these teeth, in contrast to the majority of other mammals, are not dimer but polymer. The different lamellae that compose the elephant tooth correspond, according to Bolk, to the members of a tooth family. To explain the fact that these lamellae follow one another mesiodistally and the members of a tooth family follow one another linguolabially Bolk assumes a 90-degree torsion of the tooth. The phylogenetic history of elephants, however, has shown that the earliest members of the Proboscidea had molars that do not correspond in the least with the expectations of Bolk's theory. Paleontologists have thus generally refuted this theory.

Differentiation theory

The differentiation theory maintains that even the most complicated mammalian molar has originated from a uniform tooth anlage. While the concrescence theory found its principal proponents among embryologists and dentists, the differentiation theory in the special form of the tritubercular theory had its main adherents among the paleontologists. To discuss this theory it seems better to begin with its original content than with its present status (see B. Patterson, 1956), because the terminology proposed

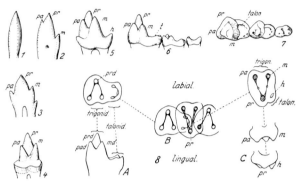

Fɪɢ. 129.—Diagrams to illustrate the tritubercular theory I. Explanation in the text. After Osborn, from Peyer (1937), in Bolk-Göppert-Kallius-Lubosch, *Handbuch der Vergleichenden Anatomie der Wirbeltiere* (Vienna and Berlin: Verlag Urban & Schwarzenberg, 1931–39), by permission.

in the original version has been retained regardless of whether the original sense has been retained.

The schematic, graphic representation of the tritubercular theory furnished by Osborn and here illustrated (Fig. 129) has been reproduced over and over in textbooks and is so clear that nothing need be added. The starting point forms simple conical teeth as they may be found in very many reptiles. This condition of the dentition Osborn calls "haplodont" (from *haplos,* "simple"). It need hardly be pointed out here that the simple conical teeth of toothed whales and dolphins have originated from more complicated teeth by secondary simplification. From the haplodont tooth the protodont tooth is derived. It is distinguished from the haplodont by its little side cusps. The triconodont tooth is formed by the formation of notable anterior and posterior accessory cusps from these at-first-insignificant cusplets. In the upper jaw its primary middle cusp is called "protocone"; the anterior (mesial) accessory cusp, "paracone"; the posterior distal cusp, "metacone." The corresponding cusps of the teeth of the lower jaw are characterized as such by adding the ending "-id"; thus they are called "protoconid," "paraconid" and "metaconid." The three points lie in a straight line parallel to the edge of the jaw. Then the accessory cusps change their position relative to the main cusp so that they form a triangle with the main cusp. This triangle is called "trigon" in the upper jaw, "trigonid" in the lower jaw. The difference in terminology is due to the fact that the two triangles have different orientations in the upper and lower jaws. In the upper jaw the protocone lies lingually, paracone and metacone buccally (labially); in the lower jaw the protoconid is labial, paraconid and metaconid are lingual. The further differentiation took place as a perfection of the occlusion. In the mandible a heel or talonid was added to the trigonid, in the upper jaw a talon formed in that a second lingual cusp developed next to the protocone, a so-called hypocone. Thereby, the originally triangular structure of the tooth crown became quadrangular (Fig. 130).

A further complication in the crown relief took place in such a way that intermediate cusps occurred along the trigon, a protoconule between protocone and paracone and a metaconule between protocone and metacone. Furthermore, a stylar shelf along the labial rim of the crown of the upper molars developed at this stage of molar evolution (B. Patterson 1956).

In the lower jaw three cusps developed on the talonid: counting labiolingually, hypoconid, hypoconulid and entoconid. Thus, a six-cusped tooth originated from which later a four-cusped tooth evolved in a variety of ways. In the ancient, primitive forms trigon and trigonid are considerably higher than are talon and talonid respectively. In geologically younger mammals this difference is lost.

In many mammals the evolution of the premolars and the molars did not remain at the stage of the tritubercular or tuberculo-sectorial or tribosphenic tooth; a further differentiation took place that led to high functional efficiency of the dentition. Prior to characterizing these different evolutionary directions we may briefly mention the extent to which the tenets of the tritubercular theory have proved correct in their original form

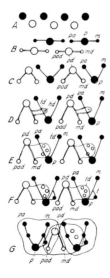

Fig. 130.—Diagrams to illustrate the tritubercular theory II. Explanation in the text. Black symbols, upper; white symbols, lower dentition. After Osborn, from Peyer (1937), in Bolk-Göppert-Kallius-Lubosch, *Handbuch der Vergleichenden Anatomie der Wirbeltiere* (Vienna and Berlin: Verlag Urban & Schwarzenberg, 1931–39), by permission.

and how far newer investigations have led to their modification. For a critique of the Cope-Osborn tritubercular theory see Butler (1941).[1]

As the name "protocone" suggests, the original tritubercular theory looked upon this cusp as the homologon of a simple conical reptile tooth, or the main point of a reptilian tooth that possesses side cusplets. Important arguments were furnished against such a view. One of them concerns the time of the occurrence of this cusp in ontogeny. If the protocone indeed represents the main cusp of a protodont tooth, the argument goes, then its anlage should occur early in ontogeny. This is, however, not so in man, insectivores and ungulates, according to M. F. Woodward (1896). In these forms the paracone is formed first. More important seems to me the circumstance that the premolars do not easily fit into the scheme proposed for the genesis of the molars by Osborn. W. B. Scott thus proposed a special terminology for the description of the premolars, in which the cusps are simply numbered as protocone, deuterocone, tritocone, tetratocone, and "-conid," respectively. Comparative considerations show that the mode of formation of the premolars and the molars can hardly be different in a fundamental way.

In the premolars of the upper jaw the cusp that becomes the protocone is an initially insignificant, late-developing structure that cannot be considered to have been derived from the main cusp of a protodont tooth. For this reason, the protocone of the molars likewise is probably not derivable from the main cusp of a reptile tooth.

According to investigations, primarily by W. K. Gregory (1921), the original main point of the upper molar corresponded to a cusp called "amphicone," from which the paracone and the metacone originated. The theory based on the assumption of a principle correspondence in the structure of the premolars and the molars is called "premolar-analogy theory." [2] It is preferable to the original form of the tritubercular theory. For the protoconid of the molars of the lower jaw, neither the time of its ontogenetic appearance nor the comparison with the premolars presents any difficulties for the original interpretation.

The tritubercular theory originally contained the assumption that the tritubercular molar form had originated from a triconodont condition in such a way that the anterior and posterior cusps of a triconodont tooth had changed their positions. Against the assumption of such a "cusp rotation"

---

[1] Recently Vandebroek (1964) proposed a radically different system of crown cusp terminology.

[2] This designation probably was meant to merely indicate that the differentiation of the premolars takes place in the same way as in the molars, and has no bearing at all on the question of morphological homology of premolar and molar cusps.

speaks primarily Wortman (1903), followed by most students since then; Vandebroek (1964) favors it.

Recently Kraus and Jordan (1965), dental embryologists who have studied in very great detail the developing crown relief of the human teeth, suggested a new theory concerning the origin of the mammalian cheek teeth. The crown relief of human premolars and molars increases in complexity from a simple mound to a multicusped structure with a far more pronounced crown relief than that of the errupted tooth. This offers the possibility of comparing various developmental shapes of these teeth with cheek teeth of primitive mammals, and the authors suggest a certain similarity between specific ontogenetic stages and examples from the early phylogenetic history of the mammals. This theory starts with the simple conical reptilian tooth as the morphological base as does the tritubercular theory, but is at present derived mainly from human data. The authors suggest similar studies of a variety of mammals to assess the comparative anatomical significance of the ontogenetic crown differentiation.

The detailed content of the theory need not be discussed here, since future work along this potentially promising approach is bound to lead to modification of the present views.

Already, in very old forms, as in the triconodonts and symmetrodonts, a basal, ring-shaped enlargement of the tooth crown, a cingulum, occurs in varying ways. From such cingulum formations strong cingulum cusps may originate (Pl. 82-a). In highly differentiated molars the cingulum gives rise to all kinds of marginal pillars (styli) that will be discussed later.

In a general comparison of mammal and reptile teeth, the mode of attachment should be considered. Among other types of tooth fixation, thecodonty occurs quite often among reptiles. In this type of attachment the teeth are implanted in depressions in the jaw bones, much as the mammal teeth are emplaced in their alveoli. There are, however, notable differences between the mode of attachment of the mammalian teeth (gomphosis) and the thecodonty of the reptiles. In the mammal teeth a root forms by the narrowing of the pulp cavity to form a basal root canal. This ends in a fine opening, the *foramen apicis radicis dentis*. In multirooted molars several root canals originate from a uniform pulp cavity. In reptiles the pulp cavity is not restricted basally, but remains generally wide open. If, exceptionally, there is a closure at the base, this comes about in a totally different way (see p. 138).

During their formation the roots of the mammalian teeth have a relatively wide lumen (Pl. 67-a).

The number of roots is not constant. It is known that in man this number may vary even in teeth of same position in the dentition; for example, in the first left upper molar. Canine teeth are usually single-rooted; but occasionally they may be double-rooted, especially in some primitive forms, as in the hedge hog. Although in general a pronounced complication of the tooth crown accompanies multiple roots, there are no strict relations between crown form and root differentiation.

Among the modern mammals only few have retained relatively primitive conditions in the structure of the molars; these are some of the lineages of marsupials, the insectivores, the bats and the primates. Most of the others became specialized and deviated greatly from the original tritubercular form. For most of the placental mammal orders it may, however, be demonstrated step by step by a great amount of fossil material that even highly complicated molars have originated from simple tritubercular forms.

The tooth forms of the different mammal groups will be discussed later. First we shall introduce a few terms used to characterize the different molar types.

The starting point for all Monodelphia (placental mammals), and according to Simpson (1936) also for the Marsupialia, are simple tribosphenic tritubercular forms (Fig. 131). Also in the symmetrodonts the three cusps of the tooth are arranged in a triangle, specifically an isosceles triangle; in the trituberculates or pantotheres it is usually a scalene triangle. A further difference lies in the fact that there is no talonid in the symmetrodonts, but a talonid is common in the more advanced trituberculates. For these reasons, Simpson (1925) created for the symmetrodonts a separate mammal order.

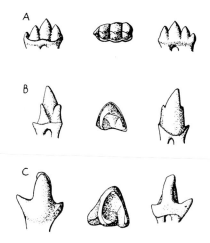

FIG. 131.—Triconodont, symmetrodont and pantothere lower teeth: *A, Priacodon,* tricondont, 3.5:1; *B, Spalacotherium,* symmetrodont, 5:1; *C, Dryolestes,* pantothere, 11:1. After Simpson, from Romer (1945).

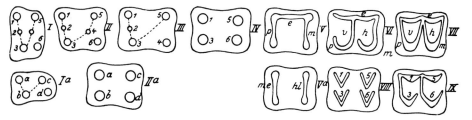

Fig. 132.—Diagram to illustrate the tritubercular theory. Designations of the form elements of upper molars: 1, paracone; 2, protoconule; 3, protocone; 4, metaconule; 5, metacone; 6, hypocone; *p*, protoloph; *e*, ectoloph; *m*, metaloph; *v*, prefossette; *h*, postfossette. After Osborn, from Peyer (1937) in Bolk-Göppert-Kallius-Lubosch, *Handbuch der Vergleichenden Anatomie der Wirbeltiere*, (Vienna and Berlin: Verlag Urban & Schwarzenberg, 1931–39), by permission.

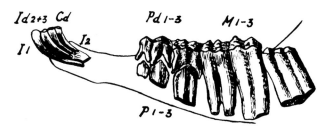

Fig. 133.—Tooth replacement in a 20-month-old sheep. From Owen (1840–45).

Molars with six well developed cusps are found primarily among the ancient mammals. The six-cusped type was a transitional stage to the more modern four-cusped type, which has evolved in the different groups by reduction of different individual cusps.

The teeth of the earliest monodelphous mammals are generally bunodont (from *bunos*, "hill"); that is, they are provided with cone-shaped cusps and are at the same time brachyodont—low-crowned and provided with well developed roots. A change in the tooth shape evolved in certain forms of mammals in that the cusps became connected to form yokes (Fig. 132). Such teeth are lophodont (from *lophos*, "yoke"). On upper molars a protoloph (fore yoke), ectoloph (outer yoke) and a metaloph (back yoke) may be distinguished; in the lower molars an anterior metalophid, a posterior hypolophid, and occasionally a third yoke formed by the hypoconule.

In the "even-toed" ungulates evolution led to a different change of the molars. The originally conical cusps changed into so-called half-moons. Teeth of this kind are called "selenodont" (from *selene*, "moon") (Fig. 133). The concave side of these half-moons faces laterad in the upper jaw, mediad in the lower jaw. Corresponding to this arrangement of the half-moons and the differentiation of the jaw articulation, the grinding stroke of the chewing motion takes place primarily from the outside inward and from the inside outward. In this manner extraordinary chewing results are achieved.

An entirely different type of dentition evolved in the carnivores. The oldest carnivores possessed in the premolar and molar section of the dentition tuberculated teeth. Of these, two antagonists on each side—in modern carnivores the last premolar in the upper jaw and the first molar in the lower jaw—became carnassials (Pl. 67-b). With their sharp cutting edges that glide by one another in a ginglymic jaw motion, they form a break-shear apparatus. Dentitions of this sort are called "secodont."

The extent of the tooth-bearing area is restricted to the jaws in mammals. Palatal dentitions, in contrast to some reptiles, do not occur in mammals. This might possibly be related to the formation of a secondary palate.

The earliest herbivores among the tetrapods were certain Permian cotylosaurs. Through the whole of the Mesozoic era we see how the evolution of the carnivorous reptiles runs in step with the differentiation of their primary prey, the herbivorous reptiles. In the Tertiary period this improvement of the weapons of offense and defense took place among the carnivorous and herbivorous mammals. It is, however, not true that the herbivorous mammals could be derived from the herbivorous reptiles. The latter were specialized forms that became almost wholly extinct, without leaving descendants.

According to the sparse information that we have about the earliest mammals, it is assumed that they fed like the modern insectivores, that is, not only on insects, but on all kinds of small invertebrates and perhaps also on a little vegetable matter. In place of the well known, but not accurate, term "insectivore," Ludwig Döderlein proposed the term "animalivor." The order Insectivora includes a number of generally primitive, but in various ways specialized, mammals. Common representatives are the hedgehogs, the shrews and the moles.

As a systematic criterion, the mode of feeding is usable only with caution, because in different, unquestionably natural, groups of mammals there are both carnivores and herbivorous forms; for example, among the marsupials. Even among the Carnivora there are omnivorous forms and the giant panda (*Ailuropoda melanoleuca*) feeds exclusively on bamboo shoots. The extinct cave bear is assumed to have also been a vegetarian.

Durophagous specialization of the dentition, that is, adaptation to handle hard-shelled food, is easily recognizable among fishes and retiles as a special phenomenon in that the ordinarily pointed teeth have become half-spherical pavement blocks or even large flat plates. Mastication is usually a mere crushing of the food. In mammals corresponding feats are not unusual; they are accomplished by simple bunodont molars that cannot be regarded

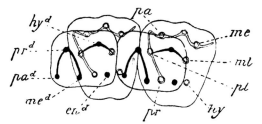

FIG. 134.—Occlusion relations of ungulate molars, upper and lower molars projected one onto another. After Osborn, from Zittel, *Grundzüge der Paläontologie* (Munich and Berlin: Verlag R. Oldenbourg, 1923) by permission.

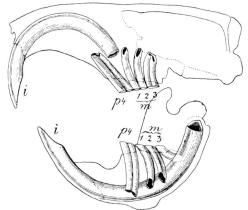

FIG. 135.—Implantation of the teeth in the rodent *Geomys*. After Bailey, from Weber, *Die Säugetiere* (Jena: Gustav Fischer Verlag, 1928), by permission.

as specialized. Among the carrion-feeding hyaenas the increased load on the teeth is reflected in a generally robust construction of the entire skull.

During phylogenetic development durophagous specialization opened up food sources for the mammals that would not have been available to them without such modification of the dentition. Among the factors that enhanced the functional efficiency of the dentition in mammals are the changes in the trigeminus musculature, related to the differentiation of a new joint for the articulation of the mandible. A step forward of very great significance was the gradual perfection of the occlusal relationships, a process that took place primarily in the late Mesozoic and early Tertiary.

The example of the crocodile shows that the teeth of the upper jaw are not opposed to those of the mandible, but alternate with them. The opponents of the teeth of the upper jaw thus do not meet their antagonists but reach into the spaces between the lower teeth. With the evolution of cusps arranged in a tritubercular fashion, the gaps between the upper and lower teeth in the closed mouth were diminished; but not until a talonid in the lower teeth and a talon in the upper ones developed did the upper and lower teeth meet one another directly (Fig. 134).

The hardness of the food consumed leads to severe wear of the tooth crowns. This wear is compensated for in a wide variety of mammal groups in that the teeth do not cease to grow at the end of the youth of the particular animals, or even earlier (Fig. 135), but become continuously growing teeth. In other cases, growth ends finally with high age, but the teeth have meantime become hypselodont, that is, they have attained notable height. Thus, they remain functional for a long time after growth ceases even if wear is considerable. In a totally different way the wear problem is met in the sea cow *Trichechus* (see p. 291).

The jaw motion of the pantotheres, corresponding to the tritubercular structure of their molars, was probably primarily ginglymic. From such primitive conditions mechanisms of jaw motion evolved that permitted real trituration, the horizontal displacement of the lower tooth row across the upper row. In the modern herbivorous ungulates this displacement takes place in an ectal-ental direction, from inside outward and from outside inward; in the rodents it is propalinal for gnawing, from back to front and front to back. Accompanying these modes of jaw motion, the apical portion of the tooth crown evolved into an efficient trituration device by the folding of the enamel in adaptation to the different directions of jaw movement. Despite continuous wear, the chewing surface of the tooth is never ground smooth. It remains rough because the enamel, by its greater hardness, is worn less than the dentine. Where enamel folding is intensive, so that the relief of the tooth surface consists of deep, narrow valleys and alternating crest structures, crown cementum is often deposited in the depth of the valleys. The crown cementum is softer than the dentine. This process results during wear in an even more elaborately modelled relief of the rough chewing surface; because not two but three tooth hard substances are worn off unevenly according to their differences in hardness.

A particular kind of durophagous specialization occurs in the dentition of the rodents (see p. 295).

With the rejection of Bolk's concentration theory, there results a simpler and more natural interpretation of the tooth replacement in mammals. This replacement is not different in principle from that of the reptiles and the rest of the non-mammals. One difference consists in the number of successive tooth generations. The reptiles are in general polyphyodont, the mammals at the most diphyodont, sometimes even more or less monophyodont. For this reason, intensive search was made to see whether there might not be highly reduced remains of a larger number of tooth generations in mammals. For the tooth anlagen of a cross row in a polyphyodont dentition of a non-mammal, the rule that the earliest-formed anlagen lie most labial, the last-formed ones most lingual applies without exception.

W. Leche (1909, 1915), M. F. Woodward (1896) and other students described vestigial anlagen in mammals that were located lateral to the milk teeth. They interpreted this so-called side lamina corresponding to this position (Pl. 68-a) as the last remains of a prelacteal generation. Similar structures, lingual relative to the anlagen of the permanent teeth, were looked upon as remains of a post-permanent tooth generation.

Most mammals are diphyodont, but the duration of functioning of the lacteal dentition is not the same in all of them. In primitive insectivores, for example in *Hemicentetes,* the teeth are changed only at the beginning of the adult condition. In man the milk dentition still plays a considerable role functionally. In certain pinnipeds, for example in *Phoca vitulina* and in *Phoca barbata,* the lacteal dentition is still produced in anlage, but it does not reach functional state and is instead resorbed largely before birth. These forms are practically monophyodont; the same applies to the toothed whales. In *Echidna* only a so-called egg tooth is left. It appears highly questionable whether there are definitely identifiable remains of tooth anlagen present in *Myrmecophaga.* On the other hand, there exists not the slightest doubt that toothlessness is a secondary phenomenon also in the mammals.

Among the marsupials, in each jaw quadrant only a single tooth, the last premolar, is changed. This evidence led to extensive discussions that revolved mainly around the question as to which of the two generations in monodelphous mammals this single tooth generation of the marsupials belongs, as well as around the question of the interpretation of the marsupial dentition in general. A number of reasons suggest that the peculiarity of the marsupial tooth replacement is to be regarded as an early specialization. As will be discussed later, this might be related to the mode of feeding of the young.

The process of eruption of the milk and permanent teeth which is particularly of clinical significance has received intensive study by dentists, but this cannot be discussed here.

Figures 136 and 137 each represent a stage in the tooth replacement of the lion and the hedgehog.

Data about the first appearance of the tooth anlagen and the temporal course of their differentiation, about the beginning and progress of calcification, about formation of the roots as well as the time of eruption of the lacteal and permanent teeth, are found in tables in the anatomical and particularly the dental literature. These were compiled on the basis of an enormous mass of observations, and often include the occasionally notable width

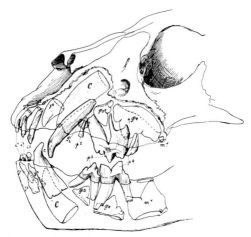

FIG. 136.—Tooth replacement in the lion. The already partially calcified teeth of the permanent dentition are emphasized by dark toning. From Weber, *Die Säugetiere* (Jena: Gustav Fischer Verlag, 1928), by permission.

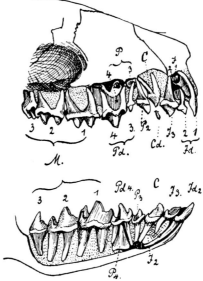

FIG. 137.—Tooth replacement in the hedgehog. 1.8:1. After Leche, from Weber, *Die Säugetiere* (Jena: Gustav Fischer Verlag, 1928), by permission.

of variation. In compressed form one of these tables is appended to the text (see p. 320).

The third molar in man usually erupts between the 19th and 25th year, but often very much later, a feature which has earned for it the name "wisdom tooth" ("Weisheitszahn," "dent de sagesse," "dent opsigone").

For a long time it has been suspected that the individual teeth in the mammalian dentition are not separate morphological entities, subject to individual phyletic change, but that they are members of morphogenetic fields. Under this concept phyletic changes in form affect the whole tooth series of a region, as for example the molar tooth series, where a phyletic change is assumed to affect the entire molar field, rather than an individual molar tooth. Butler (1939) analysed this problem and produced convincing evidence in favor of the morphogenetic field concept as applied to the mammalian dentition.

Tooth formulae

In systematic discussions of mammals it is often necessary to give information concerning the dentition. Thus, abbreviations and tooth formulae were devised that permit, in the shortest possible form, precise statements. The terms "incisors," "canines," "premolars" and "molars" are abbreviated to I. C. P. and M. The simplest formula for the permanent dentition consists of a horizontal line above which is noted how many teeth of each category are present in half of the upper jaw; below the line the corresponding numbers for half of the mandible are entered, for example for the dog:

$$\frac{I\ 3\ C\ 1\ P\ 4\ M\ 2}{I\ 3\ C\ 1\ P\ 4\ M\ 3}$$

or simplified: $\dfrac{3\ 1\ 4\ 2}{3\ 1\ 4\ 3}$

Such a formula merely shows what is determinable by direct inspection. More revealing, but partly hypothetical, is the following presentation in which each tooth of a tooth category is listed with a serial number; for example for man:

$$\frac{I\ 1\ I\ 2 - C\ 1 - P\ 3\ P\ 4 - M\ 1\ M\ 2\ M\ 3}{I\ 1\ I\ 2 - C\ 1 - P\ 3\ P\ 4 - M\ 1\ M\ 2\ M\ 3}$$

The underlying principle in this way of writing the formula starts out from the observation that the formula $\dfrac{3 - 1 - 4 - 3}{3 - 1 - 4 - 3}$ (44 teeth) is very prevalent among monodelphous mammals of the early Tertiary. Notably larger tooth numbers occur in only a few specialized groups among modern monodelphous mammals, the toothed whales and porpoises, the sirenians (*Trichechus*), and the xenarthra in the giant sloth *Priodontes*. A minor increase is found in the African dog genus *Otocyon*. Most modern mammals have fewer than 44 teeth. The suspicion that their tooth formulae have arisen by reduction from the formula $\dfrac{3\ 1\ 4\ 3}{3\ 1\ 4\ 3}$ may often be attested by paleontological data.

If, thus, instead of the summary notation $\dfrac{\text{I 2}}{\text{I 2}}$, the formula is written

$\dfrac{\text{I 1 I 2 } -}{\text{I 1 I 2 } -}$ it expresses the interpretation that of the three incisor teeth, the last one, counted from the symphysis, has been lost in both the upper and lower jaws. In the same way $\dfrac{\text{P } - \text{ 3 4}}{\text{P } - \text{ 3 4}}$ states that of the original four premolars the first and the second above and below are missing.

Comparison with closely related forms and paleontological information usually provides reliable information as to which teeth have been lost phylogenetically. But there are instances in which this cannot be determined with certainty. For this reason, certain authors do not count the premolars from front to back as they do the other teeth, but instead from back to front. This procedure is found primarily in veterinary-anatomical works, but occasionally also in the paleontological literature (for example, H. G. Stehlin). As a justification for this, it is argued that the boundary between the premolars and the molars is a safer starting point from which to count than the region behind the canine, where the dentition often shows reductions. Against this, it may be pointed out that the vast majority of placental mammals may be derived with certainty, or at least with the greatest probability, from early Tertiary forms with the formula $\dfrac{\text{3 1 4 3}}{\text{3 1 4 3}}$. The assumption that reductions in the anterior premolar area are more common than reduction further back is a reliable rule of thumb. Thus subtracting the number of premolars in a given example from the number of premolars (4) of early placental mammals yields in most cases with reasonable certainty the extent to which the premolar dentition has been reduced. A formula that uses ordinal numbers in cases where it must be assumed, for any reason whatever, that a tooth has been reduced not at the end of the row but from somewhere within the row, is much more hypothetical. This uncertainty remains the same whether the tooth count is started from the front or from the back.

The different method of counting premolars may lead to misunderstandings, especially if only a single tooth, for example P 1 or P 4, is mentioned. If the premolars are counted from back to front, in contrast to all other teeth, the disadvantages of this method of counting outweigh, in my estimation, the unquestioned advantages. In the present work we shall, in conformity with the practice of most paleontologists, as well as with usage in leading dental, human anatomical, and zoological works, count from front to back.

If, in the notation of a single tooth, the ordinal number in the abbreviated designation of the tooth category is added as an exponent, for example M^3, this means that the tooth is in the upper jaw; if the ordinal number is a subscript, for example M_3, it represents a lower molar. Teeth of the lacteal dentition are usually designated by lower case letters for the tooth categories.[1] Thus p 4, or p d4 (or dp4) designates the fourth (last) milk premolar. In German papers the milk premolars are often also called milk molars. This designation seems to me unacceptable, because molars are characterized by the fact that they either have no predecessors or, as is often assumed, no descendants. In the latter case, the molars belong to the milk generation; thus the designation of milk premolars as milk molars is misleading.

If for the designation of teeth only the human dentition is at issue, a mere numbering is acceptable, in conjunction with angle marks. In this method, the second upper right molar would be noted as $|7$, the second lower, left premolar as $\overline{5|}$.

In the tooth formulae the milk dentition is also to be considered. To include the milk dentition, the more elaborate formulae containing the order numbers are generally used instead of the abbreviated ones that contain only summary information. In the case of *Tarsius tarsius:*

$$\frac{\begin{array}{l}\text{id} - 2, 3 \text{ cd pd} - 2, 3, 4 \\ \text{I} - 2, 3 \text{ C} \quad \text{P} - 2, 3, 4 \text{ M} - 1, 2, 3\end{array}}{\begin{array}{l}\text{I} - 2, 3 \text{ C} \quad \text{P} - - 3, 4 \text{ M} - 1, 2, 3 \\ \text{id} - 2, 3 \text{ cd pd} - 2, 3, 4\end{array}}$$

Often the lacteal dentition is written immediately above and below the horizontal line, as in Max Weber's *Die Säugetiere.* It seems to me to convey the more sensible concept if the teeth of the permanent dentition occupy this position in the formula. Although many investigators assume that the molars belong to the lacteal tooth generation, in the formulae they are by convention written in the row of the permanent teeth.

The formula $\dfrac{3\ 1\ 4\ 3}{3\ 1\ 4\ 3}$ from which the majority of tooth formulae of the modern mammals originated by reduction is, except for those already mentioned, applicable only in the realm of the Monodelphia, the placental mammals. The comparable basic tooth formula for the marsupials is $\dfrac{5\ 1\ 3\ 4}{5\ 1\ 3\ 4}$. In certain modern marsupials, for example in *Myrmecobius,* a larger number of cheek teeth occurs. To distinguish between premolars and molars among these cheek teeth is often impossible with any degree of certainty, especially in fossil forms. In such cases, therefore, following the

---

[1] Sometimes the letter d (for deciduous, impermanent) is added.

proposal of H. Winge (1893), the teeth behind the canine are simply numbered serially as postcanine teeth.

Histology and histogenesis of mammalian teeth

The structure of the teeth of man and many mammals has been studied already in such depth that there exists a vast literature on the subject. For lack of space, it is not possible to give an adequate survey of this literature. I restrict my discussion to the emphasis of a few recent broad presentations which I will follow unless first-hand investigation was available to me. These are Wilhelm Meyer, *Lehrbuch der normalen Histologie und Entwicklungsgeschichte der Zähne des Menschen* (1951) ; Josef Lehner and Hans Plenk, *Die Zähne* (1936); Wolfgang Bargmann, *Histologie und mikroskopische Anatomie des Menschen* (1951). Among older works I used are J. Howard Mummery, *The microscopic and general anatomy of the teeth* (1924) and Charles S. Tomes, *A manual of dental anatomy* (1923).

Enamel

In the teeth of man a hard, shiny layer of enamel covers the dentine of the crown. This enamel cover is also present in general on the teeth of mammals. It may, however, in rare instances, be missing either partly or completely: partially, for example, on the lingual surface of the gnawing teeth of rodents (see p. 293), on the tusks of the boar and on the tusks of the elephants; completely, for example, on the teeth of Xenarthra (see p. 276).

Technique of investigation

Investigation of enamel is difficult because the enamel dissolves completely during the decalcification necessary for the preparation of microtome sections, and because ground thin-sections give no clues as to the relations of the soft parts. The cautious, slow decalcification of objects already embedded in celloidin retains the enamel to some extent (see Lehner and Plenk, 1936, p. 529). The so-called petrification method proposed by Koch and developed by Weil (1888) is intended to overcome this difficulty: teeth with their surrounding soft parts are fixed, stained in bulk, dehydrated in alcohol with increasing concentration to absolute alcohol, transferred from there to xylol (or other resin solvent) and, finally, to a solution of a grindable resin (for example, gum Damar) ; after the hardening of this medium, ground thin-sections may be made. This process constitutes progress and was widely employed. It was also used by us in a number of instances.

In the main, however, we developed our own process for the present investigations, in which the technical difficulties were avoided in a different way:

Microtome sections, through tooth material fixed with the usual reagents, decalcified with an acid and stained with dyes of different kinds, suggest that the original condition of the tissues has been notably changed during all these procedures. For this reason, the specimens together with the soft parts—without prior fixation—were deeply frozen and cut into very thin slabs with the aid of a special cutting device, so that they could be studied with a phase-contrast microscope, despite the fact that this procedure does not produce sections as thin as can be made with a microtome. In addition, vital staining was employed, for example, with methylene blue. This technique (Peyer, 1959b) produces very good results. No doubt tissues exposed to such deep-freezing also suffer certain changes; but these might not be very significant in the area of the teeth, and changes brought about by this procedure are different from those caused by fixation, decalcification, dehydration and staining. Thus a comparison of the preparations obtained by these different processes is of some interest. It was further noted that the use of phase contrast permits recognition of structural details in enamel, dentine and cementum in ordinary ground thin-sections that are not visible without this instrument.

Despite the fact that the enamel dissolves completely during decalcification, study of dentine, cementum and the pulp cavity required the preparation of numerous microtome sections. These proved unexpectedly very useful also for the investigation of the enamel. It was noted thus that the enamel, while in process of formation and hence apparently not yet much mineralized, is not entirely dissolved during decalcification. During its deposition and immediately thereafter it is stained so intensively with different dyes that no structures of any kind are visible. Only a little later, the enamel is already so well mineralized that it disappears completely during decalcification. Between these two stages, however, the structure of the organic base of the enamel is easily recognizable for a short time. The systematic search for such places of developing, but not yet completed, enamel formation led to instructive findings.

The enamel layer of mammalian teeth does not lie exposed on the dentine, but is covered with the so-called Nasmyth's membrane (Pl. 68-b). Even though this cover is a mere film, it is of great functional significance, since it is a horny, keratin-containing structure which protects the enamel against the effects of acids. Acid resistance of this enamel surface membrane is evidenced by the fact that it remains intact as a more or less coherent membrane during decalcification of the tooth, while the enamel is destroyed. The histological character and the mode of formation of

Nasmyth's membrane have been interpreted in very diverse ways; see for this the discussion in Lehner and Plenk (1936, pp. 562–67). In contrast to Mummery (1924), who thought that the enamel surface membrane consists of cornified cells of the enamel epithelium, it is now usually regarded as a cuticular formation of the ameloblasts that forms at the conclusion of enamel production.

The surface of the enamel of human teeth and of the enamel surface membrane is not entirely smooth, but reveals fine furrows and between these minute ridges that appear more distinctly if the surface has been rubbed with graphite (Pl. 68-c). These so-called imbrication lines (*Perikymatien*) are related to the so-called striation of Retzius.

This striation which appears on ground thin-sections (Pls. 69-a and 69-b) is brought about by the fact that deposition of enamel is not continuous but is discontinued in rather regular intervals; in ground thin-sections this discontinuity results in fine contour, or incremental, lines that often have a brownish color. According to newer investigations this color is considered to be an optical effect rather than a pigmentation.

The less obvious Hunter-Schreger's striation comes about in a different way; it is visible, according to Pickerill (1913), especially in reflected light (Pl. 70-a) and is interpreted as another optical phenomenon related to the fact that the enamel prisms (see below) often show places of notable change in their course. Thus it happens in a ground thin-section that portions of longitudinally hit prisms (parazones) alternate with portions of cross-cut prisms (diazones). The striation results from differences in the reflection of light by the parazones and diazones (Pl. 70-b).

The well established designation "enamel prisms" for the elements composing the mammalian enamel is formally applicable only in extremely rare cases; while the so-called prisms extend through the entire thickness of the enamel layer from the dentine-enamel boundary to the crown surface, their courses are by no means straight; most unprismatically they are angularly bent once or several times and are often twisted in a more or less complicated fashion (Pls. 69-c, 73-b; Color Plate VIII, a).

Size and form, structure, arrangement and mode of formation of the enamel prisms have been the subject of discussions for a long time; but despite investigations with the electron microscope, a generally accepted interpretation has not been reached in all points even now.

The length of the prisms varies with the different thickness of the enamel layer. According to a generally held view, here also adopted, the prisms penetrate the entire thickness of the enamel. The consideration that in strongly vaulted tooth portions an area of the crown surface occupied by a given number of prisms is larger than the corresponding surface at the dentine-enamel boundary, posed the question whether the diameter of the prisms increases at such points toward the periphery, or whether an intercalation of prisms occurs peripherally. Measurements made by Pickerill (1913) showed an increase in diameter in human teeth. Branching of enamel prisms, as suggested by Mummery (1924, Fig. 15) for the warthog *Phacochoerus,* can hardly, because of their mode of formation, be considered as a serious possibility. In the particular figure by Mummery a merely apparent branching of prisms may have resulted from prisms that lay in other levels of the section, but that because of slight bending came to lie in the optical plane of the picture.

The diameter of the prisms ranges in man from 3 to 6 μ according to von Ebner; this agrees with the measurement of W. Meyer (1951) who describes them as 4 μ thick at midlength, slightly thinner toward the dentine, and slightly thicker toward the surface. This order of size agrees with the diameter of the ameloblasts.

Cross section pictures of enamel prisms vary not only in different genera, but also with the different age of the teeth and the stage of formation of the prisms. Directions of cut that are not squarely across the prisms result in different pictures. Besides five- and six-sided prism outlines there occurs also the so-called arcade form.

There are notable differences of opinion about the structure of the enamel prisms. All investigators, however, agree that the prisms show a cross striation (Pl. 69-c). Since this cross striation appears especially prominently during slow decalcification of ground thin-sections, it is generally assumed that it might be related to a rhythm in the mineralization of the prisms. There is no unanimity concerning the question whether an outer rind-zone can be distinguished by different composition from a more central zone in the fully developed prisms. During the process of mineralization such a distinction seems to be the case according to several investigators. Mineralization is said to start from a central portion corresponding to a prolongation of Tome's process of an ameloblast cell, which has been compared to a wick. In the fully formed prism, the border layer of the prism is said to be emphasized as prism sheath by greater stainability, according to Lehner and Plenk (1936, p. 545), which would suggest a lesser degree of mineralization. Whether there is a particular interprismatic substance between adjacent prisms has been discussed for a long time. About the presence of such a substance a number of investigators have expressed their opinions, for it particularly V. Ebner, against it particularly Kölliker and Waldeyer. According to Peter (1957), renewed investigations with the electron microscope do not permit sharp differentiation into the three components: prism, prism sheath and interprismatic substance. The latter and the prism sheath "are often mixed up in the descriptions." According to the views of Helmcke, with which Peter agrees, "the enamel prisms contact one another directly in the fully developed condition without a specific interprismatic substance and are tightly intertongued with each other whereby the boundary faces run irregularly back and forth. The transition from one prism to another may be recognized in the change of direction in the position of the crystal axes.

"In their positional relations the crystals are not oriented parallel to one another, rather they arrange themselves, radiating apart after the fashion of a comet trail—as three, three-dimensional feather-plumes around an imaginary axis" (Helmcke, 1954). Thereby, each of these plumes appears as an individual prism in the overall picture. There remains the possibility that the axis around which the individual elements arrange themselves during the process of crystallization could be dependent upon the ameloblast cell during the formation of the enamel substance.

Individual crystals of hydroxyapatite have since 1944 been isolated from human enamel, and later also from that of animals, by several investigators, and made amenable to study by the electron microscope.

Also in our own investigations, which were restricted to light microscopy, we did not find any interprismatic substance. This was seen particularly clearly in those places, already mentioned, where newly formed enamel for a short time after its formation, but prior to its full mineralization, permits recognition of its structure (Pl. 71-a). Such places furthermore permit observations that might be of decisive significance regarding the view concerning the mode of formation of the enamel.

In the older literature there were two opposing views concerning this. According to one view, enamel forms by the successive transformation of the ameloblasts; according to the other, by secretory activity of the ameloblasts. Most of the more recent investigators consider enamel to be a cuticular formation produced by secretion (see literature in Lehner and Plenk, 1936).

My own arguments against the second, generally held view are the following:

What remains in section preparations, after not especially careful decalcification of teeth, of enamel in process of formation, is an organic ground substance.

The form elements that may be seen clearly in this substance correspond in all details with the form of the prisms in the fully developed enamel. In many cases, particularly in many rodents, the form both of the individual enamel prism and that of its precursor in the organic ground substance are so complicated that formation of the organic ground substance of the enamel by continued secretion seems hardly probable. The observations suggest rather the origin of a prism by growth of the ameloblast process. But in a prestage of the prism formed this way, mineralization might take place in such a way that mineral salts in solution could enter the process from the ameloblast cell and be precipitated therein.

This interpretation of our observations differs from earlier views that assumed a transformation, in that this transformation involves only a cell process formed by the ameloblast and not the ameloblast cell as a whole.

As already noted, there exists between that layer of forming enamel, immediately prior to its full mineralization, in which the precursors of the enamel prisms are clearly discernible one from another, and the ameloblasts a layer in which the organic ground substance of the enamel has just been formed. This layer stains so intensively with iron haematoxylin, or in azan preparations, that no distinct form elements can be recognized, and the whole layer seems to be a homogenous mass (Pl. 72).

Our investigations by phase contrast of unfixed, unstained preparations revealed that even in this layer the precursors of the future enamel prisms are sharply delineated one from another. We shall call this layer, which appears opaque in stained sections and which borders onto the ameloblasts, the first prestage of the enamel; as the second prestage we shall designate the slightly older zone, immediately prior to mineralization, where also in stained sections the organic ground substance of the future enamel prisms is recognizable (Pl. 72; Color Plate VIII, b).

Excellent objects for distinguishing the two prestages of the enamel are the continuously growing incisor teeth, for example of the mouse or the rabbit. Since mineralization begins at the tips of the teeth and progresses toward the base, it is completed at the cutting edge and over most of the tooth surface. Thus, the enamel is entirely dissolved in this region during decalcification. Bordering this artificial vacant space toward the tooth base is the second prestage, in which the form of the future prisms is sharply discernible. The first prestage, whose structure is visible only under phase contrast, follows clear to the end of the growing tooth. Plate 73-a shows a corresponding temporal and spatial sequence of phases of the enamel formation in the anlage of a human milk tooth, in which, however, fully developed enamel is not yet present (Color Plate VIII, c).

An illustration of a section through the tooth anlage of a pig embryo, published by Held (1926), corresponds with our observation (Pl. 71-b). The structures labeled as young enamel prisms presumably represent the second prestage of enamel, because the first prestage tends to be opaque in stained sections and because fully mineralized enamel is lost during decalcification.

Plate 71-b shows furthermore that the enamel prisms do not lie in the straight line extension of the longitudinal axes of the ameloblasts, but are angularly bent over. This characteristic seems to be widely distributed. The ameloblast processes of Tomes are slightly narrower than the ameloblasts. Mummery (1924) assumed that the layer of ameloblasts is bounded both toward the *stratum intermedium* (of the enamel pulp) and against the forming enamel by membranes. Newer investigations have revealed that neither is a membrane, but rather a terminal reticulum (Lehner and Plenk, 1936).

Numerous investigators have described droplet-shaped inclusions within the ameloblasts (see Lehner and Plenk, 1936), which are especially prominent in iron-haematoxylin preparations.

Instead of sharply circumscribed cell inclusions, the whole cell portions that are adjacent to the forming enamel may show the same staining characteristics as the first prestage of enamel (Pl. 73-b). Since these inclusions behave in the presence of stains similarly to the organic ground substance of the enamel immediately after its formation, it may be suspected that they represent the fluid primary ground material of the enamel, which becomes transformed into the ground mass only after it has reached the ameloblast processes consisting basically of an organic strutwork.

Enamel in *Crocodylus* (see p. 141) forms comparably in that the first prestage of enamel is stained so intensively with different dyes that no structural detail may be observed; also in the second prestage the stratification of the enamel is visible and, less sharply defined, a radial striation corresponding to the course of enamel prisms (Pl. 58-b). The intensively staining droplets within the ameloblasts were also observed in *Crocodylus* and *Varanus* (Pl. 59-a and b).

Plate 74-a and b, a cross-section close to the posterior end of an incisor of a hamster, shows vascular capillaries entering from the surrounding connective tissue between the cells of the outer enamel epithelium. A similar picture of a rat tooth was published by Mummery (1924, Fig. 74).

The so-called prism bundles (Schmelzbüschel) which have more recently been described by Schaffer (1933), Lehner and Plenk (1936) and W. Meyer (1951) are structures, restricted to the enamel layer, that begin at the dentine-enamel boundary and extend into the enamel usually for only a short distance (Pl. 75-a). They are characterized by the fact that the prisms in their area, as may be suspected from a certain stainability, contain more organic substance than do the other prisms. These structures, not very aptly called plumes (Büschel), have rather the forms of lamellae since they are composed of differently bent prisms. These prism bundles are thought to represent metabolic pathways.

The enamel lamellae begin, in contrast to the prism bundles, at the enamel surface and may extend through the entire thickness of the enamel layer and even a little into the dentine (Pl. 75-b). They are usually considered to be scars from injuries to the living tooth (Lehner and Plenk, 1936).

The birefringence of the enamel, which is especially impressive in mammals because of the relative thickness of the enamel layer, is of great practical importance for comparison with the tooth hard substances of other vertebrates. This applies particularly to the selachians, whose teeth do not show phenomena comparable to the birefringence of the mammalian enamel, and to the teeth of many fossil ganoid fishes, to *Lepisosteus,* and to many teleost teeth whose enamel possesses the same type of birefringence as does mammalian enamel.

The phylogenetic change in form of the enamel prisms

My attempt to understand the structural evolution of the enamel prisms in the course of the evolution of the mammals was predicated on the fact that I had available for study thin-sections of a tooth of one of the oldest known mammals, a triconodont from the Rhaetic.

The enamel layer of these teeth is very robust (Pl. 76-a and b). The dentine is traversed by tightly crowded, parallel dentinal tubules that show branching in the vicinity of the enamel layer. Under low-power magnification, the enamel is set off sharply against the dentine. Higher power shows, however, that many dentinal tubules enter the enamel and probably usually reach close to its surface. The striation of Retzius is clearly evident. Particularly striking is the simple shape of the prisms that run nearly straight and at about a right angle to the tooth surface.

For a comparison with synapsid reptiles of the later Triassic and with trituberculates and other early mammals, which would be of great interest, I had no material available. It may be assumed, however, that the trituberculates had simple relations of the enamel prisms similar to the triconodonts. This assumption is based on the fact that the teeth of the most primitive and oldest order of modern monodelphous mammals, the insectivores, have very simply formed enamel prisms (Pl. 77-a and b).

Enamel relations as simple as those in the shrew, hedgehog and mole are also found among the bats, which are relatively closely related to the insectivores. The primates including man may be added to the insectivores; they too are characterized by a relatively simple structure of the enamel prisms. In a number of mammal orders, in contrast, far-reaching specializations in enamel have occurred, particularly in the rodents whose dentition is subjected to particularly heavy use. Undoubtedly, the extremely complicated structure of the enamel prisms of some modern rodents (for example, the guinea pig) (Pl. 77-c) has evolved in the course of phylogeny from less complicated conditions.

The above considerations, despite their incompleteness, may indicate that a phylogenetic understanding of the structural history of the enamel prisms is potentially possible.

Dentine

While the enamel, except the earliest, incompletely mineralized stages, disappears without a trace during decalcification, there remains after decalcification of the dentine a fabric that is not greatly different in microtome sections and ground thin-sections and which permits the recognition of the structural makeup of the hard substance. The inorganic structural elements of the dentine (in the enamel it is hydroxapatite) have so far not been isolated by electron microscopy. Peter (1957) writes: "While in the enamel the last inorganic structural element could be found as a single crystal, the inorganic substance occurs in the dentine in a form which does apparently not permit its resolution even with the electron microscope to its individual components. By contrast, in the organic fraction of the dentine ground substance, individual fibrils have been demonstrated as structural elements by electron microscopic techniques. The arrangement of these fibrils was represented as a dense network, both in thin-sections and in surface replicas.

"In the light microscope fibers of the dentine ground substance have already been described. They cannot correspond, however, to the individual fibrils, but should be regarded, in view of their dimensions, as aggregates of individual fibers. The cross section of the fibers seen in the light microscope amounts to about 0.3 μ, cited from Meyer (1951) after von Ebner, and from Orban (1927); in contrast the fibrils visible in electron microscope pictures—themselves divisible into fibrils—are about five times smaller and not resolvable in the light microscope."

Under low or moderate magnification the dentine of mammals presents almost without exception the picture of an orthodentine, pierced by uniformly distributed dentinal tubules. These run, tightly crowded, in a course at about a right angle to the tooth surface, from the pulp cavity to the dentine-enamel interface. These dentinal tubules are usually branched near the periphery; but even in the deeper layers of the dentine, finer side twigs leave the main tubule at more or less regular intervals, which anastomose with neighboring tubules.

The dentine layer that lies adjacent to the pulp cavity is as in the other vertebrates, at first not fully mineralized and is therefore selectively stainable. Particularly intensive color contrasts result with azan staining and with iron haematoxylin. Since this layer subsequently changes to dentine, it is called predentine. W. Meyer (1951) proposed instead of predentine the expression "uncalcified dentine." The elimination of the well established term predentine seems to me unnecessary because it expresses clearly a prestage that has not yet acquired the characteristics of the finished tissue. In English the expression "odontogenetic zone" is in use.

We now consider the content of the dentinal tubules, a question which, although it concerns dentine in general, will be discussed in the example of the mammals only to avoid repetitions.

During the first few decades of the nineteenth century, dentinal tubules had become known almost exclusively from pictures of ground thin-sections of teeth. Concerning the relations of the tubules to the soft parts no precise ideas were possible, because of the state of the microscopic techniques of that time and because the cell theory had not yet become generally accepted. Only guesses were possible and one of these was that the tubules contain a fluid. John Tomes was the first to recognize that a process of the odontoblast cell—later called Tomes' fiber, after him—reaches into the dentinal tubule and extends through it. Until recently, all investigators confirmed Tomes' observations. But in 1957 W. Warwick James—known for his competence in jaw surgery, and by an inclusive work on the dentition of the primates and other odontological studies—published a lengthy paper entitled "A further study of dentin," in which he attempted to show that the dentinal tubules do not contain cell processes of the odontoblasts, but merely tissue fluid.

The findings of many authors as well as my own do not permit me to follow these views, especially since the dentinal tubules in mammals, reptiles, amphibians, Osteichthyes and Chondrichthyes show in longitudinal, oblique and true cross-section pictures a central strand that usually is stained slightly darker (Fig. 138). In view of the great regularity with which

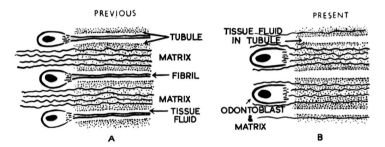

Fig. 138.—Schematic presentation of different views concerning the structure of the dentine. According to the traditional view shared by us, the odontoblast sends a cell process into the dentinal tubule (diagram *A*); according to the views of Warwick James, the dentinal tubule contains merely tissue fluid (diagram *B*). From James (1957).

these structures recur in all preparations, it is difficult to believe that it represents only a central product of coagulation of a tissue fluid. Furthermore, such a central strand is visible under phase contrast even in preparations that have been sectioned deeply frozen without prior fixation or decalcification.

It may be demonstrated with great clarity on suitably stained sections that the odontoblast processes reach into the tubules in the predentine and extend from there into the dentinal tubules (Pl. 78-a).

But, I have never observed that fibers enter the walls of the dentinal tubules, and thus the dentine, directly from the odontoblast cell without passing through an odontoblast process. It seems, however, quite possible that collagenous material might be imparted to the wall of the dentinal tubules and to the dentine ground substance by way of the often observed lateral branchlets which the odontoblast process sends into the lateral branches of the dentine tubules. Nobody denies that the space between the odontoblast process and the wall of the dentinal tubules might be filled, *intra vitam,* by fluid (Pl. 78-b).

The walls of the dentinal tubules are distinguished from the remaining dentine by a slight, but nevertheless detectable, greater resistance to the actions of acids and alkalis (Pl. 78-c) (W. Meyer 1951, and his Fig. 62). On the other hand, the designation of the wall of the dentinal tubules as Neumann's sheaths rests on an error by Neumann (1863). This author mistook the elements remaining after intensive action of acid on dentine as remains of the walls of the dentinal tubules; but in reality, as Meyer has demonstrated conclusively and as is clearly evident from Meyer's Figure 60, these are not parts of the walls of the tubules but are the odontoblast processes themselves.

Since then, this wall zone of the dentinal tubules has been investigated and discussed repeatedly, but opinions have remained divided. We follow here the discussion of v. Saal (1930), reviewed by Zangerl (1933), who furnished a schematic drawing (Fig. 139). v. Saal was not content to investigate histologically the finished dentinal tubules, and included in his discussion considerations of the mode of growth of the dentine. Starting with the observation that young dentinal tubules have a larger diameter than older tubules he suggested the possibility that the narrowing of the lumen of the dentinal tubules might take place periodically and that thus a number of "Neumann's sheaths" might be formed successively, the youngest being innermost. Sheaths formed earlier are said to be present only in remnants that soon cease to be distinguishable from the ground mass of the dentine.

There remains further the question whether the "Neumann's sheath" is

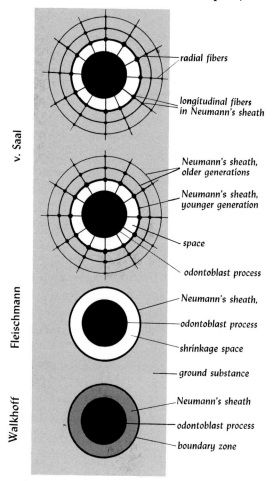

radial fibers

longitudinal fibers
in Neumann's sheath

Neumann's sheath,
older generations

Neumann's sheath,
younger generation

space

odontoblast process

Neumann's sheath,

odontoblast process

shrinkage space

ground substance

Neumann's sheath

odontoblast process

boundary zone

v. Saal

Fleischmann

Walkhoff

Fig. 139.—Schematic presentation of the different views concerning structure of Neumann's sheath. Walkhoff (1924), Fleischmann (1905), v. Saal (1930). Redrawn from Zangerl (1933).

developed in uniform strength all along the length of the tubules. Observations on teeth of *Didelphys* as well as on human teeth led Zangerl (1933) to the conclusion that ring-shaped zones occur at regular intervals along the course of the sheath in which "Neumann's sheath" shows a somewhat different chemical behavior.

Van Huysen (1961) published a histo-radiograph of a ground thin-section of a human tooth, which shows the dentinal tubules in cross section. Surrounding the lumina of the tubules there are radio-opaque rings of more highly calcified dentine. In the lower half of his figure 1-c there are, however, also some tubules whose walls are without such radio-opaque rings. The latter may correspond to the zones described by Zangerl (1933) which were interpreted as less mineralized zones along the course of a dentinal tubule possibly serving as metabolic pathways.

Quite aside from Neumann's error, Meyer proposed to avoid the term "Neumann's sheath" because this sheath is not separable from the mass of the dentine. This reason does not seem to me to be valid, since, for example, the predentine cannot be isolated from the dentine either (see p. 208).

W. Meyer (1951) believes that the odontoblast process fills the lumen of the dentinal tubule entirely *in vivo*. He assumes that in places where there is a free space (as clearly seen in the excellent photograph *loc. cit.*, p. 40, Fig. 56) between the odontoblast process and the wall of the dentinal tubule, it is the result of shrinkage during fixation of the specimen. I cannot agree with this interpretation because a comparable space is also visible in unfixed sections prepared in deep-frozen condition and investigated by phase contrast.

A phenomenon that appears clearly on ground thin-sections are the so-called interglobular spaces: air-filled spaces in dry-preserved dentine that are bounded by semiglobular projections of the hard substance (Pl. 79-a). On microtome sections they do not appear because the areas in question are occupied by uncalcified dentine *intra vitam* and in fixed material. W. Meyer (1951) thus suggests changing the term "interglobular spaces" to "interglobular areas." With increasing age these areas become smaller by progressing calcification of the dentine. According to W. Meyer (1951), the dentinal tubules may show ampulla-like enlargements near the interglobular areas. The interglobular areas usually lie close to the dentine-enamel boundary in a layer whose section-picture corresponds to the course of a contour line of the dentine. The so-called Tomes' granular layer occupies a comparable peripheral position, present particularly in the dentine of the tooth roots. This name, recalling an earlier period in tooth research, no longer applies. The structures referred to are not granules, but fine structures similar to interglobular areas, with which dentinal tubules or their branches probably communicate and which probably anastomose with very fine canaliculi in the cementum.

The localization both of the interglobular areas and the Tomes' granular layer suggests a certain functional significance of these structures in the sense of bringing about a connection between dentine and cementum.

The enamel-dentine boundary has been the object of numerous studies since Sir John Tomes noted in 1849 that in marsupials (*Macropus, Bettongia*) dentinal tubules enter into the enamel. This condition is not restricted to marsupials, but is widely distributed (Pl. 79-b). According to W. Meyer (1951), odontoblast processes are sometimes applied to the enamel prisms in the form of endplates. Although the sections available to me did not permit any absolutely certain observations, I did gain the impression that the odontoblast processes in the enamel never enter the prisms but extend between them. Larger, club-shaped odontoblast processes that enter the enamel are called "enamel spindles" or "enamel clubs."

Dentine deposited within the pulp cavity long after the formational phase of the tooth is usually designated as "secondary" or "irregular dentine"; according to the degree of irregularity Reich (1907) distinguished three grades of irregularity. Dentine formed reactively to strengthen the wall where there is danger of an opening of the pulp cavity is usually called "replacement dentine" or "protection dentine." Spherical dentine structures, that lie either free in the pulp cavity or are attached to its wall, are called "free," or "adherent" denticles. Plate 80-a, a portion of a vertical section through the molar of a very old seal, shows the filling of a narrow place of the pulp cavity by spherical structures that produced a peculiar arrangement of the dentinal tubules.

The Howship's lacunae that appear in the resorption of dentine are seen in Plate 80-b, a specimen of a freshly shed human milk incisor.

Cementum

Although bone tissue is absent in chondrichthyes (for exceptions see p. 59), it often plays a great role as attachment bone in the dentitions of Osteichthyes. In the amphibians the bony pedecel of the frogs, renewed during each tooth replacement, may here be recalled (see p. 127). Among the reptiles there are notable examples of bone of attachment particularly among the Squamata. A true tooth cementum, that is, a layer of bone deposited on the dentine without entering into a bony connection with the jaw bone, is found in the ichthyosaurs of the Jurassic and Cretaceous (see p. 146). The basal parts of crocodile teeth that are inserted within alveoli also possess a thin layer of cementum (Pl. 57-c).

In the ontogenetic development of the mammalian tooth, the cementum appears relatively late. Since it is, as already mentioned, identical with bone the cells that form it are usually simply called "osteoblasts." Some authors prefer the name "cementoblasts," to emphasize the negligible differences from ordinary bone tissue.

Where the layer of cementum attains only small thickness, the formational cells are not being enclosed into the ground mass (see Stern, 1964). Such cementum is called "primary," or better, "cellfree"; as secondary or cell-containing cementum rates a layer of greater thickness in which the cells enclosed in the ground mass are usually arranged in superimposed layers (Pl. 81-a).

As seen in sections of relatively young tooth anlagen, the cells that are to form the cementum are often originally not in the immediate vicinity of the places where subsequently cementum is to be deposited. Such places are the dentine of the tooth root, and, for example, in many perissodactyls, artiodactyls and rodents, the enamel layer of the deeply folded tooth crown. Thus root cementum and crown cementum are distinguished. The tooth crown, as long as the formation of enamel is not yet completed, is covered by the cells of the inner enamel epithelium. For this reason, deposition of cementum on the enamel becomes possible only after the enamel epithelium has been destroyed. This destruction is initiated by an invasion of mesodermal cells that wedge themselves between the ameloblasts. Soon thereafter the mesodermal elements get the upper hand and the remains of the enamel epithelium disappear completely. These successive stages may be followed in one and the same preparation in a rodent or lagomorph molar, where at the base of a narrow, deep enamel fold there is still present intact enamel epithelium but further up there is already a continuous layer of osteoblasts; between these two places the various stages of the invasion of the enamel epithelium by the mesodermal cells may be observed in the section (Pl. 81-b). At the root of the fully formed mammalian tooth, the dentine is covered by a layer of cementum. However, the root dentine is likewise not available for cementum deposition during tooth development for a long time, since it is also at first covered by ectodermal cells which we, in contrast to Mummery (1924, p. 330) consider to be a part of the enamel epithelium. Thus here again there has to develop an invasion with subsequent destruction of the ectodermal cell layer by mesodermal cells, before any cementum can be deposited. The destruction in this area is not quite as complete as in that of the tooth crown, since remnants of the enamel epithelium may remain in place, and have been described as Malassez' remains.

Root cementum is present in all mammals, while crown cementum evolved only in mammal groups in which the cheek teeth have to perform particularly punishing chewing functions.

The boundary of the cementum of the root and the enamel of the crown may be differentiated in a variety of ways in human teeth. The cementum may overlap the enamel, or the two layers may meet without overlap, or there may be a space between them where the dentine is visible at the surface. The different conditions depend on age; for example, overlap has not been observed in juveniles, but occurs in advanced age in 62.5 percent of the cases studied (Mummery, 1924).

A particularly thick layer of cementum occurs in teeth of the South American Xenarthra, in which the tooth crown possesses no enamel. Of great functional significance is the cementum in those types of cheek teeth that consist of a number of antero-posteriorly arranged transverse lamellae, in that it holds these lamellae together in a unit. This applies for example in the capybara, *Hydrochoerus*.

Still relatively little is known regarding the origin of cementum in mammals. Paleontology has been able to suggest the direction, since it could identify the group of reptiles where the first appearance of cementum may be expected, namely, among the synapsids. The same is true of other questions, as for example that of tooth replacement, where some progress has been made recently (Crompton, 1962, 1963; Fourie, 1963; Hopson, 1964). Because the synapsids are extinct, because the fossils are often rare specimens, and because preparation of the material is often fraught with difficulties, the odontological descriptions are usually restricted to what can be seen externally. Only little has become known of the histological relations. It is, however, to be hoped that further studies of synapsids will furnish insights regarding the genesis of the cementum in mammals.

Alveolar-dental membrane

Between the layer of cementum of the root and the bone of the wall of the alveolus there is a layer of tissue which is of great significance clinically in man: the alveolar-dental membrane or periodontium. Its anatomical characters are variously interpreted. According to one view, particularly represented by dentists (compare, e.g., Mummery, 1924) the membrane is thought to be a uniform, discrete structure. Another opinion, clearly expressed, for example, in Figure 596 of the 18th edition of Ellenberger and Baum's *Handbuch der vergleichenden Anatomie der Haustiere* (1943), holds that the cementum and the wall of the alveolus each possess their own periosteum, a situation practically obscured by the rich development of Sharpey's fibers (Pl. 2-b). By means of the periodontium the tooth is anchored in a springy fashion in the alveolus. This anchoring is achieved by connective tissue fibers and fiber bundles that are anchored in the cementum and in the periosteum of the alveolar wall (Stern, 1964). The arrangement of the connective tissue fiber bundles corresponds well with their intended function. The alveolar periosteum is richly supplied with vessels that originate largely from the vessel supply of the pulp cavity. There are also vessels leading from the alveolar wall to the alveolar-dental membrane. The nerve supply of the alveolar-dental membrane likewise comes largely from nerves leading to the pulp cavity. According to Mummery, the alveolar-dental membrane remains sensitive, however, even when the nerve that leads through the *foramen apicis radicis dentis* has been destroyed by the formation of an abscess. The alveolar-dental membrane, furthermore, contains numerous lymph vessels of different caliber.

The gingiva

The gingiva is connected with the mucous membrane of the mouth at the inner side of the lips, at the floor of the mouth and at the base of the palate. It is distinguished from the mucous membrane of the mouth by the fact that it heals without scar following injuries, a unique peculiarity, and by the absence of a submucosa: it is intimately welded to the periosteum of the alveolar edge. The gingiva surrounds the tooth neck as a cuff whose inner surface lies opposite the basal portion of the enamel of the tooth crown, but remains separated from it by a furrow. This part of the gingiva lacks papillae (Fig. 140), while the part that leads into the mucous membrane of the mouth possesses them.

Survey of the forms

Monotremata

The monotremes, geographically restricted to Australia, and today represented only by the duckbill (*Ornithorhynchus*) and the spiny ant eater, are unquestionably the most primitively organized of modern mammals. The spiny ant eater lives on ants and other insects. It is toothless except for an egg tooth that enables slitting the egg shell during hatching. The duckbill, which has a powerful horny beak, was likewise thought to be toothless until it was discovered that young animals, before they have reached a third of their size, have in the upper jaw four and in the lower jaw three multituberculated teeth (Fig. 141). A horny plate takes over the place of the teeth. From the form of the lower jaw, Abel (1919) believed it possible to infer the original presence of incisors. The teeth of

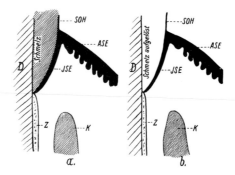

FIG. 140.—The edge of the human gingiva in vertical section: *a*, prior to decalcification; *b*, after decalcification; *sch*, enamel surface membrane; *D*, dentine; *Z*, cementum; *K*, alveolar bone; *JSE*, inner enamel epithelium. From W. Meyer, *Normale Histologie und Entwicklungsgeschichte der Zähne des Menschen* (Munich: Carl Hanser Verlag, 1951), by permission.

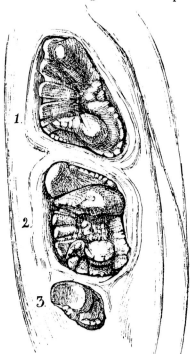

Fig. 141.—Dentition of the duckbill *Ornithorhynchus* (young individual 316 mm long), the three teeth of the lower jaw. After C. Stewart, from Weber, *Die Säugetiere* (Jena: Gustav Fischer Verlag, 1928), by permission.

Ornithorhynchus confirm the general rule of thumb that toothlessness in gnathostomous vertebrates presents a secondary condition. An attempt was made, although without success, to derive the teeth of *Ornithorhynchus* from the teeth of the extinct multituberculates (see Fig. 125). Unfortunately, fossil monotremes are known to date only from the Pleistocene of Australia.

Mesozoic mammals

In the section on the synapsid reptiles it was already noted that the mammals at the very end of the Triassic rose from a highly varied group, the cynodonts after the extinction of the vast majority of the synapsids (p. 175). From the two last periods of the Mesozoic era, the Jurassic and the Cretaceous, a time span of about 100 million years, only very few adequate remains of mammals are known. During this period the reptiles were the dominant animals on land. The mammals played only a very insignificant role. Without exception they were small. The rare specimens consist generally of isolated teeth or of tooth-bearing jaw fragments (see, for example, B. Patterson, 1956). Not until the beginning of the Tertiary period do remains of mammals occur more frequently in the fossil record. In the older literature, the few then-known Mesozoic forms—with a question mark, to be sure—were usually placed among the marsupials.

Even though the last decades have brought considerable advances in the knowledge of the Mesozoic mammals, we nevertheless still know very little concerning the very long time during which a significant phylogenetic differentiation of the mammals must have taken place, before they assumed dominance following the demise of most of the reptile orders. The following are some groups that have been distinguished; but their relationships have not yet been adequately determined (for details see Simpson, 1961).

Triconodonta

The crown of the cheek teeth consists of three tubercles arranged in a straight line. Minor additional cusps may arise from a marginal cingulum. The earliest remains occur in the Rhaetic of Hallau, Switzerland (Pl. 82-a); there are also finds from the Dogger of Stonesfield, England, from the uppermost Jurassic (Morrison formation) of North America, and from the English Purbeckian. The youngest triconodont thus far known is *Astroconodon denisoni* Patterson from the Trinity Sands (Albian) of Texas (B. Patterson, 1956). The triconodonts most likely represent a side twig of the early evolution of the mammals that became extinct without giving rise to descendants.

Multituberculata

The multituberculates are, as the name implies, characterized by possession of multitubercular cheek teeth. Of the incisor teeth, one in each jaw quadrant is specialized as a gnawing tooth; above there may be additional smaller incisors. Following the incisors there is a large diastema. Canini are absent. The last premolar has a shape characteristic in the multituberculates; it is often very high, striated on the flanks, and modified as a cutting device.

As mentioned earlier (p. 175), forms with similar multituberculated molars from the Rhaetic and Liassic belong to the reptiles. For this reason, the name Multituberculata is today only used in the restricted sense for the forms distributed primarily in Cretaceous time.

Symmetrodonta

The representatives of this group were formerly included among the trituberculates (panthotheres) that will be discussed below. As in the latter, the three tubercles of the molars are arranged in the form of a triangle. It

Fig. 142.—Lower jaw of the pantothere *Amphitherium* from the middle Jurassic of Stonesfield, England. Medial view. 2:1. After Simpson, from Romer (1945).

is an isoceles triangle, however, while in the trituberculates it is obliquely distorted. In contrast to the trituberculates, there is no talonid behind the trigonid in the symmetrodonts. On the basis of these characteristics, Simpson (1925) included these forms in a group separate from the trituberculates.

Panthotheria

The pantotheres are known from a single genus, *Amphitherium* (Fig. 142) from the Jurassic of England and North America. The upper molars are transversely elongated and possess one prominent lingual cusp. Aside from some morphological and occlusal features, the molars are said to be quite distinct from the tribosphenic pattern (Simpson, 1961).

Marsupialia

The living marsupials constitute in many aspects of their organization an ancient group geographically restricted to Australia, North and South America. The standard reference to the marsupial dentition is Bensley (1903). According to the differentiation of the dentition, three groups are distinguished.

Polyprotodonta, with up to $\frac{5}{4}$ incisors,

Diprotodonta with $\frac{3-1}{1-1}$ incisors, and

Caenolestoidea with $\frac{4}{3}$ incisors that stand between the former two.

In the last group, the innermost incisors are enlarged and lie horizontally. The caenolestids are restricted to South America. Polyprotodont marsupials were once widely distributed. Cuvier discovered in the Eocene gypsum of the Montmartre in Paris the famous "sarigue fossile" (*Paratherium*), a fossil opossum. Since then, numerous forms have become known from the Tertiary and from the Cretaceous.

Except for a few bats that are less restrained in their distribution by physiographic features, and a few genera of rodents for which transport across arms of the sea ways on drifting rafts seems probable, a dog and man, the monotremes and the marsupials are the only authochtonous mammals of

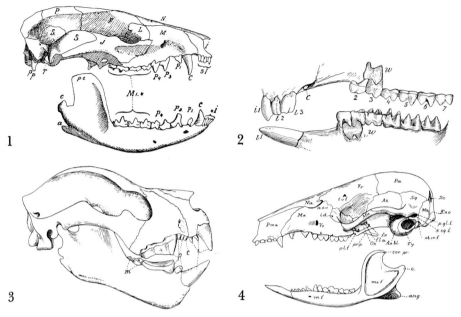

FIG. 143.—Dentitions of marsupials: 1, *Didelphys marsupialis* after Winge; 2, *Halmaturus ualabatus*, after Tomes; 3, *Thylacoleo carnifex*, after Smith-Woodward; 4, *Caenolestes* after Dederer. Compiled from Weber, *Die Säugetiere* (Jena: Gustav Fischer Verlag, 1928), by permission.

the Australian region. It is assumed that primitive, probably polyprotodont, marsupials had already reached Australia in Mesozoic time. From them there evolved, besides newer polyprotodont forms, numerous diprotodont marsupials. The terms "marsupial badger," "marsupial wolf," etc., show that the Australian marsupials became adapted to a great variety of modes of life and filled a variety of ecological niches, but remained marsupials in the basic aspects of their organization. As may be seen from the examples illustrated, the variety of modes of life manifested themselves also in the dentition (Fig. 143). The marsupial dentition appears primitive insofar as the polyprotodontids and the caenolestoids possess a larger number of incisors and sometimes a larger number of postcanine teeth than do the placental mammals. Beyond this difference it is probably highly specialized, especially with respect to tooth replacement. Thus of the entire dentition, only a single tooth, the last premolar, is changed. M. F. Woodward (1896) and Dependorf (1888) both state that the replacement tooth in the Diprotodonta even belongs to the same generation as the tooth which it replaces, i.e. a Pd4 is said to assume the position of the Pd3 that has fallen out. The replacing tooth, in a variety of marsupials, not only replaces its predecessor, but also the tooth in front of it. The comparison of the tooth generations of the marsupials with those of the placental mammals is still subject to debate. The peculiar tooth replacement of the marsupials has been related to the mode of rearing the very young. The teats on which the young are attached are said to fill the mouth cavities so completely as to retard the early development of the dentition.

The *processus angularis* of the lower jaw is bent strongly inward in all marsupials. Whether this feature also applies to all the fossil ones is naturally questionable. With regard to the histological construction of the teeth it is noted that the dentinal tubules, often reach well into the enamel, a fact already emphasized by J. Tomes (1849). The polyprotodonts are partly insectivorous (animalivorous), as the marsupial mouse *Antechinus*, partly they have become carnivores with secodont molars, as the marsupial wolf *Thylacinus*. The insectivorous *Myrmecobius* is characterized by the large number of teeth in its dentition: I $\frac{3}{3-4}$ postcanines $\frac{8}{8-9}$. Supernumerary molar teeth are known to occur fairly frequently in a number of species of kangaroos.

Thylacosmilus from the Pliocene of South America is peculiar because the upper canine is enormously enlarged, much as in the true saber-toothed cats which belong to the Carnivora (Fig. 144); a similar feature occurs

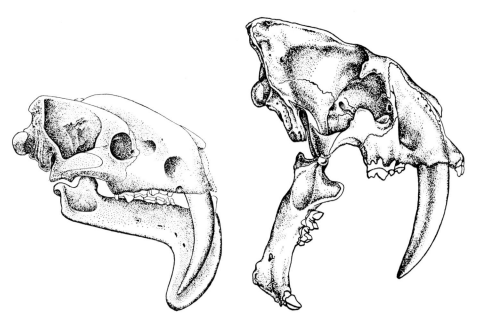

FIG. 144.—Skulls of the extinct marsupial *Thylacosmilus* (*left*) and the extinct saber-toothed cat *Smilodon* (*right*), in lateral views. From Romer (1945).

already in the Upper Eocene creodont *Apataelurus*. This striking feature is not an indication of close relationship, but rather represents convergent evolution.

The extinct *Diprotodon* from the Australian Pleistocene was a giant with a skull about one meter long. It may, like the modern wombat *Phascolomys*, have eaten bulbs and roots.

The kangaroos possess, corresponding to their vegetarian diet, tubercular molars. The last premolar of *Bettongia*, which belongs to this kinship group, is high and striated on the sides, as in certain multituberculates (Fig. 145) ; this characteristic was formerly interpreted (in the presence of only incomplete remains) as possible evidence of kinship. But this, too, appears to be convergent evolution. The most far-reaching reduction of the dentition is found in the polyprotodont marsupial *Tarsipes*, which gathers insects and nectar from flowers with its long tongue. The teeth became small, rod-shaped structures.

Insectivora

The so-called insectivores, without exception small, often nocturnal animals, do not feed on insects alone, but on all manner of small animals. European representatives are the hedgehog, the shrew and the mole; there are also Asiatic hedgehogs, lacking a spiny fur, and a host of genera on Madagascar such as the tenrec *Tenrec, Hemicentetes,* and *Setifer.* On the African mainland there is the fish-eating *Potamogale,* the Cape golden "mole," *Chrysochloris* and the *Macroscelidae;* and on the Antilles the genus *Solenodon.*

The East Asiatic Tupajidae formerly considered to be insectivores are now placed among the primates but this assignment has recently been disputed (Campbell, 1966). For comparative anatomical reasons, and because of their disjunct distribution, the insectivores have long been considered a very old, original group of placental mammals; fossils from the uppermost Cretaceous of Mongolia and North America supported this interpretation (Fig. 146).

The premolar and molar portions of the dentition show very simple relations. In the Madagassic tenrecoids, tritubercular molars still occur; they show a V-pattern of the ectoloph and the group is called "Zalambdodonta" because of the similarity of the tooth pattern to the inverted Greek letter lambda, in contrast to the Dilambdodonta (hedgehogs, shrews and moles) which show a W-pattern.

The dentition may be specialized in its anterior portion, as in the shrews where the first incisor is notably enlarged (Fig. 147). In *Sorex* the tips of the teeth are stained red; in *Crocidura*, by contrast, they are white. A

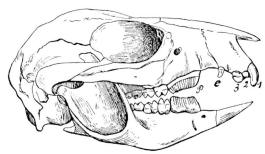

FIG. 145.—Skull of the diprotodont marsupial *Bettongia*: *P,* the laterally grooved cutting pre-molars. After Zittel, from Weber, *Die Säugetiere* (Jena: Gustav Fischer Verlag, 1928) , by per-mission.

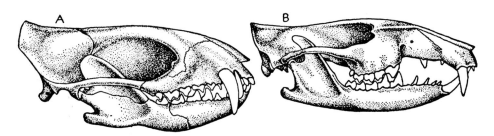

FIG. 146.—Insectivores from the Cretaceous of Mongolia: *B, Zalambdalestes; A, Deltatheridium.*
A, about 1.5:1; *B,* about 1.3:1. After Gregory and Simpson, from Romer (1945) .

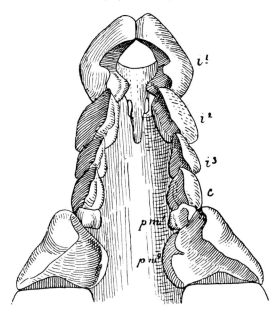

FIG. 147.—Upper incisors, canines and premolars of the shrew *Crocidura montana.* The tooth labeled *Pm*[1] is interpreted as *Pm*[3] by others. After Dobson, from Weber, *Die Säugetiere* (Jena: Gustav Fischer Verlag, 1928) , by permission.

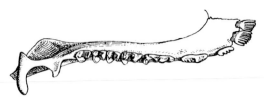

FIG. 148.—Lower jaw of *Cynocephalus*, view of the tritural surface; the incisors are comb-shaped. From Weber, *Die Säugetiere* (Jena: Gustav Fischer Verlag, 1928), by permission.

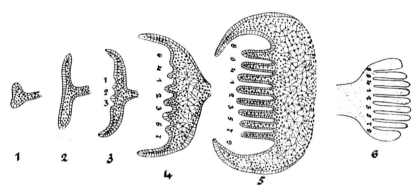

FIG. 149.—Development of a comb-shaped lower incisor of *Cynocephalus*. The numbers refer to the succession in which the prongs of the definitive tooth (6) occur. After Dependorf, from Weber, *Die Säugetiere* (Jena: Gustav Fischer Verlag, 1928), by permission.

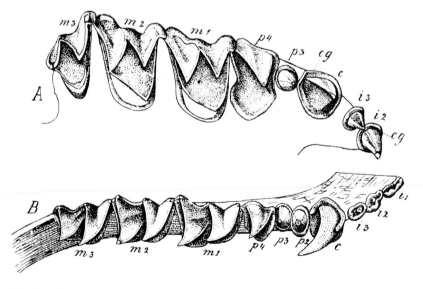

FIG. 150.—Dentition of the bat *Corynorhinus (Plecotus) townsendii* shows the so-called W-pattern of the cheek teeth: *A*, upper teeth, *B*, lower; *cg*, cingulum. After Allen, from Weber, *Die Säugetiere* (Jena: Gustav Fischer Verlag, 1928), by permission.

similar staining of the teeth occurs not only in certain rodents, but also, although rarely, among freshwater fishes, for example in loricariids. The significance of this is not known to me. According to Klunzinger (1870–71), a species of the needlefish *Belone* of the Red Sea has the tips of the teeth stained green.

The canine may approach in shape that of the incisors. Where, as in *Soriculus,* the fourth premolar became very large and caniniform, the premolars in front of it, P2 and P3, may be impaired in their development. Thus they remain very small. P2 may be missing. P1 generally is absent. Where the first lower incisor became excessively large, as in *Sorex,* the two following incisors may be lost.

As regards tooth replacement the Tenrecoidea probably show the most generalized relations; the milk teeth generally remain functional until the adult condition of the animal. According to Leche (1909, 1915) and Weber (1928), there is a tendency, among the hedgehogs, toward a reduction of the milk dentition; in the talpids there are different stages of reduction.

Of the two insectivores of the Cretaceous of Mongolia, *Deltatheridium* is the more generalized form, while *Zalambdalestes* already points toward the Erinaceoidea. Pantolestoidea and Mixodectoidea are forms from the Eocene which, because of certain specializations, are not regarded as direct ancestors of the modern insectivores.

As mentioned already in the previous section, the notably simple form and arrangement of the enamel prisms belongs among the numerous primitive characters of the insectivores.

Dermoptera

The "flying lemur" *Cynocephalus* (Fig. 148) of Southeast Asia and the Sunda Islands, is difficult to classify in the mammalian system and is usually cited as the representative of a separate order, Dermoptera. Many of its anatomical features are related to the possession of a flight membrane, with which the animal is able to glide through the air. Other features of its organization have an ancient aspect. The dentition is specialized in that the lower incisors terminate in a number of cusplets (Fig. 149). These are used to comb the fur, but according to other views this feature is related to the exclusively herbivorous character of the diet. The molars have retained the three-coned insectivore type.

Chiroptera

The bats have originated, beyond doubt, from the insectivores. The organization of the bats is characterized by a combination of primitive characters with adaptations to flight.

The less numerous, relatively large, frugivorous Megachiroptera (fruit bats), which live in the tropics and a few subtropical regions of the Old World, are distinguished from the very much more numerous, smaller, mainly insectivorous Microchiroptera that have a nearly world-wide distribution.

The molars of the fruit bats are blunt-coned corresponding to this diet, in contrast to the pointed-coned molars of the Microchiroptera (Fig. 150). Little is known concerning the prehistory of these forms. The oldest known remains, *Archaeopteropus,* are from the Oligocene of Italy.

The unbelievably large numbers of genera and species of Microchiroptera also show a notable variety in the differentiation of the dentition which cannot be discussed here in adequate detail for lack of space. The differences concern primarily the anterior portion of the dentition. The incisors may be reduced in variable measure whereby the premaxillae are also involved by this reduction. Many tropical bats are suspected of being vampires. Often this suspicion is not justified. In true vampires, the dentition shows an adaptation to this mode of feeding: the upper jaw bears on each side an enlarged incisor that has been modified as a cutting instrument. The canine also has a cutting edge (Pl. 82-b).

The teeth of the milk dentition of the bats have generally become rod-shaped, pointed hooks. They help the nursing young to attach themselves to the teat of the mother (Fig. 151). The bat molars show the W-pattern of the ectoloph that is also commonly seen in insectivores (Fig. 150).

Well preserved remains of Microchiroptera are known from the Eocene of Europe and North America. Acquisition of the ability to fly occurred probably in Paleocene time, since the forms of the Middle Eocene are already perfect fliers. Certain Paleocene specimens of teeth and jaw fragments are assumed to belong to the bats; an unmistakable identification is unfortunately not possible, because remains of the arm skeleton that would provide information concerning the degree of transformation of the extremity are not available so far.

Taeniodonta and Tillodontia

The small, extinct orders of the Taeniodonta and the Tillodontia from the early Tertiary may be briefly mentioned. The dentition shows, besides primitive relations of the molars, rodent-like specializations of the incisors (Fig. 152) (B. Patterson, 1949).

Primates

Usually grouped together as primates are the lemuroids, the tarsier *Tarsius* and its fossil relatives, the Anthropoidea including the New World

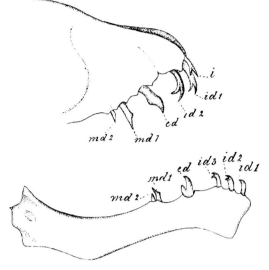

FIG. 151.—Milk teeth of the bat *Pipistrellus atramus*, which serve to fasten the young to the mother during flight. After Tauber, from Weber, *Die Säugetiere* (Jena: Gustav Fischer Verlag, 1928), by permission.

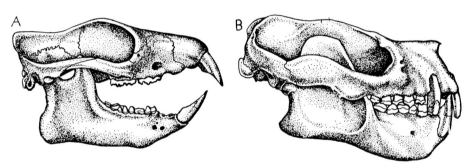

FIG. 152.—Skulls of tillotherians and taeniodonts, two representatives of aberrant early Tertiary mammal orders: *A, Tillotherium; B, Psittacotherium* (taeniodont). *A* about ⅕, *B* about ¼ natural size. After Marsh and Wortman, from Romer (1945).

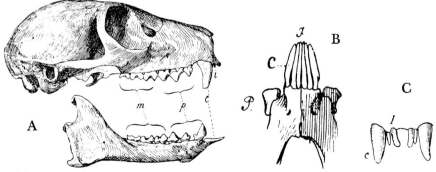

FIG. 153.—Lemur dentitions: *A,* skull of *Lemur macaca; B,* anterior end of the lower jaw of the same species; *C,* upper anterior teeth of *Nycticebus.* From Weber, *Die Säugetiere* (Jena: Gustav Fischer Verlag, 1928), by permission.

monkeys, the Platyrrhini, and the Old World monkeys, the Catarrhini, and the hominids. Among the Catarrhini, the Cercopithecoidea (macaques, baboons, langurs) and the Pongidae, that is the man-like apes (gibbon, orangutan, chimpanzee, gorilla and related fossil forms) are distinguished. The hominids are classified close to the pongids.

Following Romer (1945), the Lemuroidea will here include the tupajids, primarily arboricole squirrel-like tree shrews distributed in South East Asia. These assume an intermediate position between insectivores and lemurs. W. K. Gregory thus called them "preprimate insectivores." Their affiliation with the lemuroids is supported by, among other things, the closure of the orbit by an orbital ring and the differentiation of the olfactory lobe of the brain, but doubts have recently been voiced regarding this interpretation (Campbell, 1966).

When it was attempted, long ago and unsuccessfully, to arrange animals in a single ascending line according to the level of their organization, it was obvious that the monkeys and man must be placed at the upper end of this ladder. For a presentation of the relations of the dentition this did not work, however, because the dentition of man is in no way particularly highly advanced. It is, in fact, so little specialized that it is best discussed with that of the primates, following the still more primitive insectivores.

Lemuroidea

The "schlotternden Lemuren" (shivering lemurs) that were called by Mephistopheles for Faust's burial go back to ghosts that swished around at night, according to an ancient popular Roman belief. With the lemurs of zoology they have only the name in common; perhaps because these animals are predominantly nocturnal forms.

Most, and especially the most, primitive lemuroids live on the island of Madagascar. The African continent contains a few additional genera; the family Lorisidae occurs in Africa and South Asia.

The fact that there are so many ancient mammals on Madagascar—besides lemuroids there are also numerous endemic insectivores—is probably correctly interpreted as indicating that this island was separated from the African mainland already in earliest Tertiary time, and that the modern carnivores thus could not reach it.

From the characterization of the Madagascar lemurs the following features may be emphasized: "orbit and temporal fossa in broad connection, only superficially bounded by an orbital ring. Tympanicum ring-shaped, not contributing to the formation of the bulla auditiva. The carotis interna enters the brain case through the basisphenoid. Foramen entepicondyloideum present, centrale carpi usually free." Because of these and other characters the lemuroids have for a long time been interpreted as very primitive mammals for comparative anatomical reasons. Fossils, not from Madagascar, but from the early Tertiary of North America and Europe, have confirmed this view.

From Madagascar, fossil lemurs are known only from the Pleistocene, but in a whole suite of partly giant forms. The skull length of *Megaladapis* measures more than 30 cm, that of *Archaeolemur* more than 13 cm.

In contrast to the original monodelphian formula $\frac{3\ 1\ 4\ 3}{3\ 1\ 4\ 3}$, the dentition of the modern Lemuroidea has suffered a mild reduction in the anterior portion; it is $\frac{2\ 1\ 3\ 3}{2\ 1\ 3\ 3}$, and in the milk dentition $\frac{2\ 1\ 3}{2\ 1\ 3}$. The number of the premolars may be reduced to $P\frac{2}{2}$ (in the Indrisinae) or to $P\frac{1}{0}$ (in *Daubentonia*). The upper incisors are usually small in the lemuroids, those of the left side separated by a space from those of the right side. The lower incisors of *Lemur* are elongated and lie flat. They are tightly joined laterally by the incisiviform canines (Fig. 153).

Particular relations of the dentition are seen in *Daubentonia* (Fig. 154). Both above and below there is an anterior tooth strongly enlarged, probably I l, which has permanent growth. Behind there follow in the permanent dentition a diastema and in the upper jaw a P^4, in the lower jaw an M_1. For this reason, *Daubentonia* was originally placed among the rodents, until experience showed that rodent-like differentiation of the anterior-most teeth may occur in the most different kinship groups. The front teeth of *Daubentonia* are not used for gnawing proper, but rather for "the biting of holes in order to obtain the soft parts of fruits beneath the rind, the marrow within the sprout, the insects beneath the bark, whereby the long slender middle finger is used as an aid" (Weber, 1928). In the Pleistocene *Megaladapis* the upper incisors are missing completely; its upper canine, however, is greatly enlarged. Its anatagonist P_2 has become caniniform. The transformation of the lower canine into an incisor-like tooth, in *Lemur*, is a specialization that occurred late. In the early Tertiary lemuroids the canine is caniniform both above and below.

Tarsioidea

The features that led to the removal of the tarsier *Tarsius* (Fig. 155) from the lemuroids, and the creation for it of a separate suborder Tarsioidea, cannot be discussed here in detail; but we can mention that in the early Tertiary of North America and Europe there occur besides lemuroids also unquestionable relatives of *Tarsius*. In contrast to the situation in the

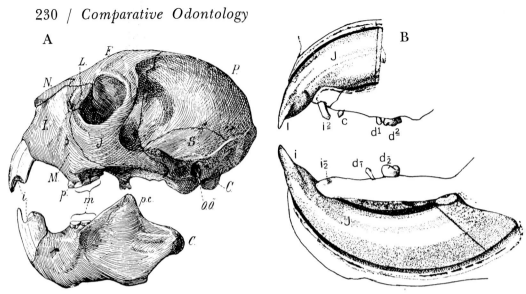

FIG. 154.—Dentition of the aye-aye *Daubentonia madagascariensis: A,* skull of an adult specimen, ¾ natural size; *B,* dentition of a male in process of tooth replacement; *i,* milk incisors; *d,* milk premolars; *I.* permanent incisors. After Peters, from Weber, *Die Säugetiere* (Jena: Gustav Fischer Verlag, 1928), by permission.

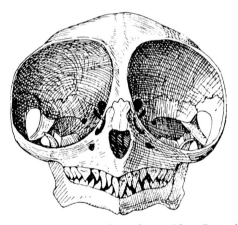

FIG. 155.—Skull of *Tarsius tarsius* seen from front. After Burmeister, from Weber, *Die Säugetiere* (Jena: Gustav Fischer Verlag, 1928), by permission.

lemuroids, the upper inner incisors of *Tarsius* are in contact with one another. The lower canine is caniniform; it stands nearly vertical.

Already in the Oligocene there existed in North America only very few lemuroids and tarsioids. In the later Tertiary they are absent in this area. Important reasons suggest the supposition that the platyrrhinous monkeys now restricted to South America arose from primitive primates that in the early Tertiary reached South America from North America across the land bridge then in existence.

Anthropoidea

Platyrrhini

The monkeys of the New World are called Platyrrhini because the cartilaginous nasal septum is in general very broad, in contrast to the Catarrhini, the Old World monkeys. But this not very significant feature is accompanied by much more profound differences. Among others these concern the dentition. Its formula in the Catarrhinous monkeys and in man is $\frac{2\ 1\ 2\ 3}{2\ 1\ 2\ 3}$, but in the Platyrrhini, for example in the family Cebidae, $\frac{2\ 1\ 3\ 3}{2\ 1\ 3\ 3}$, or in the family Hapalidae, $\frac{2\ 1\ 3\ 2}{2\ 1\ 3\ 2}$. The small delicate Hapalidae are arboreal. They feed on fruits, but notably also on insects. In the Jardin Goeldi in Pará, Brazil, I could observe how a marmoset showed joyous excitement when a keeper offered it a captured cicada in passing.

The dentition of the Hapalidae (Fig. 156) shows primitive features in the tritubercular structure of its molars. But, in comparison with the cebids, the loss of the last molar is to be considered as a specialization.

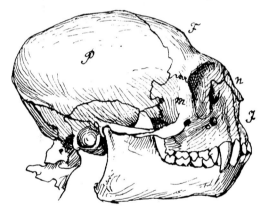

Fig. 156.—Skull of the tamarin *Leontocebus geoffroyi.* From Weber, *Die Säugetiere* (Jena: Gustav Fischer Verlag, 1928), by permission.

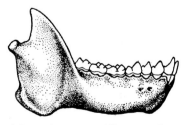

Fig. 157.—*Parapithecus fraasi* from the Lower Oligocene of Egypt; the oldest fossil find of a catarrhinous monkey. After Schlosser, from Romer (1945).

The best known cebid, often represented in zoological gardens, is the capucine monkey *Cebus capucinus*. Of the members of the group we might mention the long-armed spider monkey *Ateles*, which has sometime been called the "gibbon of the New World"; the howling monkey *Alouatta*, in which the body of the hyoid bone is blown up to form a resonance chamber; the saimiris *Saimiri*; the Sakis *Pithecia*; and finally the woolly monkey *Lagothrix*.

In their dentition these forms show notable differences of which only a few may be mentioned here. The lower incisors, that stand generally more or less vertically, are positioned horizontally both in the Pithecinae and the Hapalidae. The canines vary in relative size. In the Cebinae they have a conical shape; the upper C protrude beneath the lips. Where the food consists primarily of insects, the premolars and the molars are acutely cusped as in *Aotes*. A diet of leaves is correlated with considerable size of the molars in *Alouatta*. In the latter genus the lower molars are in part five-cusped, inasmuch as the anterior, inner cusp on the trigonid has been retained.

The fossil Platyrrhini are also restricted to South America, as far as is presently known. So far only very little is known about them. *Homunculus*, discovered and described by Ameghino, unquestionably belongs here. From the Miocene of Colombia is known *Neosaimiri* Stirton.

Catarrhini

The oldest find so far of a catarrhinid monkey is the small lower jaw of *Parapithecus fraasi* from the lower Oligocene of the Fayum of Egypt (Fig. 157). Placing this genus among specific primitive primates of the Eocene has not been possible because of the sparseness of the material. Using dentitional relations, Bolk attempted to demonstrate genetic ties between the Platyrrhini and the Catarrhini, by assuming that the first molar of the Catarrhini had originated from the last deciduous premolar of the Platyrrhini by becoming a permanent tooth. This hypothesis, for which there are no convincing arguments, has been rejected emphatically by W. K. Gregory. Also for paleogeographic reasons there is no necessity for a hypothesis that derives the Catarrhini from the Platyrrhini, since there appears to be no doubt that the Platyrrhini were also restricted to South America during the Tertiary.

A. S. Romer distinguished Cercopithecidae, Pongidae, and Hominidae.

CERCOPITHECIDAE

The Cercopithecidae (Cercopithecoidea, Simpson, 1931; Cynomorpha Huxley, 1872) include the majority of the catarrhinous monkeys: all those forms that do not belong to the Pongidae, the group that stands most closely to the hominids, the true man-like apes.

From the group of the macacs we may mention *Macaca sylvana* L. (*Inuus ecaudatus* E. Geoffroy) as the only monkey still living in Europe, restricted, to be sure, to the rocks of Gibraltar. Since it was common in ancient times in North Africa, it served Galen for his anatomical studies. To the macacs belong further the rhesus monkey and numerous additional Asiatic species. Baboons are characterized by a long snout and strong cheek bones. The genus *Cercopithecus*, (from *kerkos*, "tail," and *pithekos*, "monkey") is distributed in many species over Africa. The Colobinae are a special subfamily with the African *Colobus* and the Asiatic genera *Presbytis* and *Nasalis*.

As in all Catarrhines, the dentition of the cercopithecids shows both above and below two incisors, a canine, two premolars and three molars (Pl. 83-a). According to Weber (1928), "the lower outer incisors are not larger than the inner ones, often smaller. The anterior lower P has a pointed crown and a sharp crest faces the posterior edge of the upper C. M_3 is usually large." In the usually four-cuspid molars the anterior cusp pair and the posterior one are each connected by a transverse crest. In the last lower M a hypoconulid may occur.

The variety in the differentiation of the dentition is correlated with differences in the mode of feeding which may be insectivorous to carnivorous, frugivorous or exclusively herbivorous.

In the herbivorous Colobinae the cross crests on the molars are particularly well developed, the jaw movement is predominantly antero-posterior, and the jaws are short. In the other forms the jaws are often long, the movement of the jaws mostly ginglymic, and the molars sometimes very large.

Of fossil cercopithecids we may mention, besides the already noted *Parapithecus fraasi*, whose affiliation with the catarrhini is not beyond dispute, *Mesopithecus* from the Pontian of Pikermi, *Libypithecus* from the Pliocene of Egypt, and *Dolichopithecus* from the Villafranchian of Senèce in France.

PONGIDAE

Of greater interest than the multitude of "ordinary" catarrhinous monkeys are, for many readers, those forms that permit the recognition of more or less far-reaching correspondences with the human body, and are thus called "man-like" or "great apes." To these belong, among the living representatives, the gibbon, *Hylobates* that lives on the Sunda Islands; the orangutan, *Pongo satyrus*, restricted to Sumatra and Borneo; and the two African forms, the gorilla (*Gorilla gorilla*) and the chimpanzee *Anthro-*

pithecus troglodytes (*Pan,* Oken). Since the last three genera are more closely related to each other than they are to the gibbon, they are juxtaposed as Ponginae to the Hylobatinae. The modern forms have been augmented by a number of fossil genera and species in recent years and these are to be further discussed below.

In the dentition of the Hylobatinae, the straight tooth rows diverge posteriorly. The canines exceed the premolars notably in height (Fig. 158). The upper P have generally three, the lower ones two roots. The first upper P is bicuspid, the first lower one single-cusped. In the upper molars the trigon is clearly evident; the hypocone is reduced. In all three lower molars, besides the protoconid, the metaconid, the hypoconid and the entoconid, there is also a hypoconulid.

For the orangutan, gorilla and chimpanzee I select the following notes from the detailed account of the dentition in the *Traité de Paléontologie* by Piveteau (1957).

The upper middle incisors are larger than the lateral ones. Below, all incisors are of about the same robustness; only in the orangutan are the lower lateral incisors slightly more robust than the middle ones. The canine always protrudes beyond the level of the remaining teeth, most notably in the chimpanzee, less so in the orangutan and still less in the gorilla. The upper premolars are bicuspid; generally they have three roots. The normal number of cusps on the upper molars is four. In the gorilla (Fig. 159) the cusps are higher than in the other two genera and conical. The enamel shows only an insignificant amount of wrinkling. In the orangutan and the chimpanzee the enamel is intensively wrinkled; in connection with this the cusps may become indistinct.

The lower first P is of conical form, the second is bicuspid. The lower P are generally two-rooted. In the orangutan the three lower M have a reduced

FIG. 158.—Lower teeth of the gibbon *Hylobates leuciscus.* 2.8:1. After Hürzeler, from Piveteau, *Traité de Paléontologie,* vol. VII (Paris: Masson et Cie, 1957), by permission.

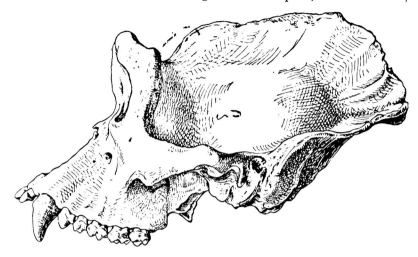

Fɪɢ. 159.—Skull of the gorilla. After W. K. Gregory and Raven, from Piveteau, *Traité de Paléontologie*, vol. VII, (Paris: Masson et Cie, 1957), by permission.

hypoconulid that forms a vestigial third lobus. An outer cingulum is present. In the gorilla the cusps are clearly differentiated and the wrinkling of the enamel occurs as grooves on the inner faces of the cusps. The hypoconulid lies close to the labial edge of the tooth crown. Between metaconid and entoconid a supplemental cusp may appear. In front of the protoconid there lies an "anterior pit" (*fovea anterior*), behind the hypoconulid and the entoconid a "posterior pit" (*fovea posterior*).

In the chimpanzee the hypoconulid is wedged between the hypoconid and the entoconid, so that it does not protrude backward as an indication of a third lobus. Anterior and posterior pits are clearly expressed (Pl. 83-b).

Fossil forms

The oldest find of a great ape is that of *Propliopithecus* from the lower Oligocene of the Fayum of Egypt (Fig. 160). Only the right half of the lower jaw without the incisors is preserved. The available portion is, however, so characteristic that its affinity with the anthropomorphi is not doubted by anyone. *Propliopithecus* was smaller than all modern forms. The canine is small and positioned vertically. The first P (P3) has a strong outer cusp, an inner cingulum, and a very weak post-median cusp. The second P (P4) is differentiated into a high anterior and a notably lower posterior portion. In the first and following molars the paraconid has disappeared. All three molars have five cusps. A crest connects metaconid and protoconid. Entoconid and hypoconid are also connected by a transversal crest. The hypoconulid approaches the hypoconid. The second molar is of

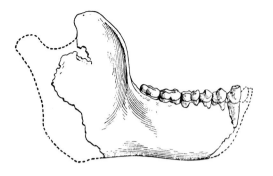

Fig. 160.—*Propliopithecus haeckeli* from the Lower Oligocene of Egypt, the oldest fossil find of an anthropomorphous ape. Lower jaw external view (slightly enlarged) and preserved lower teeth seen from above. After Schlosser, from Weber, *Die Säugetiere* (Jena: Gustav Fischer Verlag, 1928), by permission.

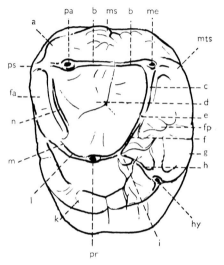

Fig. 161.—First upper left molar of *Pliopithecus*. 7.3:1. After Hürzeler, from Piveteau, *Traité de Paléontologie*, vol. VII (Paris: Masson et Cie, 1957), by permission.

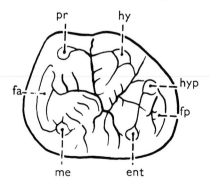

Fig. 162.—*Dryopithecus,* pattern of a lower molar. After W. K. Gregory and Hellman, from Piveteau, *Traité de Paléontologie*, vol. VII (Paris: Masson et Cie, 1957), by permission.

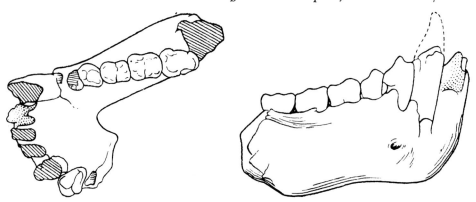

FIG. 163.—*Limnopithecus,* an anthropomorphous ape from the Miocene of Kenya, Africa. After Le Gros Clark and Leakey, from Piveteau, *Traité de Paléontologie,* vol. VII. (Paris: Masson et Cie, 1957), by permission.

about the same size as the first. In the third M the portion formed by the hypoconulid is narrower. Thus an indication of a third lobus results. All three molars have a clearly differentiated outer cingulum.

Georges Cuvier was convinced that the primates had arrived on the scene in geologically relatively recent time. This view became untenable in 1834, only two years after Cuvier's death, when an unquestionably gibbon-like ape was found by Ed. Lartet in the Miocene of Sansan. It received the name *Pliopithecus* (Fig. 161); another find belonging to the same genus, from sediments of about the same age, comes from Göriach in the Steiermark. As characteristic for the lower molars of *Pliopithecus* a small, triangular pit is described, bordered on one side by a crest that connects the protoconid with the hypoconid, and on the other by two spurs, one of which originates at the protoconid, the other at the hypoconid. Additional details may be gathered from Figure 161.

An anthropomorphous ape, *Dryopithecus fontani,* was discovered by Alfred Fontan in 1856 in the Middle Miocene of Saint-Gaudens (Haute Garonne, France), and described by Ed. Lartet. A further find, a mandible, was described by Gaudry in 1889. The wide geographic distribution of this genus is documented by numerous specimens of single teeth. As W. K. Gregory (1921) has pointed out, the lower molars are characterized by a typical furrow pattern that is significant in anthropomorphous apes generally; it has the shape of a Y. The unpaired furrow extends between metaconid and entoconid, and the paired furrows enclose the hypoconid (Fig. 162).

The finds of anthropomorphous apes of lower Miocene age in East Africa were a surprise and have been described since the thirties by A. T. Hopwood and W. E. Le Gros Clark. The latter finds came from the island Rusinga

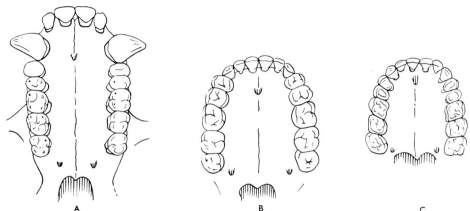

Fig. 164.—Upper tooth arcades of *A*, gorilla; *B*, *Australopithecus*; *C*, an Australian. 1:2.4. After Le Gros Clark, from Piveteau, *Traité de Paléontologie*, vol. VII (Paris: Masson et Cie, 1957), by permission.

in Lake Victoria. Of the genera proposed by Hopwood, one, *Limnopithecus*, is thought to be a relative of the Hylobatinae; the other, *Proconsul*, is placed in the phyletic vicinity of the chimpanzee and gorilla (Fig. 163).

From the Siwalik hills cynomorphous and anthropomorphous primates were described in 1886 by Lydekker. One of the latter received the name *Sivapithecus*. Additional material was discovered by Yale University expeditions in 1933 and 1935, among it three additional genera of anthropomorphous apes: *Bramapithecus*, *Sugrivapithecus* and *Ramapithecus*. According to Piveteau, *Ramapithecus* is a member of the Ponginae closely resembling the hominids.

In 1925 Dart described under the name *Australopithecus africanus* a not quite completely preserved skull, from the locality Taung in Betschuanaland (north of Kimberley), as that of a hominid. This interpretation was at first received skeptically until the well known student of the fossil faunas of the Karroo, Robert Broom, emphatically agreed with it (Fig. 164). Broom himself found, near Sterkfontein west of Johannesburg, a portion of a skull which he named *Australopithecus* (later *Plesianthropus*) *transvaalensis*. Then followed the finds of *Paranthropus robustus* from Kromadraae and *P. crassidens* from Makapansgat. The localities Taung, Sterkfontein and Makapansgat are thought to be about the same age, Upper Villafranchian. Swartkrans and Kromadraae are said to be somewhat younger. Since most of these finds are skulls, the dentition is more completely known than in the fossil forms discussed so far.

A detailed description cannot be attempted here. In the general characterization I shall follow Piveteau (1957). The upper incisors often have the shovel shape commonly seen in man. In *Paranthropus* the medial ones are more robust than the lateral ones. The lower I stand vertically in the mandible; their lingual surface is concave. The canines surpass the neighboring teeth in height insignificantly if at all. No sexual dimorphism of the canines is present. In the two upper P, outer and inner cusps are separated by a depression of complicated form. The lower P differ from those of the Ponginae; they resemble those of the hominids. The molars are very robust. The last is the largest. In the two anterior upper molars the hypocone is well developed and separated from the trigon by a clear furrow. In the third M metacone and hypocone are reduced.

Of the lower molars the first shows clearly the *Dryopithecus* pattern in the furrowing of the crown surface. Between hypoconulid and entoconid a *tuberculum sextum* is present; the mode of wear of the cheek teeth corresponds to the condition in the hominids.

The Australopithecidae are, at any rate, very closely related to the hominids, but the relations between the two groups have not yet been fully clarified. For *Australopithecus,* brain case capacities of 450 to 700 cm³ have been determined. These figures seem relatively high if one considers that for the gorilla, whose body is larger and heavier than was that of *Australopithecus,* the largest brain case capacity determined amounts to 685 cm³.

Many students regard the age of these finds as too recent for them to be ancestors of man. Piveteau thinks they possibly represent early hominids belonging to a side line that was displaced southward in the African continent by superior competitors.

From the Monte Bamboli in the Toscana (Italy) came finds of dentitions of a primate described in 1872 by Gervais under the name *Oreopithecus bambolii* (Pl. 84-a). Gervais interpreted *Oreopithecus* as a form intermediate between the cynopithecids and the pongids. This opinion was also held by Schlosser, who at first had different views. He created the family Oreopithecidae between the Cynopithecidae and the Pongidae, while other students expressed the opinion that the genus belongs to the Cercopithecidae. J. Hürzeler (1949, 1958) was able to demonstrate that the later presentations had been based on inadequate plaster casts. Restudy of the then available material led him to place *Oreopithecus* among the Pongidae, and even among the Hominidae; thus the genus assumed greater significance. Hürzeler's tenacious efforts to procure additional specimens met with great success; finally a nearly complete skeleton was obtained. Study of this, perhaps to date the most exciting find of a fossil primate, should lead to a clarification of the systematic position of this form.

While *Australopithecus* stands close to the hominids, but is usually not placed within this group (Tobias, 1965), *Pithecanthropus* (Pl. 84-b) and *Sinanthropus* are generally accepted as hominids. To the famous finds of

Pithecanthropus erectus discovered by the Dutch military physician, Eugen Dubois, in 1891 in Trinil on Java, further important material was added in the nineteen-thirties through the efforts of von Königswald. In China systematic search for material began about 1920 in Choukoutien (in the vicinity of Peking). It progressed with great intensity until 1937. The results were gratifying: six more or less complete skulls, as many mandibles, a large number of isolated teeth, and some fragments of limb bones were discovered. The specimens, unfortunately, were lost during the second World War; however, very good casts are available, made in New York in connection with the study of the material by Weidenreich.

Sinanthropus is so close to *Pithecanthropus* that the use of a different generic name is hardly justified. *Meganthropus palaeojavanicus,* characterized by its notable size, belongs probably to *Pithecanthropus,* according to Le Gros Clark; probably to *Homo* sp. according to Tobias and von Königswald. The type of dentition corresponds to that of the hominids. There is no diastema. The upper middle incisors are larger than the lateral ones. The first lower P is bicuspid. The often notable complication of the relief of the crown surface of the molars and the persistence of the "*Dryopithecus* pattern" are valued as ancient features. We might mention also that the pulp cavity is very wide and that a *tuberculum sextum* is common in the lower molars.

Gigantopithecus blacki described by von Königswald is presumably also large. So far, only four isolated teeth have become known and these were procured in apothecary shops. Because fossil bones and teeth have been used for therapeutic purposes in China since ancient times, apothecary shops are well supplied with materials of this sort. It was probably a tooth obtained from an apothecary in Peking that led later to the trail of *Sinanthropus.*

Forms such as *Pithecanthropus* and *Sinanthropus* that belong to the hominids, but have not generally been included in the genus *Homo,* have been grouped together as "archanthropiens" by Piveteau; as "paleanthropiens" forms belonging to the genus *Homo* but differing from the species *H. sapiens;* and as "neanthropiens" the fossil forms that fall within the definition of *H. sapiens,* including modern man.

That there existed in the Quaternary forms specifically different from *Homo sapiens* was realized in 1856 by the initially much discussed find from Neanderthal. This idea was formalized in 1864 by W. King's proposal of the name *Homo neanderthalensis.*

Today neanderthal men and forms closely related to them, that have sometimes received different species names, are known not only from numerous old-stone-age stations in Europe, but also from Palestine, South and

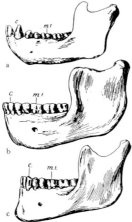

Fig. 165.—Chin shape of *a*, chimpanzee; *b*, *Homo heidelbergensis; c*, *Homo sapiens*. After Le Gros Clark, from Peyer, *Die Zähne*, Verständliche Wissenschaft, vol. 79 (Berlin: Springer Verlag, 1963), by permission.

East Africa (see Tobias, 1965), and East Asia. Since more complete finds are also available, interpretation of the finds no longer depends to such a high degree on the often minute differences in the formation of the teeth, as in the case of many early anthropomorphs where further criteria are often lacking.

A discussion of the dentitional features of the hominids that do not belong to the genus *Homo,* described in numerous publications, may here be ignored because of the insignificance of the differences from living man. In part, these are structures that occur also in living man, even though more rarely. But there are considerable differences in the differentiation of the chin, because the shape of the human chin evolved only within the hominids (Fig. 165). Despite the recent discovery in many parts of the world of numerous remains of hominids that cannot be included in the species *H. sapiens,* the question concerning the special prehistory of man has not yet found an unequivocal solution. These problems, however, lie beyond our present task.

Study of the changes of tooth form that have taken place among the hominids has left Piveteau with the impression that these changes have wrought a simplification in the form. He thus considers the very simple tooth forms as they occur in modern man as a secondary acquisition.

Homo sapiens

Man is also among the best investigated organisms in the matter of teeth and dentition. In addition to almost innumerable special studies, the human dentition has been adequately characterized in very many excellent readily available summary works, for example: Spalteholz (1909), De Terra (1911),

Widdowson (1946), Scott and Symons (1964), Sicher (1952), Piveteau (1957), R. C. Wheeler (1958 and 1962), and many others.

In view of this wealth of easily accessible information, characterization of the human dentition will here be restricted to the barest minimum. Less known, however, are the ontogenetic stages of crown development and these merit at least passing mention.

Permanent dentition. The incisors (Pl. 85) are shovel-shaped and have straight cutting edges. In the medial pair of teeth, the cutting edge may show two slight notches giving the crown a three-lobed appearance. This feature is soon removed by wear. The conical roots are about $1\frac{1}{2}$ times as long as the crowns are high. Of the four pairs of incisors, the medial pair is larger than the lateral pair in the upper jaw; reversed size relations apply in the mandible.

The canines are conical and pointed, not notably higher than the adjacent teeth. Upper and lower canines resemble each other closely in form, but the lower ones are usually slightly smaller.

The two premolars in each quadrant of the dentition correspond to the third and fourth post-canine teeth of the primitive monodephian tooth formula (see p. 198). In dental works they are usually called biscuspids, a description applicable only to the hominids. The first upper P has a (larger) buccal and a lingual cusp, separated by a deep furrow. The root is usually divided into a labial and a lingual branch, sometimes forming separate roots, sometimes merely indicated by mesial and distal vertical furrows; rarely there are three roots. In all cases the root canals are separate.

The second upper P resembles the first, but is slightly smaller and shows a minor difference in the crown relief. The root is only rarely divided.

The lower P do not always fit the designation "biscuspid," since the lingual cusp of the first may be severely reduced and the crown of the second may bear three cusps. The first lower P is the smallest of all premolars; the outline of its occlusal surface is nearly round. There is generally a single root, but in very rare cases dual roots occur.

The premolars of the permanent dentition of man differ from the molars in their considerably simpler form. Molars are usually considered teeth that have no successors, and which therefore belong to the milk dentition. In this connection it is of some interest that the second milk premolars notably resemble the molars.

The upper molars are generally provided with four cusps. The outline of the trituration surface is slightly rhomboidal. The crown relief of the first molar is fairly constant, four cusps being always present. Three roots occur, two in buccal and one in lingual (palatinal) positions. Segregation into the different roots does not take place immediately beneath the crowns, so that there is a mutual root portion. The buccal roots are often curved, their tips pointing toward each other. The crown relief of the second upper molar is less constant than in the first and the tooth is slightly smaller. The tips of the two buccal roots tend to become joined by cementum more often than in the first molar. One of the buccal roots may be united with the palatinal root, but the root canals remain separate. The third upper molar is smaller than the second and is quite variable in its form.

The lower molars of man do not show the striking form differences from the upper molars as, for example, do those in the horse. Detailed study has revealed, however, that in principle the same differences exist in man between the upper and lower portions of the dentition. This conclusion is the result primarily of comparisons with lower primates and with fossil forms.

The first lower molar has five cusps, three in buccal and two in lingual positions on the crown relief. The trituration surface is elongated in mesio-distal direction. There are two curved roots, of which the anterior is larger. The second lower molar bears four cusps that occupy the four corners of a rectangular chewing surface. The two roots are more often united than in the first molar. The third lower molar usually has five cusps, similarly arranged as in the first molar. This tooth is much less variable than the third upper molar.

Milk dentition. In polyphodont vertebrates the size differences of the teeth of young and old individuals are bridged by more or less numerous intermediate sizes. In the diphyodont dentition of man the size difference between milk teeth and their permanent successors is sudden and considerable. While the color of the permanent teeth is ivory, that of the milk teeth is white. As J. H. Mummery has pointed out, the color difference is most impressive in six- to seven-year-old children. Another difference consists in the fact that the enamel cover, where it borders the cementum of the root, is often thickened and ends abruptly; in the permanent teeth the transition is gradual. In its period of function, the milk dentition of man lies between the extremes of early resorption and prolongation of the functional significance to adult age.

The milk incisors resemble, except for minor details, their successors. The same is true of the milk canines. The crown relief of the first upper milk premolar resembles that of its sucessor; the crown of the first lower milk premolar is highly variable. The second milk premolars both above and below resemble the molar crown pattern, which in view of the functional significance of these teeth is hardly surprising. The upper milk premolars have three roots, the lower ones two.

Ontogenetic differentiation of the tooth crown. The study of ontogenetic tooth differentiation has in the past been restricted largely to histological concerns. The morphological changes that affect the tooth crown during its formative stages have only recently become known in adequate detail, and then only for man and to a lesser degree for the Rhesus monkey (Kraus and Jordan, 1965). From this fine study appears evidence that the morpho-differentiation of the crown relief progresses from simple to complex conditions, and that the crown relief of different teeth is the more similar the younger the stages are. For example, all four deciduous premolar teeth of man begin with an elongated, globular crown relief on which one large cusp is soon in evidence. Thereafter, additional cusps develop in such a way that the crown relief of different teeth at comparable developmental stages shows a remarkable correspondence, for example between P^2 and M^1 at stages V and VII (Kraus and Jordan, 1965). In general the crown relief in these ontogenetic stages is much more pronounced than in the fully formed, erupted teeth, which is partly due to the thick enamel blanket of human teeth that tends to smooth out the relief.

It is probably still too early to appraise the full significance of these developmental crown relief patterns; a broader comparative anatomical base would be very helpful. The comparisons of selected developmental stages of the human crown relief with functional teeth of dinocephalians and mesozoic mammals are not in all cases convincing; but too little is known at present, both of developmental patterns in primitive modern mammals and about the dentitions of mesozoic forms, to make such comparisons more than an interesting exercise.

Carnivora

Even if not all mammals included in this order are truly carnivorous, that is, eat meat (there are insectivores and even vegetarians among them), there are nevertheless certain forms that embody the epitome of the predator, for example the tiger or the lion. The carnivore character is clearly reflected in the dentition. The well developed incisors are almost always present in the primitive number of three on each side; the sometimes very large "caniniform" canines that extend usually very much beyond the crowns of the neighboring teeth, received their name from the development in the dog (*canis,* "dog"). Most significantly, however, in modern carnivores the last premolar in the upper jaw and the first molar in the mandible have become carnassials (*dentes lacerantes*) in most forms. Both upper and lower carnassials are secodont; that is, they have sharp cutting edges that run parallel to the edge of the jaw. During jaw movement, which in carnivores is ginglymic (controlled by a hinge joint), the two cutting edges (one side of the jaws at a time) glide along one another after the fashion of scissors or tin snips. A small amount of lateral motion of the mandible against the upper jaw is possible and even necessary in the chewing act (Scapino, 1965).

The prehistory of the carnivores is already fairly well understood. Uncertainties in the delimitation of groups develop in early Tertiary forms where the distinctions of carnivores from insectivores may pose difficulties. In the earliest Paleocene there already lived numerous species of primitive carnivores, the creodonts. This rich array of early carnivores might be related, in the last analysis, to the tremendous differentiation of the flora characterized by the rich development of the angiosperms or flowering plants, according to the views of some paleontologists. This development meant a betterment of the possibilities of the food supply for the herbivorous mammals, which correspondingly underwent a notable radiation. With the increase in the number and variety of herbivorous mammals, the carnivores that depended on them as prey could naturally increase in number of species and individuals.

In the phylogenetic progression of the carnivores from the Paleocene to the Present a phenomenon appears that was encountered in a similar manner among the reptiles of the Permian and the Mesozoic: a sort of evolutionary race in the differentiation of more and more perfect defensive devices among the herbivores, and increasingly more perfect offensive weapons among the predators. Sometimes this ended with the extinction of the prey, which thus doomed the predators as well.

For the differentiation and perfection of the carnivores, the dentition was not adequate by itself. Important accessories were the keen development of the sense organs and the central nervous system, speed and agility. Body size kept pace with the size increase in the prey. Considerable body size accompanied by resistant skin among herbivores may have led to special, curious specializations of the dentition in the saber-toothed cats.

Creodonta

The tooth formula of most creodonts corresponds to the maximal formula in monodelphia, $\frac{3\ 1\ 4\ 3}{3\ 1\ 4\ 3}$. Only rarely may the anterior-most premolar or the last molar be missing.

The geologically oldest, and in their skeletons and dentitions primitive, forms are the Procreodi. Their sharply pointed molar cusps closely resemble those of the insectivores. Carnassials are not present.

In the following group, the Acreodi, there are also no carnassials. The cusps of the molars are blunt. The end phalanges, being split, must have borne hooves rather than claws. Among the generally small animals of the

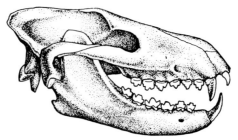

Fɪɢ. 166.—Skull of the creodont *Mesonyx,* from the Eocene of North America. About ⅕ natural size. From Romer (1945).

Paleocene, *Mesonyx* (Fig. 166), with a skull length of about 30 cm, was a veritable giant. *Andrewsarchus* from the Eocene of Mongolia was even larger.

The Pseudocreodi form the most varied group of the creodonts. They have carnassials, but in a different position within the dentition than in the modern carnivores. Either the first upper and the second lower molar, or the second upper and the third lower molar are differentiated as carnassials. *Palaeonictis* appears to be an intermediate form, in that P^4 and M^1 above, and M_1 and M_2 below show carnassial differentiation. For temporal reasons the genus cannot be considered as an ancestral form of the miacids, in which, as in modern mammals, P^4 and M_1 function as carnassials.

The Pseudocreodi include the two families Oxyaenidae and Hyaenodontidae. The oxyaenids, many of which attained considerable size, are restricted to the early Tertiary; the hyaenodontids, such as *Hyaenodon* and *Sinopa,* persisted in the tropics of the Old World into the Miocene and even into the Pliocene.

Apataelurus from the upper Eocene, already mentioned (p. 222), is interesting in that it has enlarged canines, as has the South American marsupial *Thylacosmilus* and the saber-toothed cats.

The relations of the Creodonta to the modern terrestrial carnivores, the Fissipedia, are reasonably well understood. But the taxonomic boundary between the two groups has been laid differently, depending on whether a "horizontal" or a "vertical" classification was favored. The vertical system emphasizes the phylogenetic relationships, horizontal classification the sum of mutual and distinguishing characters at a given point in time.

In the family Miacidae $\dfrac{P^4}{M_1}$ are already developed as carnassials. Since the miacids reach back very far, they lack many other characteristics of the modern carnivores. For these reasons they are placed by some students as Eucreodi among the creodonts, by others among the fissipeds, because most probably all modern carnivores have arisen from miacids.

Fissipedia

Among the fissipeds two unquestionably natural groups are distinguished, the Aeluroidea (from *ailuros,* "cat"), also called "Herpestoidea," and the Arctoidea (from *arktos,* "bear").

Aeluroidea

The viverrids, hyaenids and the felids belong to the Aeluroidea. Most primitive are the viverrids and among them certain representatives from Madagascar show affinities to Oligocene miacids (in Europe, although rare, *Genetta genetta* and *Herpestes widdringtoni*). The hyaenids, being carrion eaters, are characterized by the massive construction of the dentition; the formula is $\frac{3\ 1\ 4\ 1}{3\ 1\ 4\ 1}$, and the upper molar is vestigial.

Among the presently living cats, skull construction and dentitions are notably uniform despite considerable differences in the body size of the animals. Even the gepard *Acinonyx,* with its differing limbs, differs from the remaining felids only in a minimal feature in the structure of the upper carnassial. Catlike fissipeds existed in the Oligocene, but despite this the prehistory of the felines, the cats in the narrower sense, is debated because in the felids of the Middle Tertiary the canine is often somewhat enlarged as in the saber-toothed cats.

That true cats with relatively smaller canines could have arisen from such forms seemed questionable for theoretical reasons. The modern felines, however, probably did originate from the ancestors of the saber-toothed cats that became extinct only in Pleistocene time.

Among the latter, as also in the saber-toothed marsupial *Thylacosmilus* and in the creodont *Apataelurus,* the enormous enlargement of the canines in *Smilodon* and other saber-toothed cats necessarily brought about correlative modifications of the skull structure, especially in the joint of the lower jaw to permit a more extensive opening of the mouth, and in the faces of origin of the trigeminus musculature.

While the dentition of the saber-toothed cats was formerly occasionally considered as an excessive structure that had evolved beyond functional necessity, and which had thus led to the extinction of the species, one is now more prone to consider the fact that this structure was maintained with evidently good results for a number of millions of years.

Arctoidea

Among the Arctoidea, the mustelids (marten, weasel, skunk, wolverine, otter) are regarded as the most generalized group. Many of them lead a

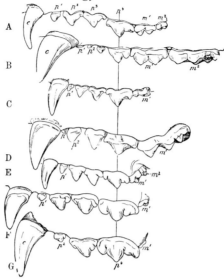

FIG. 167.—Dentitions of fissiped carnivores. The vertical line denotes the upper carnassial P^4: A, dog; B, bear; C, marten; D, badger; E, *Herpestes*; F, hyena; G, lion. After Boas, from Weber, *Die Säugetiere* (Jena: Gustav Fischer Verlag, 1928), by permission.

purely carnivorous existence. Correspondingly the dentition behind the carnassials is reduced to one tooth on each side above and below (Fig. 167). The martens have retained the full complement of premolars with the formula $\frac{3\ 1\ 4\ 1}{3\ 1\ 4\ 1}$. In related groups the first P is often reduced. Most of the mustelids are small. An extinct Miocene form from the American Miocene, *Megalictis*, reached the size of a bear.

In contrast to the felids, in which the portion of the dentition behind the carnassials has degenerated, the canids have behind the carnassials a row of molars that has been reduced only moderately or not at all. The tooth formula of the dog, for example, is $\frac{1.2.3-1-1.2.3.4-1.2}{1.2.3-1-1.2.3.4-1.2.3}$. In *Otocyon*, an African genus of dogs, the number of molars may be three above, or more rarely even four, and in the lower jaw four or even five. This results in a maximal number of 50 teeth. This is, except for toothed whales and the manatee, one of the rare cases in which a monodelphous mammal has more teeth than $\frac{3\ 1\ 4\ 3}{3\ 1\ 4\ 3}$. In *Cuon* the number of molars has been lowered to $\frac{2}{2}$, in the Brazilian *Speothos* to $\frac{1}{2}$. Among the canids, it is possible to distinguish, even though not sharply, wolves and foxes, on the basis of minor features of the dentition.

The house dog is probably the oldest of man's domestications. Domestication has led to numerous breeds that differ from one another in many striking ways. Differences also concern the form of the skull and the dentition (Fig. 168). The dentitional relations of the various breeds have been investigated in many studies by veterinary anatomists.

Canids extend back to the Eocene. They are particularly well represented in the Miocene and the Pliocene. In part they were bulky animals of considerable size, with insignificant differentiation of the carnassials but with the full complement of molars. These forms were probably not purely carnivorous; they might represent sidelines of canid evolution.

The procyonids are small, arboreal forms, restricted to the New World; corresponding to their omnivorous diet there is no pronounced development of the carnassials. Fossil representatives reach back to the Lower Miocene in North America. The procyonids reached South America only in the Late Pliocene.

The ursids are, like the procyonids, mainly omnivorous. They are distinguished from the latter, aside from greater body size and generally

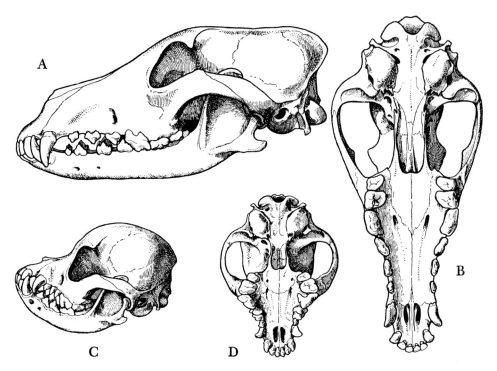

FIG. 168.—Dentitions of domesticated dog breeds: *A* and *B*, skull of a greyhound; *C* and *D*, skull of a pug. From Ellenberger and Baum, *Handbuch der Vergleichenden Anatomie der Haustiere*, 18th ed. (Berlin: Springer Verlag, 1943), by permission.

nonarboreal mode of life, also by the dentition. The last upper molar has been lost. The remaining molars have, for example in the cave bear, been elongated as a compensation, since the exclusive herbivorous diet required considerable capacity for mastication. The cave bear molars are characterized by notable wrinkling of the enamel. In what must be regarded as one of the most outstanding comparative anatomical studies ever published, Davis (1964) came to a different conclusion about the character of the enlarged, highly wrinkled molars of the cave bear and the giant panda, *Ailuropoda melanoleuca*. This animal is, as Davis has convincingly demonstrated, an "exaggerated" bear rather than a procyonid as has often been suggested primarily on the basis of the dentition alone. Davis found that the enlargement of the crown relief of the molars is a function of the skull and/or tooth size in *Ursus*. Premolar elements degenerate progressively with increased skull size among the species of *Ursus*; the molar crown pattern becomes increasingly elaborate as absolute tooth size increases. Davis furnishes convincing evidence that the cheek tooth battery in *Ailuropoda* differentiated as a whole unit, rather than in individual tooth elements. He suggests that selection acted on a morphogenetic field that included the entire cheek tooth row, with the result that all units in the field are enlarged to the same relative degree (Fig. 169). Under this interpretation the complicated molar crown pattern of *Ailuropoda* was thus not selected for in conjunction with an exclusively herbivorous diet (bamboo shoots), but represents merely a function of the pronounced overall size increase in the cheek teeth generally.

In the genus *Melursus* (India and Ceylon) the lips are large and unusually movable, the tongue is notably protrusible in adaptation to a diet of insects, honey and fruits. With the differentiation of the soft parts the inner upper incisors have been lost.

Pinnipedia

The sea lions, the walrus and the seals have been greatly modified by numerous adaptations for life in the sea, but from their overall organization there can be no doubt that they belong to the carnivores. The modifications that affected the dentition show the same essential direction as in the cetaceans: a simplification of the forms of the premolars and molars. This simplification is probably related to the difficulty of performing a true chewing act under water.

Simplification of the dentition took place in different ways in the different families (Fig. 170). In the otariids an upper incisor has been lost, but above, there are five postcanine teeth, below six. The milk dentition is changed a few weeks after birth and in many seals does not erupt at all but

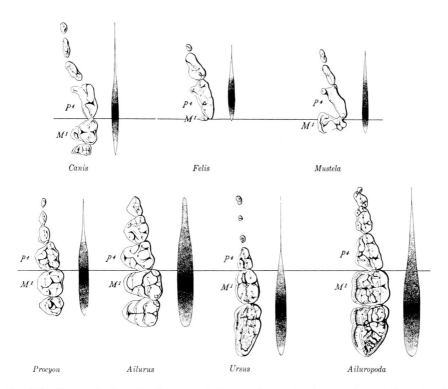

Fɪɢ. 169.—Upper cheek teeth of representative carnivores showing varying gradients in the premolar-molar field. From Davis (1964).

Fɪɢ. 170.—Secondarily triconodont cheek teeth of the seal *Leptonychotes weddelli*. After Osborn, from Weber, *Die Säugetiere* (Jena: Gustav Fischer Verlag, 1928), by permission.

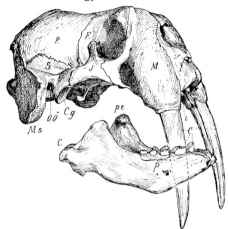

FIG. 171.—Skull of a walrus, *Odobenus rosmarus: M, maxilla; I.* premaxilla; *C,* canines; *i,* incisors. From Weber, *Die Säugetiere* 1928), (Jena: Gustav Fischer Verlag, 1928), by permission.

is resorbed already *in utero*. The walrus (Fig. 171) has above and below three incisors and enormously enlarged, permanently growing canines. The loss of the first premolar is related to the great development of the canines. The other teeth are small, blunt and single-rooted. In part, they fall out early in life.

In the form of their post-canine teeth the seals, at least in the subfamily Phocinae, have retained somewhat more original conditions in that lateral cusps are still present. Such teeth are thus secondarily triconodont, because there is no doubt that this form has evolved from a more complicated structure of the molars and premolars by simplification. In the Cystophorinae or hooded seals the cheek teeth are small and single-cusped.

Condylarthra

As long as only the modern forms of hooved mammals (ungulates) were concerned, their systematic grouping posed no difficulties. When, however, in the past hundred years a wealth of extinct more or less closely related relatives of the ungulates became known from the early Tertiary, difficulties arose. It was first thought that a stem group could be delimited from which all later ungulates had evolved. However, as more material became known and these old forms became better known, the systematists became more reserved in drawing connecting links. The ancient forms lack all characters of specialization in the particular directions that are typical for the later mammalian orders. The fossil record now available shows quite well how the earliest ungulates were organized. Yet it is not possible at this time, in the judgment of leading authorities, to delimit in a satisfactory way an inclusive group of ancient ungulates that includes all later forms, and to relate the earliest representatives of the different orders with certainty to particular genera of such an ancient group.

In the older classifications of the modern mammals, great weight was attached to the distinction between unguiculates (forms with claws) and ungulates (forms with hooves). Later, fossils showed that there are both ungulates with claws and early carnivores with end phalanges that indicate the original presence of hoof-like structures.

In addition to the few modern groups of ungulates, there is a great variety of extinct forms that belong to the hooved mammals in the broadest sense of the term.

Since the following presentation is not addressed to paleontologists particularly, but seeks a broader circle of readers, the grouping of the different orders will not follow purely paleontological viewpoints. It attempts to simplify somewhat the picture by a slightly changed presentation.

The condylarths are the Paleocene and Eocene mammals formerly considered as the stem group of all later ungulates. The best known genus, *Phenacodus* (Fig. 172) is available in whole skeletons. In its proportions and in the structure of its skull, *Phenacodus* recalls a creodont more than an ungulate, even though it had hooves. The dentition has the formula $\frac{3\ 1\ 4\ 3}{3\ 1\ 4\ 3}$. The molars are brachyodont and bunodont, six-cusped above and below. The anterior premolars are simple, the posterior upper ones tribosphenic. The canines were fairly large. Only a small diastema is present above between the incisors and the canines, and below between the canines and the first premolars.

Of other condylarths, only *Hyopsidus*, *Meniscotherium* and *Didolodus* may be mentioned. In *Meniscotherium* the cusps of the molars were selenodont (Gazin, 1965). The end phalanges, however, bore claws rather than hooves. *Didolodus* is interesting because this Paleocene form is the best known condylarth so far found in South America (Simpson, 1948).

Broadly allied to the condylarths, although no reliable genetic relations

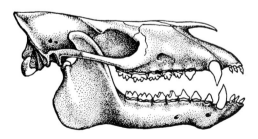

Fig. 172.—Skull of the Lower Eocene condylarth *Phenacodus*, about ⅓ natural size. After Cope, from Romer (1945).

are known, are two orders from the Paleocene and Eocene mainly of North America, the Amblypoda and the Dinocerata.

Amblypoda

The oldest known amblypod, *Pantolambda* from the Paleocene, was about the size of a sheep. Its molars are of very simple structure, the canines are moderately enlarged. The amblypods of the Upper Paleocene and the Eocene reached notable size. *Coryphodon,* a large form from the Eocene, is known also from Europe. Its teeth appear to be specialized compared to *Pantolambda.* Simons (1960) has written a monograph on the Paleocene pantodonts.

Dinocerata

The uintatheres (Fig. 173), first known from the Late Paleocene of North America, reached an even greater size than the amblypods. In the Upper Eocene there, *Uintatherium* (see H. Wheeler, 1961, for a recent review) attained the size of an African *Rhinoceros.* The name "Dinocerata" refers to the presence of large bony protuberances on the nasal bones, the maxillae and the parietals. In the dentition the upper incisors are usually missing. In the male the canines are much enlarged. The upper molars have two transversal crests converging inward; behind them is a hypocone (Fig. 174).

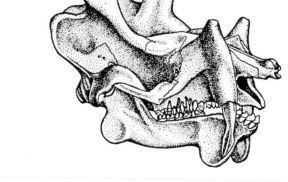

Fig. 173.—Skull of the Eocene dinocerate *Uintatherium,* about $\frac{1}{12}$ natural size. After Marsh, from Romer (1945).

Fig. 174.—Upper cheek teeth of *Uintatherium,* about $\frac{5}{12}$ natural size. After Osborn, from Romer (1945).

According to Romer (1945), whose presentation I follow, the Dinocerata are not especially closely related to the Amblypoda. Certain similarities, for example in the hand and foot, are interpreted as similar adaptations to the heavy body build.

Outside of North America the only finds known so far are from the Upper Eocene of East Asia, for example *Gobiatherium*. This situation shows how little we know of the history of this order.

Perissodactyla

Even if, among the modern mammals, the perissodactyls (unpaired hooves) and the artiodactyls (paired hooves) are grouped together as ungulates, this does not mean that they are closely related. Fossils show rather that the two groups have been separated during the entire Tertiary. Romer's statement is thus apropos: "strange as it may seem, a cow is, for example, probably as closely related to a lion as to a horse." While the earliest known artiodactyls may not be associated with the condylarths, very probably the perissodactyls are rooted in this group.

The condylarth genus *Tetraclaenodon* (*Euprotogonia*) corresponds to a high degree of the general ideas about the appearance of an ancient perissodactyl. The proportions of the limbs show that they are not yet specialized for fast walking as are those of the modern ungulates. The feet were plantigrade and pentadactyl. In the skull a series of characteristics, such as the moderate size of the brain case, the presence of a sagittal crest and the broad connection between the orbit and the temporal fossa, recall the creodonts and the insectivores.

Hippoidea

At the beginning of the famous horse series (Figs. 175 and 176) there is *Hyracotherium*, the famous eohippus of the Lower Eocene of North America and Europe. It ranked in size with a fox terrier. The tooth formula is, as always in primitive placentals, $\frac{3\ 1\ 4\ 3}{3\ 1\ 4\ 3}$. The molars were brachyodont and essentially still bunodont, but with a slight beginning of yoke formation. Above there are six cusps, below four. The anterior premolars are very simply constructed, the posterior-most has a triangular crown outline. The diastema (above between the third incisor and the canine, below between the canine and the anterior-most premolar) are not very extensive. The Palaeotheriidae are a side line that is mainly distributed in the Upper Eocene of Europe. *Palaeotherium* has already been described masterfully by Georges Cuvier from the Gypsum of the Montmartre.

Mesohippus from the North American Oligocene has the size of a German

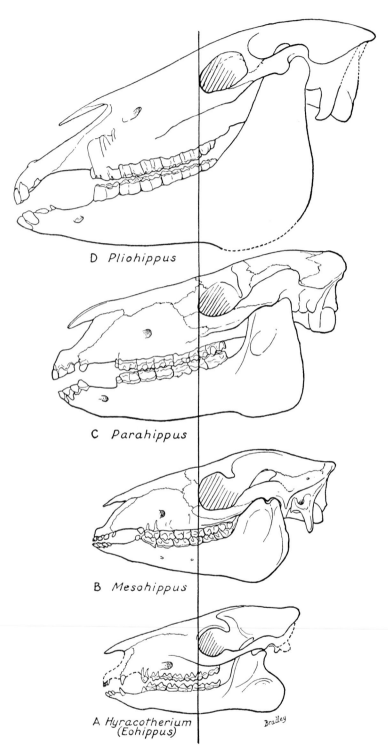

D *Pliohippus*

C *Parahippus*

B *Mesohippus*

A *Hyracotherium*
(*Eohippus*)

Bradley

FIG. 175.—Structural evolution of the horse skull. From W. K. Gregory, *Evolution Emerging*, vol. II (New York: The Macmillan Co., 1951) , by permission.

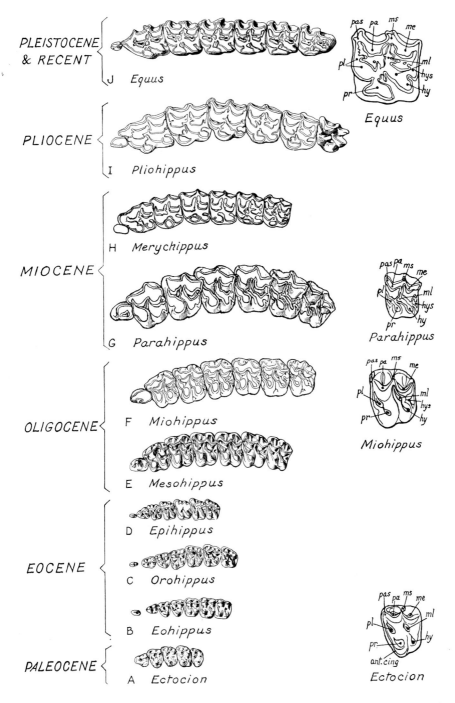

Fig. 176.—Horse series. Examples from the evolutionary sequence of the upper molars from the Paleocene to the Present. Designations of the tritubercular theory for the form elements of the premolar-molar pattern: *pr*, protocone; *pl*, protoconule; *pas*, parastyle; *pa*, paracone; *ms*, mesostyle; *me*, metacone; *ml*, metaconule; *hy*, hypocone; *ant. cing.*, anterior cingulum. From W. K. Gregory, *Evolution Emerging*, vol. II. (New York: The Macmillan Co., 1951), by permission.

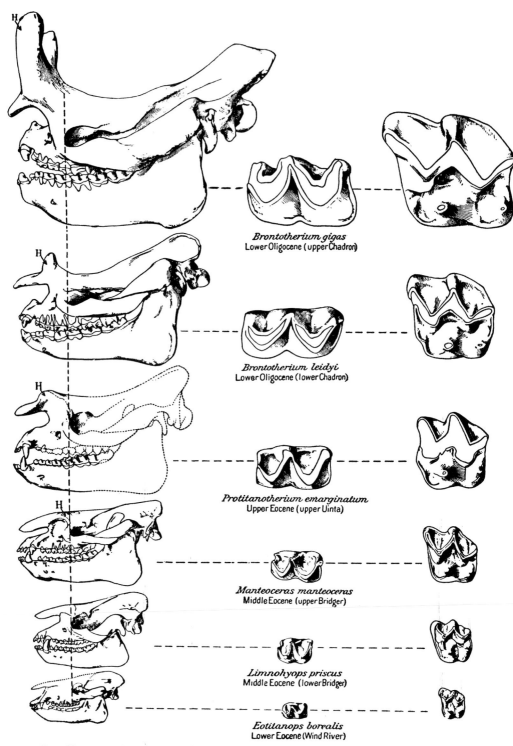

Brontotherium gigas
Lower Oligocene (upper Chadron)

Brontotherium leidyi
Lower Oligocene (lower Chadron)

Protitanotherium emarginatum
Upper Eocene (upper Uinta)

Manteoceras manteoceras
Middle Eocene (upper Bridger)

Limnohyops priscus
Middle Eocene (lower Bridger)

Eotitanops borealis
Lower Eocene (Wind River)

FIG. 177.—Evolution of the skull and molar patterns in the titanotheres. From W. K. Gregory, *Evolution Emerging,* vol. II (New York: The MacMillan Co., 1951), by permission.

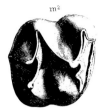

Fig. 178.—Second right upper and last right lower molars of the perissodactyl *Chalicotherium goldfussi*. 1:2.2. From Zittel, *Grundzüge der Paläontologie* (Munich and Berlin: Verlag R. Oldenbourg, 1923), by permission.

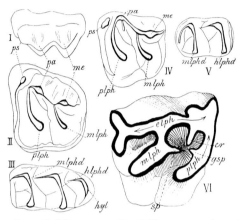

Fig. 179.—Molars of tapirs and rhinoceroses: I and II, upper molars of *Systemodon;* III, lower molar of same; IV, upper; V, lower molar of *Hyrachyus;* VI, upper molar of *Rhinoceros; cr,* crista; *elph,* ectoloph; *hlphd,* hypolophid; *hyl,* hypoconulid; *me,* metacone; *mlph,* metaloph; *mlphd,* metalophid, *pa,* paracone; *plph,* protoloph; *ps,* parastyle; *sp,* spur. From Weber, *Die Säugetiere* (Jena: Gustav Fischer Verlag, 1928), by permission.

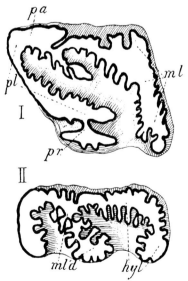

Fig. 180.—Enamel folding of the molars of the Pleistocene rhinoceros *Elasmotherium sibiricum:* I, upper molar; *ml,* metaloph; *pa* paracone; *pl,* protoloph; *pr,* protocone; II, lower molar; *hyl,* hypolophid; *mld,* metalophid. After Brandt, from Weber, *Die Säugetiere* (Jena: Gustav Fischer Verlag, 1928), by permission.

shepherd dog. The diastemas are more extensive, but the teeth are still brachyodont; the ectoloph is W-shaped in the upper molars, and the hypostyle is clearly protruding.

With the exception of the little P 1, the premolars have begun to resemble the molars, increasing the efficiency of the chewing action. *Anchiterium* is an equid, of about the same stage of differentiation as *Mesohippus,* that immigrated to Europe at the beginning of the Miocene.

In the presumed center of the evolution, North America, the genus *Parahippus* evolved. *Parahippus* is still brachyodont, but characterized by a beginning formation of crown cementum, by a connection of the hypocone with the outer yoke, and by further complications of the crown relief. *Parahippus* is interpreted as a transitional form between forest-dwelling and steppe-grazing horses.

Parahippus gave rise to *Merychippus,* the stem form of the modern horses (Stirton, 1940). It is already characterized by hypselodont teeth. According to Romer, this increase in height is related both to a more and more pronounced diet of Gramineae and to the general increase in overall size that had taken place since the early Tertiary (Fig. 175). *Merychippus* is followed by *Hipparion,* which became distributed over Asia and Europe, by *Hippidion* and *Onohippidum* that reached South America, and *Pliohippus. Pliohippus* gave rise to *Equus* (Pl. 86-a). Peculiarly, however, the horses died out completely in North America at the end of the Pleistocene. They were reintroduced by the Spaniards after the discovery of America. Accompanying the evolution of the dentition was the transformation of the limbs that led from the original plantigrade form to the present one-toed unguligrade condition. An overall account of the evolutionary picture of the horses has been written by Simpson (1951).

Titanotheriodea

The titanotheres (Fig. 177) are a group of perissodactyls formerly known only from North America. The end forms in the Oligocene reach giant size. The skull bore large horn-like protuberances. In contrast to the equids, however, the molars remained on an ancient bunolophodont level. The early extinction of the titanotheres has been related to this phenomenon.

Ancylopoda

The chalcotheres or ancylopods drew attention to themselves because they misled Cuvier to commit an interesting error. He interpreted large limb skeletons that bore powerful claws as the remains of a giant pangolin (*pangolin gigantesque*), confident in his principle of morphological correlation. When much later more complete remains were uncovered showing skull and limbs associated, it became evident that this animal, because of the structure of its skull and the character of its dentition, and despite the claws, has to be assigned to the perissodactyl ungulates (Fig. 178).

Tapiroidea

The two remaining groups of perissodactyls, the tapirs and the rhinoceroses, are characterized by the conservative structure of their molars (Fig. 179) that has remained so into the Present. Above there are an ectoloph, a strong protoloph and a metaloph; below two transversal yokes in the tapirs, two asymmetrical yokes in the rhinoceroses. In the Eocene tapir-like forms, the premolars are more simply constructed than the molars; in *Protapirus* from the Oligocene and in the tapirs already widely distributed in the Miocene, the premolars have become molariform. The structure of the limbs corresponds to the simple construction of the dentition.

The disjunct distribution of the modern tapirs suggests an earlier, much wider distribution; this conclusion has been proved correct by a large amount of fossil material.

Rhinoceroidea

What was said about the distribution of the tapirs applies equally to the rhinoceroses. The forms of the Eocene are notably smaller than those alive today, as would be expected. They were slender, relatively agile animals. The front foot inluded four toes. In the dentition the premolars had not yet assumed molar form. From these beginnings there evolved during the Tertiary a great wealth of differently constructed rhinoceroses: the Amynodontidae, with a mode of life resembling that of the hippopotamus; the short-legged *Teleoceras;* the giant *Baluchitherium;* the hornless *Aceratherium* of the Miocene; and the surviving genera of East Asia and Africa that may be distinguished by the differentiation of the horns. In the differentiation of their dentition all of these forms lack profound differences. *Elasmotherium* (Pleistocene, Eurasia) may be mentioned in this connection, since the molars are characterized by wrinkling of the enamel (Fig. 180).

Artiodactyla

As noted before, the evolutionary history of the unpaired- and paired-hoofed ungulates followed separate paths during the entire Tertiary period. The end forms of this evolution are in both cases highly specialized "modern" herbivores which, because of a similar mode of life, resemble one another in many respects, but exhibit far-reaching differences in the basic features of their organization. The earliest placental mammals were plantigrade. A faster mode of locomotion was achieved when, instead of the entire plantar face of the foot, only the toes and finally only the end phalanges were set to the ground. This development led to a reduction of the side toes that no longer touched the ground, which took place differently in the two orders. In the perissodactyls there finally remained only the third toe, in the artiodactyls, in contrast, the third and fourth. The primitive condition was in both cases a pentadactyl foot. Thus it is understandable that the terms paired-hoofed and unpaired-hoofed apply in most cases, but not always; thus the perissodactyl tapirs have four toes in the front foot, and a few very ancient artiodactyl genera have five. But the conditions referred to as "mesaxon" (axis of the foot lies within the third toe) and "paraxon" (axis lies between the third and fourth toes) are independent of the degree of reduction of the lateral digits.

Suina

To the difference in the structure of the limbs between perissodactyls and artiodactyls there corresponds an equally pronounced difference in the structure of the cheek teeth. The perissodactyls are mostly lophodont, that is, their molars show yoke formations (an outer yoke or ectoloph, an anterior yoke or protoloph, and a posterior yoke or metaloph). The artiodactyls, however, have either bunodont molars provided with cusps, as in the Suina, the pigs; or the tubercles have become half-moons and the molars are thus called selenodont, as in the ruminants. As already noted, the concave side of these half-moons faces outward in the upper molars, inward on the lower molars. This arrangement enables the efficient trituration necessary for the utilization of a diet consisting predominantly of grasses. The omnivorous Bunodontia resemble the stem forms more closely in the structure of the dentition. The limbs are also more primitive, in that they usually have four toes. In the dentition of the pig, the complete formula of the placental mammals, $\frac{3\ 1\ 4\ 3}{3\ 1\ 4\ 3}$, has been retained without any reduction whatsoever, a rare exception among the modern mammals.

Another primitive characteristic of the suids is the much simpler form of the premolars than the molars. The upper canines, or tusks, are characterized in the boar by continuous growth and are much stronger than in the female. They are curved outward and upward. The lower canines are triangular in cross section. In the American genus *Tayassu (Dicotyles)*, the peccary, the upper tusks are barely bent outward, and the posterior premolars are somewhat molariform.

Most striking are the upper tusks in *Babirussa* (Pl. 86-b). They lose contact with the lower canines, pierce the skin of the upper lip and, grow-

FIG. 181.—Complete cheek tooth series of the lower jaw of the fully grown warthog *Phacochoerus;* m_1 is completely worn down. Slightly enlarged. After Owen, from Weber, *Die Säugetiere* (Jena: Gustav Fischer Verlag, 1928), by permission.

ing permanently, describe a large arc over the snout. Peculiarly specialized are the molars of the African wart hog *Phacochoerus* (Fig. 181). M_1 and M_2 are soon worn down and fall out. The lower M_3 becomes a hypselodont tooth of such great mesio-distal extent that it borders the P_4. Following the drop-out of the anterior premolars, it finally remains as the only cheek tooth when P_4 has also been shed.

Von Köenigswald (1965) sugggested that the Siwalik pig *Tetraconodon*, which has unusually robust cheek teeth, may have evolved into a carrion feeder, in connection with the widespread occurrence of mass death and carcass accumulations, as a characteristic biotope in the Pontian (Pliocene) of Eurasia. The mouth of the hippopotamus (*Hippopotamus* and a dwarf form in Liberia) is characterized by a wide snout whose corner pegs are made up of the canines. The outermost incisor, still present in the Pleistocene ancestors (*Hexaprotodon*), has been lost in the permanent dentition. The cheek teeth, upon wear, assume a characteristic clover leaf shape which makes finds of individual teeth easily identifiable.

As noted earlier, the modern artiodactyls pose no great difficulties with respect to their major systematic grouping. Adequate clarifications of the natural grouping of the extremely numerous (and often still incompletely known) fossil forms has not yet been achieved. Depending on the characteristics used, the systematic arrangement varies from author to author. We shall again follow Romer. He contrasts with the ruminants the Suina, that is, the suids and hippopotamids and additionally a few extinct families, for example the Anthracotheriida and the Entelodontidae; but he assigns to a few ancient families, for example the Dichobunidae, as Palaeodonta, a separate position between the Suina and the Ruminantia.

The anthracotheriids are pig-like artiodactyls of notable size that were distributed in the Middle Tertiary of the Old World. They have sometimes been grouped together with the anoplotheriids as a separate group, Bunoselenodontia, because half-moon structures may occur on the two outer cusps of the molars; otherwise, however, the true suid characters seem to predominate.

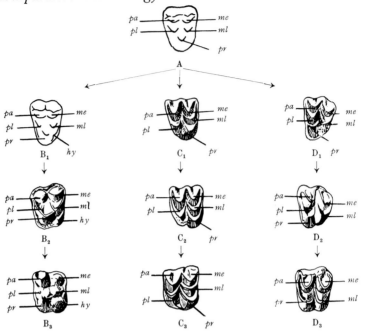

FIG. 182.—Different modes of origin of four-cusped artiodactyl molars from a five-cusped initial form with a triangular outline: (*B*) vertical series, Hypoconifera: from the cingulum a hypocone originates that forms the posterior inner cusp; (*C*) vertical series, Chaenotherioidea: the protoconule becomes the anterior, the protocone the posterior inner cusp; (*D*) vertical series, Euartiodactyla: the metaconule becomes the posterior inner cusp. After Stehlin and Abel, from Weber, *Die Säugetiere* (Jena: Gustav Fischer Verlag, 1928), by permission.

Ruminantia

Among the modern ruminants two groups of different size are distinguished, the Tylopoda and the Pecora. To the Pecora belong the Traguloidea, the Cervoidea (deer) and the Bovoidea (cattle).

In the ruminants the upper incisors are usually absent and so are the canines. The incisors of the mandible and the incisiviform canines that stand close to the incisors act against a strongly cornified palatal plate. This arrangement, in which a widely protrusible tongue may play a significant role, enables the rapid plucking of large quantities of grass. The food thus rapidly procured (in view of the ever present danger from aggressive predators) is leisurely regurgitated in a safe resting place, thoroughly mashed by mastication and then returned to the stomach for the second time. This process is made possible by the complicated mechanism of the ruminant stomach. The lower canines of the ruminants are incisiviform, except in the camelids where they are caniniform.

The upper molars of the modern artiodactyls, except in certain suids, are four-cusped. This number four of the selenodont elements has evolved in a variety of ways from the stem forms, documented by numerous finds of high geologic age. In these the teeth were triangular, but already equipped with the intermediate cusps protoconule and metaconule (Fig. 182). Above, the inner cusp was the protocone, the anterior outer cusp the paracone, the posterior outer cusp the metacone. The protoconule occurred as a later development between protocone and paracone, the metaconule as an intermediate cusp between metacone and protocone. Labially there was a cingulum, from which the outer pillar formations, the styli, originated later. Such a tooth has a rounded triangular form. The rectangular outline, as it is characteristic of the modern artiodactyls, evolved along three paths. In many other mammals a posterior inner cusp, a hypocone, originated from the cingulum. This path was followed only in rare cases among the early artiodactyls, for example in the Dichobunidae and in the Entelodontidae. These were thus grouped together by Stehlin and later by Abel as Hypoconifera.

A second modus, likewise restricted to a relatively small group, the Caenotheriidae, consisted in the inward migration of the protoconule, which thus became the lingual cusp of the upper molars. The protocone was thus displaced backward and became the posterior lingual cusp. In all other artiodactyls, which have been grouped together as Euarthiodactyla, a similar process took place; the metaconule, originally an intermediate cusp in a triangular molar form, was displaced inward and became the posterior lingual cusp. It is perfectly justifiable to attribute systematic significance to this feature. But the taxonomic value of such odontological characteristics should be carefully weighed against that of all other morphological characters.

The dentition of the camels is somewhat more primitive than that of the cervids and the bovids, in that it still has an upper incisor and behind it the canine. The stomach of the tylopods, furthermore, has not attained the complication of that of the ruminants. In the llamas of South America, the camels of Central Asia that were double-humped in the wild form have close relatives.

In the Tertiary, camels were widely distributed in North America. They may be traced into the Eocene. These old forms still had a complete dentition.

The American family Oreodontidae, which reaches back to the Eocene, had the height of its development in Oligocene time. In the Bad Lands of South Dakota, bones and teeth of these animals lie on the surface by the thousands. The limbs of the oreodontids are short and four-toed, the body-form pig-like; but the molars are selenodont, five-cusped in the earliest forms, four-cusped (by disappearance of the protoconule) in the later

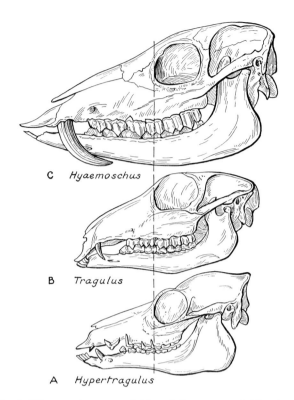

C   *Hyaemoschus*

B   *Tragulus*

A   *Hypertragulus*

FIG. 183.—Skulls of Oligocene hypertraguloid and Recent traguloids. From W. K. Gregory, *Evolution Emerging*, vol. II. (New York: The Macmillan Co., 1951), by permission.

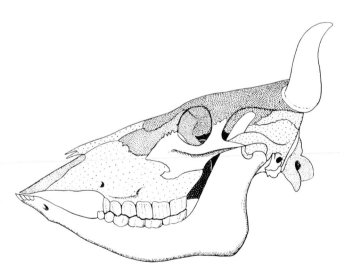

FIG. 184.—Skull of the cow. From Ellenberger and Baum, *Handbuch der Vergleichenden Anatomie der Haustiere*, 18th ed. (Berlin: Springer Verlag, 1943), by permission.

forms. In view of these anatomical peculiarities, the oreodontids have on occasion been called "ruminating pigs."

The North American Agriochoeridae had claws instead of hoofs, probably used for the digging of roots and bulbs.

The Xiphonodontidae are an Old World family. The genus *Xiphodon* from the Late Eocene Gypsum of the Montmartre was described by Cuvier. The upper molars are selenodont and five-cusped because of the presence of a protoconule. The lower canine is incisiviform. The function of the canine was taken over by the first premolar. In spite of the relatively high geologic age of the Xiphodontidae, the reduction of the toes II and V had already well progressed.

To the specialized artiodactyls belong, besides the large groups of the cervids and the bovids, two small, ancient, deer-like genera, *Hyemoschus*, living in West Africa (Fig. 183) and *Tragulus* (India, Ceylon, South East Asia). Including the extinct families Amphimerycidae, Hypertragulidae and Protoceratidae, the entire suite of forms is grouped together as Traguloidea by Romer. The modern tragulids chew the cud, although their stomach is less complicated than that of the bovids. Upper incisors are absent, as are antlers and horns; but the enlarged upper canines serve as weapons. In *Hyemoschus* metacarpals III and IV are not fused. Fossil forms show that the Traguloidea reach far back in time. In *Archaeomeryx* from the Eocene of Mongolia, the upper incisors and the upper canine are still present; the lower canine is aligned with the incisors. The function of a canine was taken over by the first premolar. This is also the case in the Protoceratidae, in which, in contrast to the modern tragulids, there developed grotesque bony protuberances on the skull.

Among the modern cervids, the small, Central-to-East-Asiatic musk deer resemble the tragulids although they lack antlers and are equipped with enlarged canines that serve as weapons. Many of the Palaeomerycidae (widely distributed in Miocene time) that gave rise to the antler-carrying deer lacked antlers themselves.

In most of the modern cervids, only the stag bears antlers. Among the fossil finds, teeth and jaws and antler remains are very much more common than whole skulls or even skeletons. Thus it is difficult in many cases to coordinate with certainty teeth and antlers. The differentiation of the dentition of the cervids is relatively modest.

In contrast to the Cervicornia, whose antlers (where present) are shed periodically, the Vellericornia (giraffe and okapi) have on the skull bony processes; the molars are brachyodont. Above, incisors and canines are absent. The lower canine is double-lobed in both animals. Fossil giraffids were distributed in the Pliocene and Pleistocene of southern Europe and

Asia; they were characterized by grotesque bony protuberances on the skull.

The bovids or cavicornia usually have on the skull a pair of bony projections that bear horns. In most cases both sexes have horns, but there are races in which both sexes are hornless. With the exception of *Antilocapra,* the North American pronghorn antelope, the horns are not shed.

The bovids are the youngest group of artiodactyls. Their evolution began near the end of the Miocene and reached great impetus in the Pliocene and Pleistocene. Today they are by far the most varied group of ungulates. Despite the great form variety in the bovids, the dentition is relatively uniform (Fig. 184). Differences involve mainly the degree of hypselodonty and in some cases the special form of the incisors.

Cetacea

The difficulties that a lung-breathing animal, moreover a mammal, had to overcome to maintain itself in the sea were extremely great. There is hardly a feature in the body of a cetacean that has not been affected by the adaptive transformations necessary to permit a permanently aquatic mode of life. Among the most evident phenomena are the mode of respiration and locomotion in the fluid medium. The nasal opening is displaced to the roof of the skull. In the whale it is incorrectly called "spouting hole": what is expelled in rapid and powerful exhaling is not a stream of water but respiratory air that contains a great deal of water vapor. Entrance of water to the lungs is prevented by automatically acting valves; the greater the water pressure, the tighter the closure of these valves. In correlation with an increase in the diving capability, numerous complex meshworks developed in the vascular system. Besides pressure regulation in the vessels, these make possible an increase in the blood volume, and thereby an oxygen reserve when respiration is interrupted during diving. The exclusively aquatic locomotion led, much as in fast-swimming fishes, to the near-perfect streamlining of the torpedo shape. The anterior limbs became functional fins, even though the basic skeletal construction of land-living vertebrates was retained. The hind limbs were lost except for a few vestiges that are not visible externally. The forelimbs (or fins) act only as steering devices in cetaceans. Forward propulsion of the body is effected by beating motions of a horizontally placed tail fin, which is not supported by skeletal structures. The dorsal fin, where present, is also supported only by a cartilage- and bone-free connective tissue core.

That the cetaceans have originated from land-living mammals has been demonstrated for a long time by comparative anatomical investigations. More recently, discoveries of fossil material fully confirmed this view.

Fossil remains of cetacea are often significant even when very fragmentary, because the degree of aquatic adaptation may be judged in an impressive way also from the structure of the dentition. As in the pinniped carnivores, so also in the Cetacea the transformation of the dentition took place in the direction of a simplification of the tooth form.

The oldest whale known to date, *Protocetus atavus* from the Egyptian Eocene (Fig. 185), still had a heterodontous dentition with the formula $\frac{3\ 1\ 4\ 3}{3\ 1\ 4\ 3}$. The molars still had a more complicated form than the premolars (Fig. 186). The bony outer nasal opening was already located farther back on the skull than in any land-living mammal, but it was not displaced backwards as far as in modern cetaceans. Otherwise the skull was similar to that

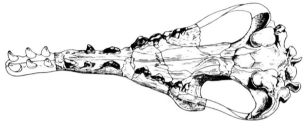

Fig. 185.—Skull of the Eocene ancient whale *Protocetus atavus*, seen obliquely from beneath. After Fraas, from Peyer (1937), in Bolk-Göppert-Kallius-Lubosch, *Handbuch der Vergleichenden Anatomie der Wirbeltiere* (Vienna and Berlin: Verlag Urban & Schwarzenberg, 1931–39), by permission.

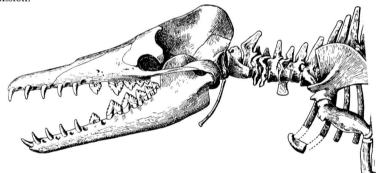

Fig. 186.—Skull of the ancient whale *Basilosaurus* (*Zeuglodon*) *osiris*. ⅟₁₃ natural size. After Stromer v. Reichenbach, from Zittel, *Grundzüge der Paläontologie* (Munich and Berlin: Verlag R. Oldenbourg, 1923), by permission.

Fig. 187.—Skull of the Miocene whale *Squalodon bariensis*. ⅟₁₂ natural size. After Doederlein, from Zittel, *Grundzüge der Paläontologie*, (Munich and Berlin: Verlag R. Oldenbourg, 1923), by permission.

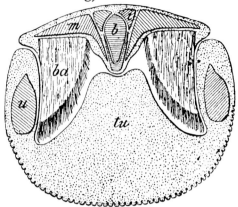

Fig. 188.—Cross-section through the anterior portion of the head of the finback *Balaenoptera: b,* cartilaginous nasal septum with vomer; *ba,* baleen; *i,* premaxilla; *m,* maxilla; *u,* lower jaw; *tu,* tongue. After Delage, from Weber, *Die Säugetiere* (Jena: Gustav Fischer Verlag, 1928), by permission.

of the creodonts. The peculiar changes that characterize the later cetacean skull had not yet occurred. These ancient whales, to which also *Basilosaurus* (better known as *Zeuglodon*) (Fig. 186) belongs, are grouped together as Archaeoceti.

The dominant whales of the Miocene were the so-called Squalodonti (from *squalus,* "shark"), so called because their teeth resemble those of the sharks *Carcharodon* or *Carcharhinus* (Fig. 187). In these forms a feature characteristic of the modern toothed whales has already evolved, the so-called telescoping of the skull. The maxillary bone is extended backwards over the frontal. It may even reach back to the supraoccipital, thus totally covering the parietal on the roof of the skull. In the baleen whales the maxilla is also extensive, but it merely sends a narrow process over the skull roof. A broad superficial covering does not take place. For this reason a few forms that do possess teeth are regarded as ancestors of the baleen whales. Unquestionable baleen whales, Mystacoceti, appear in the Miocene. There are three groups of them: the furrow whales or balaenopterids with throat furrows and separate neck vertebrae; the balaenids without throat furrows and with fused cervical vertebrae; and the thachianectids, intermediate between the former two, with few throat furrows and separate neck vertebrae (Fig. 188).

Etienne Geoffroy St. Hilaire could already in 1806 recognize a dentition in a foetus of a baleen whale. It is being resorbed, however, *in utero*. This is probably the anlage of the permanent dentition. The relations in the toothed ancestors of the baleen whales support this interpretation. Kükenthal (1889–93), however, regards this embryonic dentition as belonging to the milk dentition.

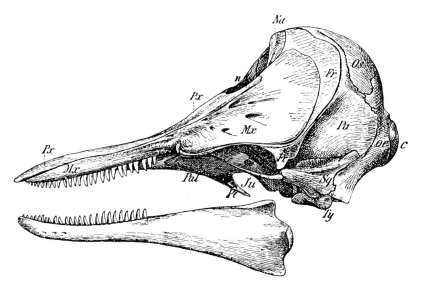

FIG. 189.—Skull of Delphinus, showing secondarily homodont dentition. After Boas, from Weber, *Die Säugetiere* (Jena: Gustav Fischer Verlag, 1928), by permission.

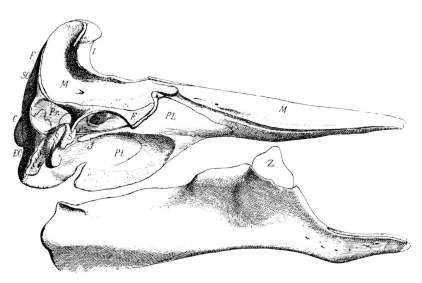

FIG. 190.—Skull of the tooth whale *Mesoplodon sechellense*: Z, single large tooth in the lower jaw. After van Beneden and Gervais, from Weber, *Die Säugetiere* (Jena: Gustav Fischer Verlag, 1928), by permission.

The baleen that furnishes the so-called "Fischbein" originates from the epidermal palatal crests. Their frayed edges form a wier in which small animals are trapped when the mouth is closed. The food consists mainly of plankton (Fig. 188).

The toothed whales whose skull construction has already been briefly mentioned have evolved in a very different way with respect to the dentition.

In the delphinids (in the narrower sense) there may occur 250 or more teeth in a long snout, all of them small and of pointed-conical form (Fig. 189). There is no question that the homodonty is secondary. How this considerable increase in the number of teeth, which in the Archaeoceti amounts to only 44, came about is not known. Other delphine-like forms as for example the "brown fish" *Phocaena*, have fewer teeth. In *Mesoplodon* (Fig. 190) each mandible bears only one, very much enlarged tooth, while the upper jaw is toothless. In the sperm whale *Physeter* only vestigial tooth anlagen are present in the upper jaw although the lower jaws bear extraordinarily large, powerful, conical teeth. According to Weber (1928), the alveoli for these teeth are incompletely developed. There is a more or less uniform furrow. A similar condition prevails in the pygmy sperm whale *Kogia*. These relations recall the condition in the ichthyosaurs of the Jurassic and Cretaceous, in which the formation of a continuous furrow is very pronounced. In the Triassic forms alveoli for the individual teeth were present.

A particular differentiation of the jaws that occurs also among fishes (see p. 109) and in ichthyosaurs (e.g., in the Liassic *Eurhinosaurus*) is found in the fossil *Eurhinodelphis*. It consists in the great elongation of the upper jaws beyond the tips of the mandible. O. Abel assumed that such a rostrum might have served for probing on the bottom.

A very extraordinary enlargement of a single tooth occurs in the male of the narwhal *Monodon* (Fig. 191); in this form the permanently growing, usually left, incisor may reach a length of over two meters. The right incisor remains hidden in the gingiva, as do both incisors of the female. This is probably the most extreme case of sexual dimorphism in the dentition.

Notoungulata, Litopterna Astrapotheria, Pyrotheria

Besides other fossils from the Pampas formation of Argentina, Charles Darwin brought back peculiarly curved, hyselodont teeth of a giant mammal which were subesequently described by Owen as *Toxodon* (from *toxon*, "arc"). Later it was found that not only the Pleistocene, but the entire Tertiary of South America contains a very rich fauna of almost exclusively endemic, now extinct mammals. With the exception of the primates, the

Xenarthra which will be described later, and a few marsupials, this fauna consists partly of ungulate-like forms, partly of peculiarly specialized mammals whose systematic affinities are not clearly determinable at this time, and which are thus treated as members of separate orders. The fossil material procured at first by Florentino and Carlos Ameghino, and later especially by expeditions of North American museums, permits a fair insight into the history of this extinct mammalian world, even though many questions remain unanswered.

It may be assumed confidently that the land connection between North and South America was interrupted at the beginning of the Tertiary period. Much as in Australia, where the monotremes and marsupials that arrived on that continent even earlier could achieve there a high degree of differentiation by isolation—free from the competition of more modern forms, so it became possible for these primitive mammals that had early found their way to South America to develop a varied fauna, because the superior carnivores and herbivores that had evolved outside of South America could no longer extend their ranges southward. Entry of the modern carnivores into South America took place much later in Tertiary time with the reconstitution of a land connection. It is possible that the extinction of the ancient herbivores of South America in the Pliocene and Pleistocene is related to this.

These zoo-geographic relations suggest that early in Tertiary time relatives of the South American ungulates also lived in North America. In *Arctostylops* (Fig. 192) such a form has indeed been recognized. An even notably earlier find from the upper Cretaceous of Mongolia, *Paleostylops*, shows that the group of primitive placental mammals, from which the South American "ungulates" arose, had an early differentiation and a wide geographic distribution.

Notoungulata

The most varied of the South American fossil hoofed mammals are the Notoungulata. Although their dentition shows many different features, it is possible to recognize a number of common characteristics. Reduction of the number of teeth is rather rare. Extensive diastemas occur only in a few very late forms. The teeth stand tightly crowded. There is a gradual transition in the form from the incisors to the molars. Premolars and molars are usually lophodont. The ectoloph is extensive; united with it under an acute angle is a robust protoloph. The small metaloph originates from the posterior end of the ectoloph. The geologically older forms are brachyodont, the younger ones may be hypselodont. From the great variety of forms only a few may be illustrated (Figs. 193 and 194).

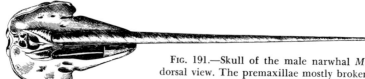

Fig. 191.—Skull of the male narwhal *Monodon monoceras* in dorsal view. The premaxillae mostly broken off to show the base of the large left and the vestigial tusks. From Peyer, *Die Zähne*, Verständliche Wissenschaft, vol. 79 (Berlin: Springer Verlag, 1963), by permission.

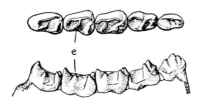

Fig. 192.—*Arctostylops*, a member of the otherwise almost exclusively South American, extinct ungulate order Notoungulata, from the Eocene of North America: $P_1 = P_4$ and M_1, views of the outer side and the chewing surfaces; *e*, the characteristic entoconid. After Matthew, from Romer (1945).

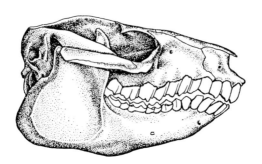

Fig. 193.—Skull of the Miocene notoungulate *Protypotherium*. About 6/10 natural size. After Sinclair, from Romer (1945).

Fig. 194.—Right upper and left lower tooth row of the Miocene notoungulate *Nesodon*. 1/4 natural size. After Scott, from Romer (1945).

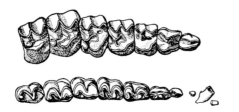

Fig. 195.—Upper and lower tooth rows of the litoptern *Diadiaphorus* from the Miocene of South America, which greatly resembles the horses in the structure of its limbs but is totally different from them in its dentition. After Ameghino, from Romer (1945).

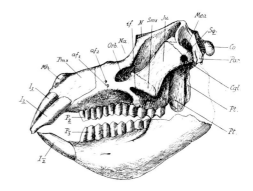

FIG. 196.—*Pyrotherium sorondoi*, a representative of a separate order of mammals from the Oligocene of Patagonia: *J*, the enlarged incisors; *p²*, the second upper; *p₃*, the third lower premolar. After Loomis, from Weber, *Die Säugetiere* (Jena: Gustav Fischer Verlag, 1928), by permission.

Litopterna

The not very numerous Litopterna are interesting because the reduction of the side toes has taken place much as in the horses. Already in the Miocene there was a genus in which the pencil bones are relatively smaller than in the modern horse. The dentition (Fig. 195) and the rest of the skeleton show, however, that instead of kinship, parallel evolution took place.

Pyrotheria

The relatively poorly known pyrotheria (Fig. 196) were large, elephant-like animals. But here again, there is no closer phyletic relationship.

Astrapotheria

The dentition of the Astrapotheria is peculiar (Pl. 87-a); the largest species of this group attained the dimensions of a rhinoceros. The upper incisors are absent, the upper and lower canines very much enlarged. Between them and the cheek teeth there is above and below each a large diastema. The position of the external nasal opening suggests the presence of a proboscis. How the dentition functioned in detail remains to be determined since similar, modern counterparts are lacking.

Xenarthra

Scaly anteater, anteater, armadillos and sloths, with their extinct relatives and the aardvark, *Orycteropus*, were united in early classifications as an order, Edentata, because the dentitions in these forms is either totally absent or very strongly reduced. This arrangement turned out, upon more intensive study, to be an unnatural conglomeration of heterogenous elements. The scaly anteater and *Orycteropus* became representatives of separate orders Pholidota and Tubulidentata.

It was found that the remaining families do form a natural group that has arisen from a common ancestry. Among other features they have in common an osteological characteristic that does not occur in any other mammal: in the lumbar region of the vertebral column there occur accessory processes in addition to the normal joint processes of the vertebral arches. The name "Xenarthra" alludes to this condition (from *xenos,* "foreign" and *arthron,* "joint").

The armadillos and their fossil relatives, the glyptodonts, the sloths and their extinct cohorts, the gravigrades, and the ant eaters are all mainly restricted to South America. What is true of the platyrrhinous primates, the notoungulates and the litopterns also applies to them: they are mammals whose ancestors had reached South America in early Tertiary time and could evolve there unmolested because of the isolation from North America and the rest of the world.

Near the end of the Tertiary, a land connection was reestablished. This led to an invasion of modern carnivores into South America and the extinction of some endemic forms, although others managed to maintain themselves; and to an immigration of hoofed mammals. In the opposite direction, some giant sloths, such as *Megalonyx,* reached deeply into North America, where they all died out. Among living forms, an armadillo extends into the southern United States and cebids into southern Mexico.

Among the Xenarthra, two subdivisions are distinguished: Hicanodonta (from *hikanos,* "adequate") and Anicanodonta. To the Hicanodonta belong the armadillos or Dasypodidae and their extinct relatives, the Glyptodontidae; to the Anicanodonta belong the sloths with their fossil relatives, the Gravigrada, and the less closely related Myrmecophagidae or ant eaters.

The Hicanodonta never have less then $\frac{7}{7}$ teeth. The greatest number of teeth, $\frac{26}{24}$, a total of 100, are present in the giant armadillo *Priodontes giganteus.* The reduction of the dentition affects primarily the anterior portion of the dentition. In *Dasypus novemcinctus* there are still an upper and two lower incisors. In the Dasypodidae there are also remains of the milk dentition. Most of the Anicanodonta have $\frac{5}{4}$ teeth. The Myrmecophagidae are entirely toothless. Interpretation of additional small deciduous denticles observed in *Bradypus* and in *Choloepus* is controversial.

Functionally the Xenarthra have become monophyodont. Their tooth forms are very simple. The dentition is almost or entirely homodont. An enamel layer is always absent. The dentine is surrounded on the outside by cementum. In the interior of the tooth there often occurs—in contrast to other mammal teeth, where the pulp cavity is smooth-walled and filled with soft tissues—a hard substance containing vessels, as already described by Owen for *Mylodon.*

True root formations never occur in Xenarthra. The pulp cavity generally remains wide open basally. The teeth grow permanently; thereby the reduction in the dentition is somewhat compensated.

Among the modern Dasypodidae, the closed jugular arch and the jaw musculature show that the dentition retains considerable functional significance. A genus from the Miocene, *Peltephilus*, still has incisors above and below.

The extinct glyptodonts are specialized compared to the armadillos with respect to their armor; instead of larger shields with moveable straps between them, the armor has become a rigid unit. The glyptodonts have $\frac{8}{8}$ teeth; the posterior ones are multilobed. The ramus of the mandible ascends very steeply and is unusually high (Pl. 86-c).

The modern sloths live high in the trees and feed on leaves. The well known multiplication of the cervical vertebrae, which represents an increase in the moveability of the neck, is probably related to this arboreal mode of life. They possess $\frac{5}{4}$ cylindrical teeth. In *Choloepus*, the two-toed sloth, the anterior-most tooth is separated from the others by a diastema; in *Bradypus*, the three-toed sloth, the teeth stand in a closed series.

Besides the simple dentition, the very complicated stomach contributes to the utilization of the leaf diet. The relatively strong jugal has a large ventrally directed process that does not reach the squamosal. It is assumed that the transition to phyllophagy, that is, to an exclusive leaf diet, halted further reduction of the dentition.

Extinct relatives of the sloths are the gravigrades or ground sloths. A few of their representatives reach giant size in the Pleistocene, for example, *Megatherium*, the giant sloth of the Argentinian Pampas formation. It probably fed on subsurface parts of vegetation, which were scratched out of the ground with enormous claws. Related to it are *Megalonyx, Mylodon* and others (Fig. 197). As is true of the modern sloths, the ground sloths had $\frac{5}{4}$ teeth. The jugular arch is interrupted; on the jugal bone there is a large ventrally directed process, much as in the glyptodonts (see above). The special importance of this process is not known.

The anteaters are totally toothless. In connection with this toothlessness virtually nothing is left of the jugular arch. Jugal and squamosum are separated from one another by a wide space. The lower jaw has become a slender rod. The musculature that serves the movement of the long tongue has attained an enormous measure, reaching clear to the xiphisternum.

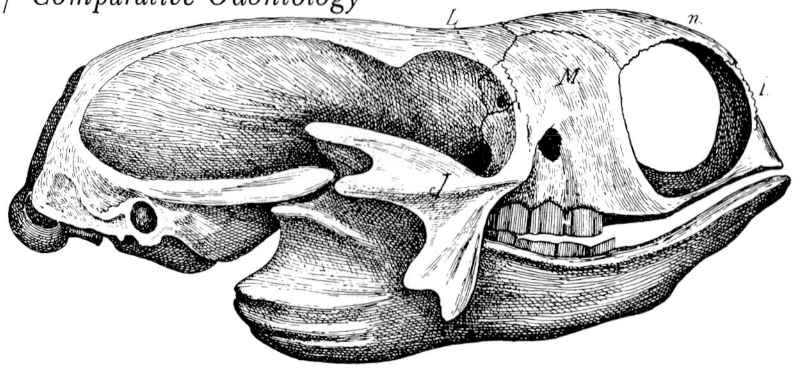

FIG. 197.—Skull of *Grypotherium darwini,* a relative of *Megatherium* which still lived with man in Patagonia. ⅔ natural size. After Burmeister, from Weber, *Die Säugetiere* (Jena: Gustav Fischer Verlag, 1928) , by permission.

Pholidota

The order Pholidota was created in connection with the division of the Edentata in three separate groups, and includes only scaly anteaters that all belong to the genus *Manis.* One of the Greek expressions for scale is *pholis;* it was preferred to the Latin *squama,* since the lizards and snakes are already called Squamata. The name "scaly anteater" ("Schuppentier" in German) is fitting for these mammals. Although horny scales occur in other mammals also, they are nowhere present in such perfection as in *Manis.* Their distribution is restricted to the tropical parts of Southeast Asia and Africa.

The diet consists of termites. In connection with this diet, morphological specializations have occurred. The dentition was lost except for a short period during embryonic development. With the reduction of the masticatory musculature, the jugular arch disappeared except for insignificant vestiges. The lower jaw became a slender bony rod (Fig. 198) . The skull is externally very similar to that of the anteaters, but this similarity does not reflect kinship, as is evident from the different arrangement of the musculature that serves the moving of the very long worm-like tongue, present in both cases, and which reaches all the way to the end of the xiphisternum. The stomach of *Manis* is, although of simple external form, very complicated in its structure. It recalls the bird stomach and is not only equipped with glands, but also with a cornified trituration organ. Except for these specializations, the anatomy of *Manis* satisfies in every respect our ideas of a generalized, ancient mammal. For this reason, it was not possible to include *Manis* in one of the larger mammal orders. Nothing is known of the prehistory of this genus except for a few remains from the youngest Tertiary, since Cuvier's "pangolin gigantesque" turned out to be a perissodactyl ungulate.

Tubulidentata

Like *Manis, Orycteropus* became the representative of a separate order, Tubulidentata, when the former order Edentata was revised.

Orycteropus, the aardvark, is distributed (three species) over large parts of Africa. Its diet consists of termites. So-called scraping claws, morphologically interpreted sometimes as hooves and sometimes as claws, are used to tear down termite nests, but the animals are also excellent burrowers. Corresponding to the character of the food, the masticatory musculature is only weakly developed. The temporal fossa, in broad connection with the orbit, is not very extensive. Since the anterior portion of the dentition is reduced, the premaxillae are small. The jugal is well developed, the jugular arch not interrupted. The simply formed teeth are columnar, rootless, and permanently growing. They have no enamel. The dentine is surrounded by a coat of cementum. The data concerning the number of teeth vary because many of the teeth drop out early. But the number of teeth formed in anlagen is extraordinarily great. In one embryo 12 milk teeth were found in the upper jaw, 14 in the lower. Of replacement teeth there was found, according to Weber, the third to sixth premolars and behind them indications of at least four molars in the upper jaw; in the lower jaw the 2. to 6. premolars and behind them indications of 5 molars. Broom (1907) writes the formula of the dention of *Orycteropus* as follows:

1. 2. 3.–1.–1. 2. 3. 4. 5. 6.   From this set there remain

       ?. 3. 4. 5. 6.–1. 2. 3. 4. 5.   in the permanent dentition

---

        2. 3. 4. 5. 6.–1. 2. 3. 4. 5.   above and below only four or

1. 2. 3.–1.–1. 2. 3. 4. 5. 6.   five teeth each.

The name Tublidentata relates to the peculiar structure of the teeth. These consist of a number of vertically oriented, six-sided prisms of which each is penetrated in the center by a narrow pulp cavity. From the pulp cavity dentinal tubules enter the dentine of the prisms (Fig. 199). These

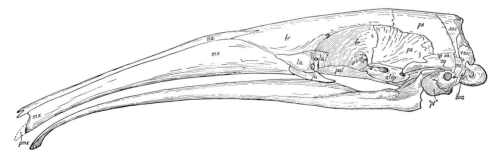

Fig. 198.—Skull of the totally toothless ant eater *Myrmecophaga* in side view. From W. K. Gregory, *Evolution Emerging,* (New York: The Macmillan Co., 1951), by permission.

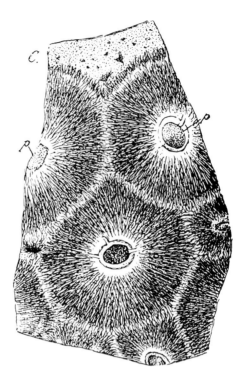

FIG. 199.—Cross-section through a tooth of *Orycteropus afer: p,* cross sections of the pulp cavity diverticula, which ascend the tooth, surrounded by polygonal dentine columns and from which dentinal tubules enter into the dentine; *C,* cementum. After Duvernoy, from Weber, *Die Säugetiere* (Jena: Gustav Fischer Verlag, 1928), by permission.

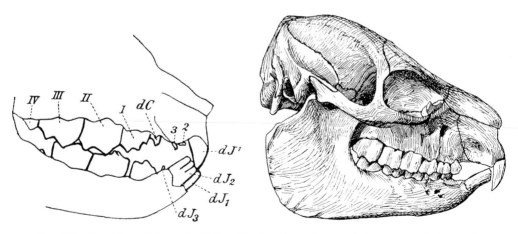

FIG. 200.—Dentition of *Procavia.* Left, milk dentition of *Procavia kamerunensis larae,* after Brauer; *right,* skull of *Procavia capensis,* adult; 1:1.1. From Weber, *Die Säugetiere* (Jena: Gustav Fischer Verlag, 1928), by permission.

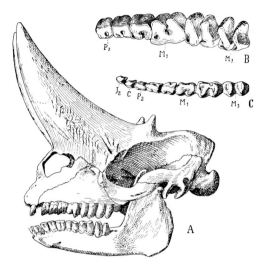

FIG. 201.—*Arsinotherium zitteli* from the Oligocene of Europe: *A*, skull in lateral view, about 1:13; *B*, upper; *C*, lower tooth rows; about 1:8. After E. W. Andrews from Zittel, *Grundzüge der Paläontologie* (Munich and Berlin: Verlag R. Oldenbourg, 1923), by permission.

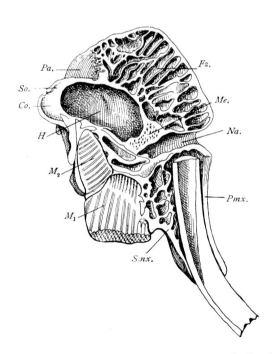

FIG. 202.—Skull of the Indian elephant *Elephas maximus*, cut sagittally: M_1 and M_2, first and second molars; *Na*, nasal cavity; *pmx*, premaxilla; *smx*, maxilla. After Zittel, from Weber, *Die Säugetiere* (Jena: Gustav Fischer Verlag, 1928), by permission.

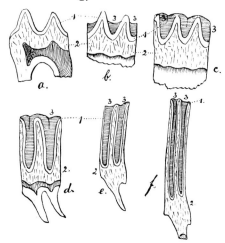

FIG. 203.—Formation of lamellae in elephant molars: 1, enamel; 2, dentine; 3, cementum; *a*, *Mastodon americanus*; *b*, *Stegodon ganesa*; *c*, *Elephas insignis*; *d*, *Elephas planifrons*; *e*, *Elephas hysudricus*; *f*, *Elephas maximus*. After Cope, from Weber, *Die Säugetiere* (Jena: Gustav Fischer Verlag, 1928), by permission.

structures appear to originate from a uniform tooth anlage (Anthony, 1934).

Unquestionable fossil remains of *Orycteropus* are known from the younger Tertiary of Samos, from France and Switzerland. *Palaeorycteropus* from the Eocene and Oligocene are not, according to Romer, certainly referable to this group. The tubulidentates must, however, undoubtedly reach far back in time. The overall generalized organization of the living species and particularly the dentition with the large number of tooth anlagen support this conclusion.

Subungulata

The four mammal orders, the Hyracoidea, the extinct Embrithopoda, the Proboscidea and the Sirenia differ greatly from one another in their mode of life and habitus. Anatomical investigations showed, however, re-markable correspondences in many features and that they exhibit certain resemblances to the ungulates. They are thus gathered together as sub-ungulates.

Hyracoidea

The modern Hyracoidea all belong to the genus *Procavia* (formerly *Hyrax*). They are distributed over Africa, Arabia, Israel and Syria. The fossil forms had about the same original area of distribution as the subungulates in general.

The dentition of *Procavia* (Fig. 200; Pl. 88-a) is of great interest in several respects. The first upper and the first and second lower incisors are enlarged as gnawing teeth and grow permanently. The upper incisor of *Procavia* differs, however, from the gnawing teeth of rodents in its triangular cross section. The lower incisors show, somewhat as in *Cynocephalus* but not as pronounced, three to four notches. It was recognized early that the lophodont molars recall formally the molars of *Rhinoceros* in miniature. Within the genus *Procavia* there occur notable brachyodont and hypselodont forms. The complete milk dentition contains three incisors, a canine and four premolars. In the permanent dentition I^2, I^3, and I_3 are missing as well as the canines. Of the extinct forms, *Pliohyrax* is known from the Pliocene of Pikermi (Greece). *Geniohyus* has on the inner side of the mandible a large pit whose significance is not known.

Embrithopoda

So far, the only representative of this order is the giant *Arsinotherium zitteli* from the lower Oligocene of the Fayum. Its dentition has the formula $\frac{3\ 1\ 4\ 3}{3\ 1\ 4\ 3}$. The teeth are lophodont and hypselodont. They stand tightly crowded. The form of the premolars is very different from that of the molars (Fig. 201).

Proboscidea

The elephants are called Proboscidea because they have a proboscis, a trunk, that functions, so to speak, as a fifth extremity. The high level of intelligence of the proboscideans may be correlated with this apparatus. The notable size and peculiar form of the skull is determined both by the condition of the dentition and by the differentiation of the trunk. The external bony nasal opening has been displaced upward and backward.

The musculature of the trunk requires attachment surfaces on the skull bones. Moving the mighty tusks and the heavy cheek teeth imposed even greater requirements on the musculature. Finally, the skull form was also influenced by the places of insertion of those portions of the thoracic musculature which serves the movement of the head. All this led to an enlargement of the skull that surpasses by far the capacity necessary to house the brain and the sense organs. Compared to the total skull size, the brain cavity is relatively small, as shown in Figure 202. The extremely thick skull wall is highly pneumatized, that is, provided with air-filled cavities.

The dentition consists of the tusks, present only in the upper jaw, and the cheek teeth. That the tusks are incisors follows from their position in the premaxilla; Goethe still considered them as canines. The permanent tusk is preceded by a milk tusk that is shed after the age of one year. The growth of the tusks is permanent. In the large-eared African elephant bulls, the tusks may reach a length of three meters; in the cows they are weaker. In the Ceylon race of the Indian elephant they may even be missing. An enamel cover is found only at the tip and is soon worn off. Otherwise, the tusk consists of dentine which, according to Mummery (1924), contains about twice the amount of organic substance as does human dentine. The permanent growth of the tusks is made apparent by the fact that bullets have been found within them and, in one instance (Pl. 87-b), even an iron spear point. As ivory, the dentine of the elephant tusks has found a great variety of uses. The elasticity of ivory results from a particular arrangement of the dentinal tubules.

The cheek teeth are separated from the tusks by a wide diastema. In each half of the jaws there is a total of only 6 cheek teeth. Of these the three earliest are milk teeth, the three following permanent molars. They are composed of a different number of antero-posteriorly arranged transversal lamellae. A lamella consists of a core of dentine, surrounded by a layer of enamel. In the narrow, deep valleys between the lamellae, tooth cementum is deposited. Since enamel, dentine and cementum differ in hardness, they are worn at different rates, resulting in the presence of a rough chewing surface at all times during the wear of a tooth (Fig. 203).

The number of lamellae (Fig. 204) increases from the first-appearing to the last tooth. It amounts in the African elephant to 3, 6, 7, 7, 8, 10; in the Indian elephant to 4, 8, 12, 13, 12–14, 16–18, 18–24. In the last upper molar of the mammoth it may reach 27–30. In the Indian elephant the lamellae, prior to wear, appear to be differentiated into denticuli or digitelli.

Only a single cheek tooth and the anterior portion of the one following next (in each quadrant) are functional at a time. Since the chewing surface lies oblique to the orientation of the lamellae, each tooth can be worn down to almost the last remains, which is of vital importance in view of the restricted number of teeth. The replacement does not take place, as is generally true in mammals, in vertical direction, but from the back of the jaw foreward. Tooth replacement is thus horizontal.

The only living proboscideans are the African elephant *Loxodonta africana* and the Indian Elephant *Elephas maximus*. The mammoth *Elephas primigenius* was a contemporary of stone-age man. In the Pliocene and Miocene there lived a whole host of proboscideans. The oldest genus, so far known, *Moeritherium* (Fig. 205), was found in the Upper Eocene of the Fayum. Its dental formula is $\dfrac{3\ 1\ 3\ 3}{2\ 0\ 3\ 3}$. In comparison to the primitive formula, there have already been reductions that correspond to diastemata,

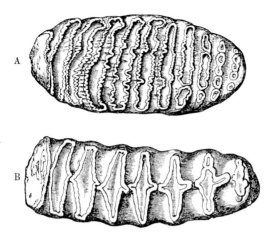

FIG. 204.—Elephant molars: *A*, upper molar of the Indian elephant *Elephas maximus; B,* upper molar of the African elephant *Loxodonta africana.* About 1:3.4. After Owen, from Weber, *Die Säugetiere* (Jena: Gustav Fischer Verlag, 1928), by permission.

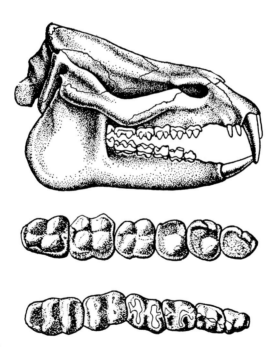

FIG. 205.—*Moeritherium,* the oldest proboscidian, from the early Tertiary of Egypt. *Above,* skull in lateral view; *middle,* upper cheek teeth; *below,* lower cheek teeth. Redrawn from Romer (1945).

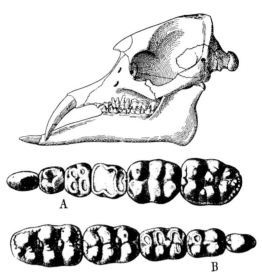

FIG. 206.—*Palaeomastodon*, a proboscidian from the Oligocene of Egypt. Skull about 1:11; *A*, upper; *B*, lower cheek teeth; about 1:3.5. From Zittel, *Grundzüge der Paläontologie* (Munich and Berlin: Verlag R. Oldenbourg, 1923) , by permission.

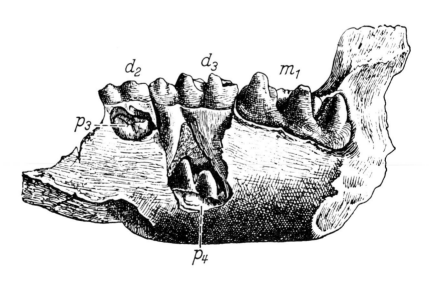

FIG. 207.—Vertical tooth replacement in *Mastodon*. After Lartet, redrawn from Zittel, *Grunazüge der Paläontologie* (Munich and Berlin: Verlag R. Oldenbourg, 1923) , by permission.

above between canine and premolars, below between tusk and premolars. The upper and lower second incisors have become tusks, but the enlargement is moderate. The brachyodont cheek teeth have four cusps that form two yokes. Thus this earliest proboscidean does not fulfill the expectations of Bolk's theory (see p. 185). Tooth replacement was still vertical. The transition to the horizontal mode of replacement took place late in geologic time.

The skull of *Moeritherium* is still elongated. Corresponding to its geologic age, *Moeritherium* does not belong to the archaic placental mammals of the earliest Tertiary; it shows already clear beginnings of specializations that led, during evolution, to the mastodonts and the elephants. The external bony nasal opening already lies farther back on the skull than should be otherwise expected. Thus it was possible to associate the highly differentiated end form of the Present with a skull type that had hardly deviated from the more normal form of the mammalian skull. In the abbreviated presentation of this evolution, primarily restricted to the dentition, I shall follow mainly Romer (1945).

The lower Oligocene genera *Palaeomastodon* (Fig. 206) and *Phiomia* that follow *Moeritherium* in Egypt are somewhat larger and more specialized. The external bony nasal opening has been displaced farther backward and upward. The tusks are stronger and the other incisors have been lost. The number of the cross yokes has increased to three. To these, accessory cusp formations have been added in *Phiomia*. Among the following mastodonts two evolutionary series may be distinguished; these have been described as "suid" and as "tapiroid."

The tapiroid forms (*Mastodon*[1] *tapiroides* in the Miocene, *Mastodon borsoni* in the Oligocene) led to *M. americanum*. In both evolutionary series the mandible becomes shortened and the lower tusks atrophy. The upper tusks, however, reach considerable length. Representatives of both lines reached North and South America (Simpson and De Paula Couto, 1957) where they became extinct much later than the European mastodonts (Fig. 207). However elephant-like the later mastodonts may look, the elephants cannot be derived from them directly. The oldest already elephant-like genus is *Stegodon* from the Pliocene of Asia. In this form the transition of the vertical to the horizontal tooth replacement, one of the most important distinguishing characters, has taken place. The mandible is very short.

From *Stegodon* evolved the African and Indian elephants, the mammoth

---

[1] In the strict application of the rules of nomenclature, *Mastodon* should be replaced with *Mammut* which, however, is bound to lead to confusion. For simplicity and clarity the generic name *Mastodon* is here retained.

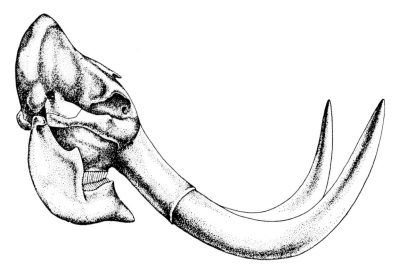

FIG. 208.—Skull of the mammoth, *Mammuthus primigenius*. 1/20 natural size. From Romer (1945).

FIG. 209.—Skull of the late Miocene proboscidian *Dinotherium;* molar, view from the chewing surface. Skull 1/17, molar about 1/5 natural size. After Gaudry and Andrews, from Romer (1945).

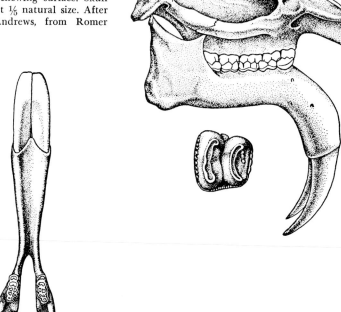

FIG. 210.—Lower jaw of the Pliocene proboscidian *Amebelodon*. 1/28 natural size. After E. H. Barbour, from Romer (1945).

(Fig. 208) and the older elephants of the Pleistocene (*E. meridionalis, E. antiquus* and *E. trogontherii*).

A further proboscidean that evidently deviated early from the main stem is *Dinotherium* (Fig. 209). It is characterized by the fact that in the end form only lower tusks are present. The molars are extremely simple. The tooth replacement is vertical. Special differentiation of the tusks is also seen in forms that evolved from mastodonts such as *Amebelodon* and *Platybelodon,* in which the two lower incisors form a kind of shovel (Fig. 210). *Gnathobelodon* lacks lower tusks; a similar shovel is, however, formed by the symphyseal portion of the mandible.

Sirenia.

The sirens that entice the passing traveler to destruction with their yearning song exist only in the phantasy of early sea-faring folk. To be sure, the zoological sirens have a kind of fish tail and mammary glands in breast position. From such observation might have come the first notion in the origin of the image of a mermaid. This is not certain, since many wonderful creations of a free phantasy, for example the Centaur, do not go back to real observations. For a zoological siren the name sea cow is more fitting, even if its intelligence does not in the least approach that of a cow.

What makes these mammals interesting is that they show many similarities with the cetaceans and are yet so different from them that a closer relationship between them is impossible. The sirenians are not, by far, as varied a group as are the cetaceans. There are only two modern genera: *Trichechus,* the manatee that lives primarily in streams; and *Dugong* (*Halicore*), the mermaid (from *hals, halos,* "salt-sea" and *kore,* "girl"). A third genus, *Hydrodamalis,* Steller's sea cow, lived in Kamtschaka and in the Bering Sea where it was discovered in 1741 and was exterminated soon afterward. The last specimen was seen in 1854 according to Weber. Two species of *Trichechus, T. latirostris* and *T. inunguis,* inhabit the east coast of America from Florida to North Brazil and the Antilles; the third species, *T. senegalensis,* the coast of tropical West Africa. The dugong, *Dugong* (formerly *Halicore*), lives along the coasts of the Indian Ocean, the Red Sea, Australia and New Guinea.

The skull is characterized by rather steeply ascending, ventrally recurved premaxillae (Fig. 211). These bear in the male a tusk each. Related to this shape and the notable size of the premaxillae is the position of the external nasal opening which is displaced backward and upward.

The lingual surfaces of the recurved portions of the premaxillae and the anterior, downcurved part of the mandible are each covered with a horny plate. These enable fragmentation of the sea weeds which form the diet of

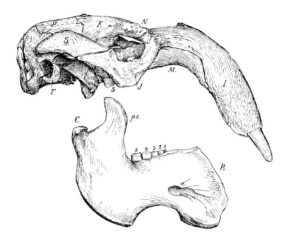

Fig. 211.—Skull of the sirenian *Halicore dugong*: *I*, premaxilla; *R*, surface for the horny grinding plate; 1–5 molars of the milk dentition. From Weber, *Die Säugetiere* (Jena: Gustav Fischer Verlag, 1928), by permission.

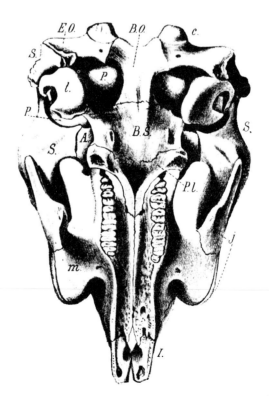

Fig. 212.—Skull of the sirenian *Trichechus latirostris*, view of the ventral side. After Vrolik, from Weber, *Die Säugetiere* (Jena: Gustav Fischer Verlag, 1928), by permission.

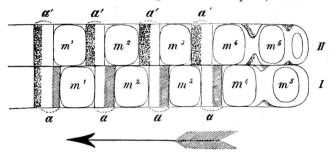

FIG. 213.—Horizontal tooth replacement in *Trichechus*. In the diagram: left, the anterior; right, the posterior end of the cheek tooth series; m_1 — m_5, the molars; in the upper row (II) already somewhat displaced forward, a and a', the partitions of the alveoli, in process of resorption (shaded), in process of rebuilding (dotted). After Hartlaub, from Weber, *Die Säugetiere* (Jena: Gustav Fischer Verlag, 1928), by permission.

Dugong. The tusk is preceded by a milk incisor which is being replaced already *in utero* by the permanent tooth. In the female the tusk does not erupt. In the anterior part of the mandible vestiges of teeth have been demonstrated in the embryo. In the maxilla there are 5 to 6 cheek teeth. Milk premolars precede the two anterior ones. "These teeth are without enamel cover, have open roots and, at first, transverse yokes as in *Trichechus* which wear off soon and change upon further growth into rootless pegs, that become enclosed in cementum and finally drop out to the last" (Weber, 1928). The jaws of *Hydrodamalis* were entirely toothless according to the account of Steller; they carried horny plates.

Trichechus (Fig. 212) has no tusks. The anterior end of the skull is not bent ventrad as in *Dugong.* Above and below there are embryonic anlagen of incisors. The cheek teeth seem to have a much greater role in the trituration of the vegetable diet—mostly seeds of *Victoria regia* and of *Pistia stratiotes*—than in the dugong. The seeds said to constitute the main diet of *Trichechus* might require greater chewing efforts than the marine *Zostera* and *Halophila* species on which the dugong feeds. It is, however, suspected that the extremely great wear of the *Trichechus* teeth results from sand adhering to the fodder.

The powerful cheek teeth of *Trichechus* stand in a tight row. Particularly interesting are their number and the mode of their replacement. In each jaw quadrant there may be present simultaneously up to eight cheek teeth, although usually only five or six (Fig. 212).

Tooth replacement is horizontal as in elephants. The teeth of the whole row are in constant motion forward. Posteriorly, new teeth are being formed; in front the worn teeth drop out. The alveolar walls that separate the individual teeth thereby undergo constant removal and reconstruction (Fig. 213).

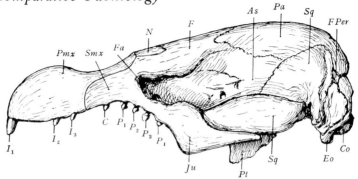

Fig. 214.—Skull of the sirenian *Protosiren fraasi* from the Eocene of Egypt. 1:3.5. After Abel, from Weber, *Die Säugetiere* (Jena: Gustav Fischer Verlag, 1928), by permission.

Although in each jaw quadrant only six cheek teeth are formed in the elephant, the replacement is practically unlimited in *Trichechus*. As many as twenty teeth may be formed in each jaw.

Increase in the original number of mammalian teeth is, except in the toothed whales, extraordinarily rare. It occurs, for example, in the African dog genus *Otocyon*, in which 50 teeth may be present. This is not a primitive condition, however, but a secondary increase. The same is true of the toothed whales, since fossils shown that the oldest whales have a heterodont dentition of 44 teeth.

For a clarification of how the multiplication of the cheek teeth comes about in *Trichechus*, additional microscopic investigations of the embryology and of the processes during replacement would be necessary. The simplest assumption is that the dental lamina keeps proliferating at the posterior end.

The prehistory of *Trichechus* is, unfortunately, not yet adequately documented by fossils (Simpson, 1932, Reinhart, 1959); but the ancestors of the *Dugong* may be followed back to forms of the Egyptian Middle Eocene which had a heterodont dentition of 44 teeth and also a complete milk dentition.

The down-warping of the anterior skull portion was not yet as pronounced in *Eotheroides* and *Protosiren* (Fig. 214) as in the later forms. Accompanying the transformation of the dentition was the progressive adaptation of the skeleton to the requirements of life in the water. In particular, the gradual loss of the hind limbs is impressively documented by fossil finds.

Of *Desmostylus* (Pl. 88-b) only teeth were known from the Miocene of California until recently; their systematic position could not be determined with certainty. Now whole skeletons from Japan have shown that *Desmostylus*, although related to the Sirenia, may not properly be placed in this order. Reinhart (1959) suggests a separate order Desmostylia for them.

As stated initially, the Sirenia are not closely related to the Cetacea. The similarities are the result of similar adaptations correlated with the transformation of original land mammals to an exclusively aquatic mode of life. Besides the similarities there are many very profound differences.

Since our presentation had to be restricted largely to the dentition, we could not mention that the Hyracoidea, the Embrithopoda, the Proboscidea and the Sirenia show many significant correspondences which suggest that the subungulates represent a group of related forms closely allied to the ancient ungulates. The fossil forms permit the assumption that the center of origin of this group may be found in Africa.

Rodentia

The order Rodentia, the rodents, will be restricted, following the more recent classifications, to the former Rodentia simplicidentata. Rodentia duplicidentata, to which the rabbits and their allies belong, are treated as a separate order Lagomorpha. For a justification of this grouping, see p. 298. The rodents are characterized as simplicidentates because they have only one pair of incisors above in contrast to the duplicidentates that have two. The gnawing teeth are characterized by permanent growth, which compensates for the strong wear so that the gnawing tooth retains the same length more or less constantly. If, for some reason, the teeth do not wear, the gnawing teeth keep on growing while maintaining their curvature, until finally they prevent the opening of the mouth. In contrast to the duplicidentates, enamel is formed only on the outer, labial side of the gnawing tooth, as seen in Plate 74-a, but occasionally it may also be present mesially and distally (Wood, 1965).

Since the enamel wears more slowly than the dentine, it always forms a sharp, protruding edge. The gnawing teeth sit in deep alveoli in the jaw bones so that, as Mummery notes, the upper alveoli describe a larger arc of a smaller circle, the lower ones a smaller arc of a larger circle.

In *Bathygerus* (Fig. 215) the alveolus of the lower incisor reaches to the mandibular joint. Behind the gnawing teeth there follows a wide diastema. This is of different extent depending upon the number of cheek teeth that have been reduced. The third incisor; the canine; and, above, the first two, below, the first three premolars are always absent. In many cases the third upper premolar is also missing. Or all premolars may be absent.

The usual number of molars in each jaw quadrant is three. In a few Australian Hydromyinae the last molar is missing. Since the premolars are also absent, the dentition is reduced to the formula $\frac{1\ 0\ 0\ 2}{1\ 0\ 0\ 2}$, that is, to 12 teeth in the whole dentition.

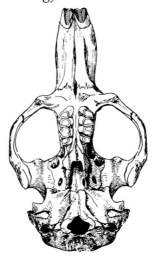

FIG. 215.— Skull of the "mole rat" *Bathyergus,* ventral view. The distance between the upper cheek tooth rows is smaller than that between the lower rows. After Weber, from Peyer, Die *Zähne,* Verständliche Wissenschaft, vol. 79 (Berlin: Springer Verlag, 1963) , by permission.

As may be gathered from the tooth numbers, the premolar battery is not of great significance in the rodents. Only in a few of the geologically oldest genera are the premolars notably simpler in form than the molars; in all others, molarization of the premolars has taken place.

The relative height of the cheek teeth shows considerable differences. There are low, brachyodont forms which are always provided with well developed roots, teeth of intermediate height, and high, prismatic forms in which root formation that terminates the growth in height occurs only late in ontogeny, and then incompletely or is even altogether suppressed.

The form of the rodent cheek teeth depends furthermore on the mode of the enamel folding which led in its broad features to a corresponding pattern, different from that of the molars of all other mammals. But at the same time it led in detail to such an enormous variety of form that its study required a precise terminology which brought about the creation of a special nomenclature that cannot be discussed here.

The basic form of the upper molars is compared by Romer to a Latin capital E, whose horizontal bars are oriented labiad; the mesial and distal crests correspond to the paracone and the metacone, and the middle crest represents a mesoloph characteristic for the rodents. Lingually, protocone and hypocone protrude; between them there may be a mesocone that originates from a middle, longitudinal crest. Further transversal structures may occur mesially and distally.

In the nomenclature proposed by Stehlin and Schaub (1951) , the transversal enamel ribs (with respect to the longitudinal axis of the tooth) are designated as outer and inner anticlines and are numbered in mesio-distal sequence, the valleys correspondingly as synclines. The longitudinal middle elevation is called longitudinal crest. So-called pits (Trichter) develop as synclines are closed off by marginal elevations.

In the hypselodont, deeply enamel-folded cheek-teeth crown cementum is deposited on the enamel in the depth of the valleys (see p. 214). Because of the differences in the hardness of enamel, dentine and cementum the chewing surface cannot be ground smooth, a great advantage in trituration.

With progressing wear of a molar it is natural that its chewing surface changes, in that, for example, shallow valleys of the original crown relief disappear completely. Thus in the detailed comparison of molar forms, the degree of wear is always to be considered.

The rodents are the most richly branched order of mammals, with about 2,800 modern species and a constantly increasing number of fossil forms. Their grouping into categories based on phylogenetic relations confronts the systematist with considerable problems, particularly in cases where the interpretation of the phyletic relations based on the morphology of the limbs leads to different conclusions than the investigation of the dentition. In the case of the bipedal jumping rodents, intensive research has shown, for instance, that this mode of locomotion has arisen in several subgroups independently. Yet molars with permanent growth occur in a variety of form assemblages that are not very closely related to one another.

The differences in the structure of the dentitions and in the jaw bones and the entire skull structure are related ultimately to variations of function, which in turn are related to changes in the differentiation of the masticatory musculature.

In view of the particular specializations that this musculature has attained in the rodents, a few notes about the masticatory musculature in mammals generally may follow here. It consists of the musculus temporalis, the musculi pterygoidei, and the musculus masseter, all of which are served by the fifth brain nerve. Areas of origin of the temoralis muscle are the skull roof and upper portion of the side wall of the skull; the place of insertion is the coronoid process of the mandible. The muscle acts to close the mouth by simple ginglymic or orthal jaw motion. The muscle is thus most notably developed in the carnivores.

The pterygoid muscles—an inner and an outer one are distinguished—received their name because they originate from the wing processes of the pterygoid bones. Their area of insertion lies at the medial sides of the mandibles. Consequently, they produce lateral displacements of the mandible. The masseter, in mammals generally, and especially in the rodents is

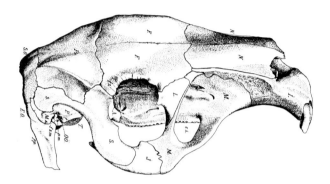

FIG. 216.—Skull of *Hydrochoerus*: *ci*, very much enlarged infra-orbital canal through which fibers of the masseter muscle extend. From Weber, *Die Säugetiere* (Jena: Gustav Fischer Verlag, 1927), by permission.

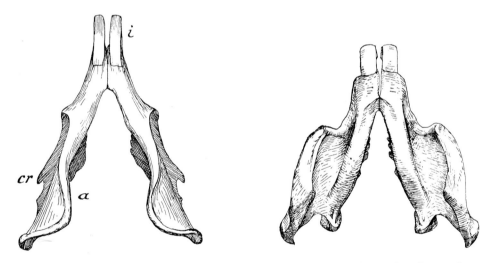

FIG. 217.—Different form of the processus angularis of the lower jaw. *Left*, sciurognathous type—the processus angularis originates from the lower face of the incisor alveolus and from the lower and posterior surface of the body of the mandible (example shown, *Marmota marmota*); *right*, hystricognathous type—the processus angularis originates from the outer surface of the incisor alveolus (example shown, *Bathyergus maritimus*). From Weber, *Die Säugetiere* (Jena: Gustav Fischer Verlag, 1928), by permission.

more powerfully developed than the pterygoidei. It originates from the outer and lower sides of the jugular arch; its place of insertion is primarily the lower outer margin of the mandible. Through the action of the masseter muscles, the lower cheek teeth are moved mainly against the upper ones. Thus the masseter is usually well developed where the molar area of the dentition has considerable extent. A special development of the masseter in concert with the specialized rodent dentition evolved in conjunction with a forward and backward displacement of the lower jaw against the upper dentition. Because the direction of a movement produced by muscle contraction is determined by the respective positional relations of the areas of origin and insertion of the muscle fibers, an enlargement of the areas of attachment resulted. This enlargement took place in different ways depending on whether the outer or the inner portion of the masseter was involved. Accordingly, three groups of rodents are distinguished: the squirrel-like Sciuromorpha, the porcupine-like Hystricomorpha and the mouse-like Myomorpha.

To the Sciuromorpha belong partly forms without particular specializations of the masseter and which have proved to be generalized also in other characters, and partly forms in which the outer portion of the masseter has extended its territory of origin far forward. In the Hystricomorpha and Myomorpha the inner portion of the masseter has expanded anteriorly in such a way that a foramen in the skull (small in other mammals) has been grossly expanded (Fig. 216). In the Myomorpha the outer masseter layer has likewise become extended forward. The places of insertion of the masseter muscles on the lower jaw are also characteristic of larger groups of rodents (Fig. 217). Several rodent groups, particularly the Anomaluroidea cannot be grouped in any of the above categories.

A description of the great variety of rodent dentitions is impossible because of lack of space. A few remarks shall suffice. One peculiarity of certain rodents is that the distance between the right and left tooth rows may be greater in the upper jaw than in the mandible. Thus the chewing plane of the teeth does not lie horizontally, but in the upper jaw runs from dorsolaterally to ventromedially and is reversed in the lower jaw.

The two halves of the lower jaw are sometimes, most notably in the squirrels, movable against each other. By contraction of a transversal muscle, the points of the lower incisors may be separated from one another, an apparatus well suited for breaking hard nut shells. In the beaver the two halves of the lower jaw are fused at the symphysis (Fig. 218).

Although numerous rodents are reported from the younger Tertiary, the order is represented in the Paleocene only by the genus *Paramys* (Fig. 219), to which Eocene material has been added (Wood, 1962). These early finds

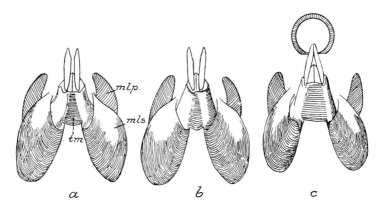

FIG. 218.—Lower jaw of the squirrel *Sciurus vulgaris: a,* in resting position; *b,* in catching position; *c,* in gnawing and wedging position (as when opening a nut); *mlp,* M. masseter lateralis, deep layer; *mls,* M. masseter lateralis, superficial portion; *tm,* M. transversus mandibulae. After Krumbach, from Weber, *Die Säugetiere* (Jena: Gustav Fischer Verlag, 1928), by permission.

show that the rodents apparently evolved from even earlier placental mammals. But they do not yet provide satisfactory information concerning the pre-history of the order.

From the Oligocene very many more finds of rodents are available than from earlier times, furnishing certain insights concerning the centers of origin of different groups. Not yet clarified is, however, the paleogeographic distribution of the hystricomorphs which appear in the Oligocene of Africa, and at the same time in South America where they reached a much greater differentiation. The North American porcupine *Erethizon* is thought to be a late immigrant from South America.

Lagomorpha

That the rabbit, shown to us in our youth in every schoolbook as an example of a rodent, and the hare should now no longer belong to the rodents, may appear to many as an unnecessary innovation. The reasons that led to the new arrangement are, however, of such weight that one cannot ignore them.

In earlier systematic treatments it had already been pointed out that the Rodentia duplicidentata and the Rodentia simplicidentata are not only distinguished by the number of upper incisors, but by many other characteristics of their organization. This distinction may also be seen from the diagnosis of the rodents in the former, broader sense, in which in all kinds of notations one had to add "with the exception of the duplicidentates." For a long time comparative-anatomical and paleontological experience had shown that the differentiation of permanently growing incisors is no reliable criterion for the interpretation of the systematic position. Different genera such as *Daubentonia* (*Cheiromys*), placed among the rodents because of this, had to be removed from this group on the basis of the remaining features of their organization. More detailed study also revealed that there existed notable differences in the differentiation of the gnawing teeth, as well as in the nature of their function. Such differences also exist between simplicidentate and duplicidentate "rodents," pertaining especially to the mode of jaw movement. In the simplicidentates it is propalinal; but not in the duplicidentates, in which the gnawing and chewing take place with simple ginglymic movements in conjunction with lateral displacement of the mandible. Correspondingly, the articular pit for the lower jaw is relatively broad in the duplicidentates. These matters led to the examination of the question whether the differentiation of the dentition of the duplicidentates supports closer phyletic relations with the simplicidentates. Intensive study revealed that this is not the case. In the division of the group into two separate orders, the name Rodentia remained with the simplicidentates, because they include most of the forms except the rabbits, hares and pikas.

In contrast to the rodents, the incisors of the Lagomorpha are surrounded on all sides by enamel, although the layer is thinner on the back sides of the teeth. Behind the functioning gnawing teeth there is a second pair of small incisors, hence the name duplicidentates. In the upper jaw there are

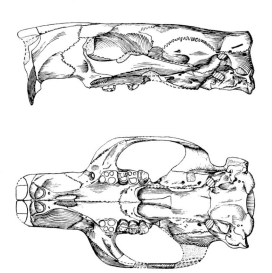

FIG. 219.—*Paramys,* one of the earliest fossil rodents from the Paleocene and Eocene of North America. About 1:1.5. From Wood, *The Early Tertiary Rodents of the Family Paramyidae* (Philadelphia: American Philosophical Society 1962), by permission.

always three premolars (Fig 220), a number that no longer occurs among rodents. In the lower jaw there are only two P. The number of molars is three above and below in the Leporidae. In the living pika *Ochotona* the M³ is missing.

The earliest, still incompletely known lagomorph is probably *Eurymylus* from the late Paleocene. The separation into the two orders probably took place much earlier. *Titanomys* from the Oligocene still has rooted molars. Otherwise the lagomorphs of the Oligocene already show permanent growth of the molars and intensive enamel folding. The genus *Lepus* (hare) (Fig. 220) and *Oryctolagus* (rabbit) (literally "a digging hare") are known only since the Pliocene. While it seems certain that the lagomorphs are not rodents and probably have not even arisen from early rodents, there remains the vexing question as to what other groups of mammals they might have come from. This frustrating problem was recently reviewed by Wood (1957), under the title, "What, if anything, is a rabbit?". According to this analysis, the origin of the lagomorphs might be sought among the early condylarths.

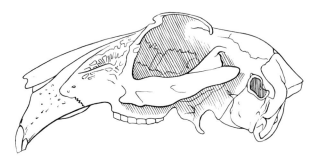

Fig. 220.—Skull of the hare *Lepus*. Note smaller incisors behind the gnawing teeth. From Peyer, *Die Zähne*, Verständliche Wissenschaft, vol. 79 (Berlin: Springer Verlag, 1963), by permission.

Postscript

Instead of the kind of summary that would require reviewing descriptive details of the dentition in the different groups of vertebrates, we shall here regard the subject from a somewhat different perspective, emphasizing important relationships and main points of view.

The short historical survey was included because a review of its history is worthwhile in any specialized study. Even so, we had to restrict our survey to odontology, ignoring the richly documented history of dentistry. Perhaps the first scientist who compared the human dentition to the teeth of different vertebrates was Aristotle. Much later, Conrad Gessner described the differences of the dentition of a shrew and a mouse in unusual factual detail. Among the major developments coincident with progress in zoology and anatomy, were the formulation of the cell theory, which enabled understanding the histological construction of the teeth; broadening of the horizon by comparative odontological material that became available through paleontological research; gradual improvement of research techniques; and the creation of scientifically oriented, government-supported, dental institutes.

Despite the absence of fossils to provide information about the origin of vertebrates, comparative-anatomical and embryological findings led to the recognition of a relationship between the vertebrates and the tunicates, as well as to the supported presumption of a distant relationship to the phylum Echinodermata. In the Agnathi (jawless vertebrates) the skeletal rods that surround the anterior end of the intestinal tube, the visceral arches, are all nearly the same shape; in the gnathostomes one pair of these arches entered the service of food intake and became a jaw arch.

One theory, formerly widely held, assumed that bone had arisen only within the gnathostomes in such a way that it originated from the so-called basal plate of dermal denticles of sharks. E. A. Stensiö could, however, show with certainty that bone occurs already in a subgroup of the Agnathi, the cephalaspids, and that the level of organization of these bone-bearing forms (formerly placed among the gnathostomes) is equal to that of the modern cyclostomes.

Among the Agnathi, the modern representatives, the cylostomes, have no dentine teeth, only epidermal horny denticles. In the ostracoderms, because of the condition of their visceral arches, a dentition was most probably absent. But the coelolepid ostracoderm, *Thelodus scoticus,* has dermal denticles that correspond structurally to those of the sharks.

The evolutionary step from Agnatha to Gnathostomata that must be postulated for weighty comparative anatomical reasons has so far not been documented by fossils.

The earliest gnathostomes are the placoderms having without exception bone and jaws. The dentition of certain placoderms is of great interest; but the investigations of W. Gross on acanthodians and arthrodires could be referred to only briefly.

The ostracoderms and the placoderms are completely strange vertebrates that appeared and became extinct in Paleozoic time. We meet, however, in the elasmobranchs, in the broadest sense, more familiar types. The earliest finds, so far, are from the middle Devonian, but the sharks and their allies probably extend farther back in geologic time. Their earlier origin is suggested by the magnitude of the differences between the sharks and the other fishes, and by the consideration that the phylogenetic development of the forms of late Devonian age, known from whole skeletons, required a considerable amount of time.

About the origin of the Chondrichtyes opinions are divided. Most students suppose that the Chondrichtyes originated from the placoderms; they are assumed originally to have had bone since lost. Others derive them in a direct line from the ostracoderms, arguing for a transition from the agnathous to the gnathostomous condition among mobile nectonic forms that may not have had bone, in contrast to the heavily armored benthonically specialized cephalaspids.

Besides the dentition teeth, many sharks, rays and skates have within the mouth cavity considerably smaller mucous membrane denticles. These I have described in detail because they have been widely neglected in the more modern literature; they are no longer even mentioned in several works. Their number varies: in many sharks, rays and skates, mucous membrane denticles are nearly or wholly absent; the mouth-throat cavity of a *Charcharodon carcharias* 4½ meters long contains over 2,000,000 mucous membrane denticles, estimated from sample counts.

As already noted by O. Steinhard, the form of the mucous membrane denticles corresponds in the different genera closely to that of the dermal denticles. An exception is the skate, with stout dermal denticles but very delicate pointed mucous membrane denticles. The form of the mucous membrane denticles may vary according to the position in the mouth-throat cavity.

The mucous membrane denticles in all instances resemble the dermal denticles in outer form and in having the same simple internal structure, even where the dentition teeth contain a core of trabecular dentine inside of a coat of orthodentine. The mucous membrane teeth are the most original tooth formations in the mouth-throat cavity; the teeth containing trabecular dentine are to be regarded as specialized structures, a fact often ignored in the favorite comparisons of shark teeth to other hard substances; to bone, for example, or to dermal hard structures of primitive vertebrates.

The mucous membrane denticles also correspond to dermal denticles in the mode of replacement. In both, the replacement anlage is formed near the surface (not at depth) between the functional denticles. Furthermore, the replacement is not governed by a dental lamina—the replacement denticles are formed randomly throughout the shagreened area.

In the tooth replacement of the dentition teeth of the sharks, a replacement tooth, to reach its place of function, must overcome not only a notable linguo-labial distance; it must at the same time change its attitude, because the tip of the replacement tooth is oriented away from the edge of the jaw and not toward it. This change of attitude may take place in a number of small, nearly equal steps, the original condition, or it may take place suddenly almost immediately prior to the assumption of the functional position. In many instances, the replacement tooth moves, tooth base first, toward the edge of the jaw, flips over and becomes fixed with its base on the outside of the edge of the jaw.

In the particular mode of tooth succession there are among sharks differences, related to the arrangement of the dental cross rows. If these cross rows are separated from one another, a replacement tooth can assume its place of function as soon as its predecessor has been shed; if the teeth of neighboring cross rows are interlaced, however, then a tooth cannot advance into its position of function until its own predecessor as well as those of its neighbors have been shed. In extreme instances of this sort, as in the lower jaw of *Dalatias,* individual teeth cannot be changed, only whole longitudinal rows all at once.

The dentition teeth of sharks show a wealth of forms, not only among different shark groups, but even within a single dentition where the size and form of the teeth may vary greatly. In one feature all selachian teeth correspond: the tooth base has a considerable size, a fact probably related to the cartilaginous character of the jaw skeleton. In the absence of bone, the various modes of tooth attachment in bony fishes and tetrapods are impossible here, and the teeth can only be fixed on the jaws by connective tissue. Such a fixation naturally requires on the surface of the tooth base an adequate area of insertion for the connective tissue fiber bundles, a requirement that may have resulted in the enlargement of the base.

In the Osteichthyes, that is, in those fishes in which bone occurs besides cartilage, no distinction between dentition teeth and mucous membrane teeth is possible, even though the pharyngeal denticles of the Osteichthyes occasionally resemble the mucous membrane denticles of the sharks. But even here there is a difference, in that the denticles are not directly attached to the gill arches in Osteichthyes, but are often fastened to peculiar little bony platelets that make the connection to the gill arch skeleton. In some instances, the teeth of the posterior gill arches may attain considerable size as so-called pharyngeal teeth.

With respect to differences in the dentition that are related to differences in the diet, we may note that the so-called predaceous fishes do not always have large cutting or piercing teeth. The catfish *Silurus,* for example, a voracious predator, is equipped with only small but numerous brush-teeth.

Feeding on hard-shelled prey has produced similar adaptations of the dentition in the most different fish groups and at the most different times of geologic history: compact cylindrical or globular teeth have been united into tooth pavements. Along the jaw edge there may be conical and in front incisiviform teeth.

Sharks and bony fishes correspond in that in both groups the architecture of the head, on which the possibilities of differentiation depend, is predelineated by the requirements of gill respiration. With the transition to lung breathing and the related reduction of the posterior arches of the visceral skeleton, the area of denticulation suffered a reduction in its extent.

The earliest amphibians, the stegocephalians, were extinct near the end of the Triassic. One of the subgroups, the labrinthodonts, is characterized by the radial folding of the wall of the tooth base. Extreme development of this folding produces a labyrinthine picture in cross-sections. Such folding also occurs in other groups of vertebrates among fishes, for example in *Lepidosteus* and *Holoptychius,* and among reptiles in the geologically younger ichthyosaurs. It is always connected with a great expansion of the basal part of the tooth. The construction may be compared to the structural shape of corrugated sheet metal, in which great strength is achieved with little material. In the trabecular dentine we see a parallel to this principle. Trabecular dentine is always covered by a layer of orthodentine, and may be compared to spongy bone surrounded by lamellar bone. In other instances, as in the placodonts and in the mammals, teeth that must withstand heavy functional demands are massive in structure.

Among the modern amphibians, the anura have only very small teeth. Furthermore, the dentition in frogs is usually restricted to the upper jaw; in toads it is entirely lacking. Tooth replacement in frogs is very intensive, however. Teeth are continuously resorbed and replaced by new ones, and even the bony pedestals are resorbed and newly erected. The young tooth anlage enters the pedestal of the functional tooth via a little portal where it develops further. In sections one sees, generally, two replacement generations of different age, in addition to the functioning generation. The intensity of this replacement suggests that the dentition in frogs may have notable functional significance despite its limitation to the upper jaw, and despite the small size and simple shape of the teeth.

The teeth of reptiles show only modest differences of form in no sense comparable to the wealth of shapes in mammalian teeth. But we nevertheless find among the reptiles, at least, if the gamut of fossil forms is included, a notable multiplicity of functional design, related principally to the differentiation of the masticatory musculature, and associated with it the differentiation of the skeletal elements of the temporal region, the palate and the mandible. Greatest mobility was achieved in the mandibular joint by the snakes, which were thus enabled to ingest undivided prey of enormous size compared to their own skull and body size. Among snakes, there are also the most extreme tooth specializations among reptiles, the venom fangs. In the grooved-tooth forms, the venom is carried to the bite wound in a shallow groove near the tooth surface. In the pipette-tooth forms, on the other hand, the groove became deeper and by the fusion of the edges of the original groove became a tube within the interior of the tooth. Because of the special requirements of this tube, the pulp cavity has come to resemble a half-moon structure, as seen in cross section.

In the groups of the synapsids, a long phylogenetic development led to a mammal-like heterodonty and finally to the formation of teeth of unmistakably mammal-like habitus. Of the numerous and varied Permian and Triassic synapsids, most were extinct before the end of the Triassic period. The mammals originated from small, still very incompletely known Ictidosauria.

The comparison of mammalian molars to simply constructed reptile teeth led to the formation of two theories: the theory of concrescence, further developed by L. Bolk to the dimer concentration theory;[1] and the theory of differentiation, which as the Cope-Osborn trituberecular theory found wide acceptance. In the original concrescence theory, it was assumed

---

[1] A very different concept of "concrescence" affecting not only mammalian molars, but all dentine teeth of vertebrates, was recently proposed by Stensiö in the form of the lepidomorial theory. For details of this see page 59.

that every cusp of a multicusped molar, for example of a multituberculate, corresponded to an originally independent individual tooth. Bolk started from the arrangement of the selachian teeth (and replacement teeth) in cross and longitudinal rows. Fusions were said to occur only within cross rows (tooth families) in such a way that the entire anlage material of a cross row (which in the polyphyodontous selachians produces many tooth generations) was in the mammals exhausted in a single tooth. Thereby those cross rows that belong to the so-called exostichos are said to produce the milk teeth; those belonging to the endostichos form the permanent dentition. Against such profound differences between exostichos and endostichos speaks the fundamental fact (however, to my knowledge, never yet voiced) that in the most labial longitudinal, zigzag row of teeth in a shark dentition, a tooth belonging to the endostichos itself achieves the position of exostichos as soon as its exostichos neighbors have been shed; whether a tooth belongs to the endostichos or the exostichos depends entirely on when during development the tooth rows are observed. The embryological arguments that Bolk marshalled in support of his theory are partly controversial, partly rejected. The so-called enamel septum is demonstrably not a partition but an enamel strand. An unbiased comparison of the tooth replacement of the mammals to the conditions in reptiles, amphibians, and fishes furnishes no evidence in favor of the necessary consequence of the concentration theory, that the replacement of teeth in mammals is a process fundamentally different from that of all other vertebrates. The factual material of vertebrate paleontology also contradicts Bolk's theory.

The tritubercular theory was, however, confirmed in its basic tenets by extensive investigations, especially of early Tertiary mammals. To be sure, some of its details proved to be untenable. It was found, for example, that the protocone does not represent the original main point of the tooth. The nomenclature was fortunately not changed because of this; the Cope-Osborn terminology remained in use even in those instances where the original meaning no longer applies. Because of an ever-increasing knowledge of the prehistory of the mammals, even very complicated mammal molars can be "carried back" convincingly to tritubercular origins.

The character of the food need not correspond, in any individual instance, to the designation of the group to which a mammal belongs; there are omnivorous and even herbivorous carnivores. In the overall picture, however, the differences in feeding are very significant. This is particularly evident in the phylogeny.

From indifferent, probably omnivorous beginnings, vegetable diet led in different groups of mammals independently to similar differentiation in an increase in the efficiency of the chewing action. A contributing factor was the improvement in the occlusion of upper and lower dentitions. The formation of a talonid increased the crown-to-crown contact of upper and lower cheek teeth. Further increases in efficiency resulted from the infolding of the enamel of the tooth crown and the deposition of cementum in the depressions of the crown relief; this development, because of the different degrees of hardness of enamel, dentine, and cementum, resulted in a rough, uneven grinding surface, even under continuous wear. Finally, the originally brachyodont teeth became hypselodont and in extreme instances root formation which terminates the growth in height of the teeth was suppressed. This development is related to an increase of tooth wear in that, by prolongation of the period of function of a tooth, the mammal is to some extent compensated for having only a restricted number of teeth available. As Romer has noted, an increase in the chewing efficiency became necessary not only with the change in diet to gramineans or other hard fodder, but also with the increase in overall body size.

Like the dentition of the earliest ungulates, that of the ancient carnivores was omnivorous, but in the latter a carnivorous diet led to a different specialization of the dentition, most typically expressed in the felids. The modern carnivores are largely characterized by the fact that the fourth premolar in the upper jaw and the first molar in the lower have become cutting carnassials. Some of the ancient carnivores did not yet have carnassials, in others more posterior teeth were differentiated as carnassials. In only one family, the miacids, from which all later carnivores evolved, the carnassials were formed by P^4 and M_1.

Many carnivores have enlarged canines. In the saber-toothed cats, they reached enormous size, and could only remain functional because a simultaneous transformation of the mandibular joint permitted an especially wide opening of the mouth. This excessive development was formerly thought to have resulted in the extinction of the saber-toothed cats, until it was suggested that this type of dentition had been in use for millions of years and that, moreover, a similar type of dentition had independently evolved in marsupials and creodonts. It is assumed today that the extinction of the saber-toothed cats was caused by the extinction of their prey. Besides examples of gradual perfection of the dentition over periods of many millions of years, the record also contains regressive developments that led to the complete loss of the dentition, for example, in the turtles and the birds. The earliest representatives of both, however, still bear teeth. The lost dentition was replaced with horny beaks; not so, however, in the ant eaters and pangolins that feed primarily on termites, procuring their prey by a long, worm-shaped tongue made sticky by the saliva. The reduction of the food does not start until it reaches the stomach, whose functional efficiency compensates for the loss of the teeth. Totally toothless forms were investigated with some success for remains of tooth anlagen entirely restricted to embryonic life. Geoffroy St. Hilaire found some in the foetus of a baleen whale.

In several orders of generally terrestrial mammals certain representatives had a pronounced aquatic life, such as *Chironectes* among the marsupials, *Limnogale* and *Potamogale* among the insectivores, *Nectomys,* *Ichthyomys* and *Hydromys* among the rodents, and *Lutra* and *Latax* among fissipede carnivores. In these latter forms the adaptation to an aquatic life takes place before our eyes, so to speak; but in pinnipeds it took place in the not-too-distant geologic past. Despite the rather far-reaching transformations related to changes in environment and food, the ancestors of the pinnipeds must certainly have been terrestrial carnivores.

In the cetaceans the situation is different. These evolved from terrestrial mammals to permanently marine forms so long ago, and the transformations associated with the aquatic adaptation are so considerable, that allocation to a definite order of mammals is not possible. In the differentiation of the dentition, pinnipeds and cetaceans correspond in that their original heterodonty has been simplified, in the dolphin to a complete homodonty and in certain seals to at least a secondarily triconodont form of the cheek teeth. The dentition of the ancient whale *Protocetus* still consists of 44 teeth, distinguishable as incisors, canines, premolars and molars.

As in the whales, in the sea cows permanent life in the water has led to far-reaching aquatic specializations including the loss of the posterior paired limbs. The modification of the dentition, however, took an entirely different course. This is understandable because the sea cows are entirely herbivorous animals that feed primarily on seaweed or seeds of aquatic plants.

Sexual dimorphism in the dentition occurs in a modest way already among fishes, for example among the rayids. In the Permian reptile genus *Dicynodon,* the male has in each jaw quadrant only a single tooth and the female is toothless; the latter was formerly described as *Oudenodon* (no-tooth). In mammals a pronounced sexual dimorphism of the dentition is not rare. The canines of the boar are considerably larger than those of the female pig; the greatest difference is in the whale *Monodon* where one of the incisors, usually the left, has become a ramrod over 2 meters long and the teeth of the female are mainly hidden within the gingiva.

That teeth serve not only the purpose of dealing with the food but may also be used as weapons need hardly be noted. This duality is seen impressively in the Musk deer and in *Tragulus* and *Hyemoschus,* both small forms related to the deer. They lack antlers; but the upper canines have become saber-shaped tusks.

Quite evidently there are relations between the dentition and the construction of a skull. It is, however, not true that the form of the bones determines the differentiation of the dentition; rather, despite its apparent rigidity, it was the bone that had to accommodate the requirements of the soft anatomy, especially of the masticatory musculature whose differentiation and localization is in turn related to the function of the dentition.

The holostylic condition of the skull in the holocephalians, and that independently evolved in the lungfishes, is assumed to be related to the large tooth plates whose efficient functioning required powerful muscles and a firm construction of the skull. The massive structure of the placodont skull seems clearly to be related to the extremely durophagous dentition. The geologically earliest proboscidea had hardly deviated in the architecture of their skull from the norm among mammals. The specialization of the dentition was undoubtedly one of the main factors, perhaps the decisive one, in the differentiation of the elephant skull.

The histology and developmental history of the teeth were treated in the main body of the text in conjunction with macroscopic relations; but the treatment of the subject here permits their connected presentation.

As emphasized before, all formation of dentine teeth is topographically restricted to the boundary of ectoderm and mesoderm (mesectoderm) even where no enamel is being formed. This must be noted because the significant role of the ectoderm in tooth formation has been very much neglected (for example, by F. Weidenreich) in comparing teeth to bone.

Ectodermal ameloblasts with very rare exceptions and mesodermal (or, more accurately, mesectodermal [1]) odontoblasts are together, involved in the formation of teeth.

In invertebrates, the ectoderm also secretes a hard substance (regularly in the two large phyla, Arthropoda and Mollusca) in the form of a so-called cuticular exoskeleton. In contrast to the vertebrates, the secretion of this ectodermal product takes place on the outside of the formational cells while the enamel is formed on the inner side, facing the mesoderm. Possibly this difference is due to the fact that the ectoderm of vertebrates is highly stratified, and in invertebrates it forms as a single layer of cells. Herein may lie the cause of the restriction of enamel formation to the vertebrates.

---

[1] It has been shown that in some instances cells originating from the entoderm may become ameloblasts. The designation "mesectoderm" is more appropriate because, as demonstrated experimentally, odontoblasts may originate from neural crest material along with gill arches. The term "mesoderm" is used here merely for the sake of simplicity.

For a long time it has been suspected that the formation of enamel is not the only task of the ameloblasts. It was assumed in particular that the ectoderm guaranteed the species-specific form of the tooth. Experimental results have shown, however, that this is probably not merely an influence of the enamel epithelium on the mesodermal tooth germ, but that a very complicated system of inductions affects tooth development during the different phases of the process.

In the tooth development of the selachians, ameloblasts and odontoblasts lie close together prior to the deposition of any substance. They are separated only by the basal membrane which, according to Kerr (1955), consists of a fine, fibrous meshwork and sparse, structureless ground substance. The space surrounded by the epithelial sheath is tightly crowded with cells of uniform appearance, that contain large nuclei and relatively little cytoplasm. The cells of the epithelial sheath are initially only slightly larger than other cells of the dental lamina and are not conspicuous in stained sections. In the succeeding stage their height has notably increased and their nuclei are sharply delineated in azan preparations, because the cytoplasm has become notably lighter. Both features suggest that the cells in this stage are in a state of increased activity. In the apical region of the tooth anlage, meanwhile, a cell-free zone has developed by the secretion of a ground substance between the basal membrane and the mesodermal cells, forming a cap over the tip of the cone of mesodermal cells. In this ground substance there soon occur fine fibers that originate partly from the basal membrane, partly from the mesodermal cell territory.

In selachians, the histological interpretation of the substance in question, and of the hard substance that results from it, is controversial. According to one view it is enamel; according to the other, which I support, it is dentine, but a dentine influenced by the ameloblasts.

According to our view of enamel, which is based on that of the mammals and the reptiles, a tooth hard substance may be referred to as enamel only if the following three conditions apply: (1) formation by ectodermal (and only in very exceptional cases by entodermal) cells; (2) centrifugal direction of growth, so that the last-formed enamel layer is most superficial; and (3) characteristic negative birefringence, a criterion practically very reliable.

The enamel of mammalian teeth originates from cell processes of the ameloblasts which undergo mineralization. No comparable mode of formation appears in the questionable substance in selachians. L. Lison believed he had found, in *Scyliorhinus,* a centrifugal growth direction of the substance in question. In his argument, a space visible in his sections was thought to have developed by dissolution of a hard substance present prior to decalcification. According to my experience with selachian teeth, however, there is never any evidence of the dissolution of a hard substance, which is easily and definitely determinable in mammalian and certain fish teeth. Furthermore, comparison of very young to more advanced tooth anlagen of selachians suggests no centrifugal direction of growth of the questionable substance; in both stages, the outermost tooth substance (which lies inside the basal membrane) is formed by the same thin layer, containing fibers at a right angle to the surface, which Kerr has called reticular on the basis of their reaction to stains. Inside this layer there is unquestionable orthodentine with a centripetal direction of growth.

Absence of the characteristic birefringence of enamel can be demonstrated best by comparing ground thin-sections of fossil selachian and reptile teeth.

Even though Tomes and Mummery retained the term enamel for the outermost layer of the selachian teeth "in order to avoid increasing the number of technical terms," they nevertheless held the view that the organic base of this layer is furnished by the mesodermal cells of the pulp cavity. At the same time, however, they pointed out that the state of increased activity, in which the ameloblasts are found during the formation of the substance in question, suggests active participation of these ectodermal cells in the formation of this outermost layer. Our own investigations confirm this view. Especially interesting in this respect is the observation in *Isurus* that during a certain stage of tooth formation capillaries enter projections of the outer enamel epithelium which in other, more pronounced instances (in teleosts) can only be interpreted as an increased supply of material from the blood that would increase the effectiveness of the ameloblasts.

That the smooth, shiny character of the crown surface extends toward the tooth base only exactly as far as the inner enamel epithelium during tooth development, also suggests a material contribution by the ameloblasts to the outermost layer of the selachian tooth.

On ground thin-sections through the teeth of *Heterodontus,* there are places where fine dark lines originate from tiny pits on the crown surface and slightly enter the tooth, diverge, become thinner, and then terminate. Similar structures, but less clearly visible without special staining, occur also in other sharks. Presumably these are reticular fibers as described and illustrated by Kerr for *Scyliorhinus.* Noting the terminological difficulties and using the term purely descriptively, Kerr calls the outermost layer of the selachian teeth enamel with the justification that this layer does not have the characteristics of dentine. But the layer in question cannot be called enamel, at least not according to our definition of enamel, which is based on the conditions in mammals, amphibians, and reptiles and which is also applicable in many fishes. We thus proposed for this layer the indifferent designation "peripheral initial zone" (the "vitrodentine" of other authors).

In all selachians, the first dentine formed is without exception an ortho-dentine, whose not-yet-fully-mineralized prestage is called predentine. The direction of growth is centripetal. In the teeth of most vertebrates, the odontoblasts on apposition of new layers of dentine retreat in closed for-mation toward the center of the pulp cavity; as they retreat they leave behind a cytoplasmic process in the hard substance produced by them, which in the teeth of higher vertebrates results in a persistent, undivided, more or less smooth-walled pulp cavity. All dermal and mucous membrane denticles and the dentition teeth in certain families of elasmobranchs (for example, the rayids and the mustelids whose orthodentine is characterized by the particular regularity of its structure) consist exclusively of ortho-dentine.

The trabecular dentine [1] never occurs by itself, but is formed beneath a coat of orthodentine. The odontoblasts that produce the trabecular dentine do not have the typical orientation during the formation of orthodentine; they may assume any position whatever within the pulp cavity. But the orientation of any given odontoblast to the hard substance formed by it is the same as that of the cells that form orthodentine. The odontoblast re-treats during dentine production, leaving a cell process behind. These odon-toblasts produce an irregular spongework of trabecles consisting of dentine whose formation is preceded by predentine.[2] The development of these dentine trabecles subdivides the pulp cavity into numerous diverticula which in larger teeth may be oriented vertically. In some cases the apical portion of the tooth may consist of orthodentine, the basal portion of trabecular dentine.

The Chondrichthyes and the Osteichthyes have evolved separately at least since the middle Devonian. Thus the differences in their organization are very considerable, for example, as reflected in the structure of their teeth and in the fact that the dentition teeth and the dermal denticles in selachians have essentially the same structure,[3] but in the Osteichthyes the dermal hard structures differ very greatly from those of the teeth.

---

[1] We prefer Röse's term trabecular dentine to the names osteodentine and vasodentine which have been used for a variety of structures.

[2] In some fossil forms the cores of these trabecles consist of a tissue resembling bone, hence the statement, for example by Ørvig, that a spongework of bone is formed first, to which den-tine is secondarily applied; this is clearly not true in all instances.

[3] See p. 59 for the interpretation of dermal denticles and teeth according to the lepidomorial theory of Stensiö-Ørvig.

From the first large subdivision of the Osteichthyes, the actinopterygians, some chondrosteans, subholosteans, holosteans and teleosts were studied; from the second subdivision, the Choanichthyes, some crossopterygians and some lungfishes.

In 1906 O. Jaekel (see Hennig, 1906) described from pycnodont teeth a special kind of dentine as tecodentine. Subsequently (Schalch and Peyer, 1919), I could show that in *Sargodon tomicus* the teeth consist of three substances: orthodentine, enamel, and a superficially enamel-like substance, here called modified dentine (= durodentine of Schmidt). In 1937 S. E. Guttormsen and I demonstrated an equivalent construction for a number of ganoid fishes. In contrast, Schmidt (1949) declared "that in one class of vertebrates, the fishes, enamel is generally and fundamentally absent," adding to this, without any justification, "the statements of Peyer (Schalch and Peyer, 1919) and Guttormsen (1937), to the effect that in certain cases true enamel occurs besides durodentine, may be shown to be in error." On describing a dentition of *Lepidotes,* I pointed out (1954) that the question could probably be decided by an investigation of the tooth development of the modern holostean *Lepisosteus.* Such a study has since been made through the help of American friends, who procured material preserved for histological purposes.

Investigation of the modern holostean shows the following: the cells of the inner enamel epithelium are not all of equal size; the cells in the apical portion of the tooth anlage are much larger, especially much higher, than the cells located more basally. Furthermore, the large apical cells of the enamel–epithelium border only that portion of the predentine which is penetrated by numerous dentine tubules, and which upon mineralization becomes the hard, shiny, modified dentine that covers the orthodentine as a cap. On the basis of these observations, it may be assumed that the apical cells of the inner enamel epithelium influence the cap of predentine which they border, as a result of which harder, shiny, modified dentine forms instead of orthodentine. The designation "modified dentine" should be used only to describe a dentine whose formation takes place in this way.

That the more basal cells of the inner enamel epithelium, which are not especially enlarged, form true enamel, may be gathered with certainty from a comparison with ground thin-sections of teeth of *Lepisosteus.* Between the inner and outer enamel epithelium there is in *Lepisosteus* a true enamel pulp containing a stellate reticulum. The boundary area between the tooth germ and surrounding connective tissue is interesting in that in many places blood capillaries enter projections of the outer enamel epithelium. These projections bring about an enlargement of the interface between ectoderm and mesoderm at a place that is very important for the exchange of material; this enlargement probably provided an additional port of entry for material from the bloodstream—not via the pulp cavity—but to the outside of the tooth anlage.

Among teleosts teeth consisting of enamel, orthodentine, and modified dentine seem to be restricted to certain families; but modified dentine has a very wide distribution, and orthodentine is always present. The best examples of true enamel in teleosts are found among the sparids and labrids. The enamel character is suggested particularly by an especially intense negative birefringence. In the presence of acids, this enamel behaves differently from that of mammals, reptiles, and amphibians in that its organic ground substance does not disappear without trace upon decalcification, but remains intact enough to permit recognition of short, straight rodlets, oriented at a right angle to the surface. It was labrids and sparids that served J. H. Mummery for the description of his "tubular enamel," a designation no longer tenable under the present interpretation; but Mummery properly recognized the physiological significance of the complicated intertonguing of the outer enamel epithelium and the capillaries. In numerous types of differentiation, such an intertonguing occurs also in very many other teleosts. The territory occupied by the enamel epithelium is always considerable. As a rule, the cell boundaries disappear in this area in early stages. Only exceptionally do they remain clearly recognizable later. In many instances this leads to very peculiar structures of which only a very few examples could be illustrated. This differentiation, called stroma formations by Mummery, requires further morphological and physiological investigation.

Trabecular dentine occurs, for example, in the pike *Esox,* but it differs from that in selachians in that the arrangement of the capillaries and the connective tissue strands appears to influence the arrangement of the trabecles; this is not as evident in the selachians.

Merluccius teeth provide a good example of vasodentine in the sense of Ch. S. Tomes, that is, a dentine penetrated by a network of fairly wide tubules that contain blood capillaries.

The histology of the teeth of the Choanichthyes is interesting in several respects. The study of teeth of *Latimeria* showed the presence of only enamel and orthodentine. R. Schweizer has noted this fact in fossil crossopterygians. Modified dentine has so far not been identified in any representative of the group. This kind of dentine is also absent in the lungfishes, in which tooth plates originate, as Semon has demonstrated, from the concrescence of many discrete individual teeth. True enamel is present beyond doubt, but it is retained only in places on the crown of the tooth plates that are not subjected to wear.

Histological study of the developing teeth of modern amphibians revealed in particular the relatively large size and thus small number of the cell elements. The unfortunately short-lived tooth chimeras, that G. Wagner obtained experimentally by implanting neural crest material from *Bombina pachypus* on young larvae of *Triton alpestris,* provide insight into the influences of parts of the anlagen on one another at different periods of development. True enamel is present both in Anurans and in urodeles; Gymnophiona could not be studied at first hand.

In the reptiles, investigations on *Crocodilus* and *Varanus* showed primarily that the formation of enamel takes place in the same manner as in mammals. Fully-formed reptile enamel, much as that of mammals, is entirely dissolved during decalcification of the specimens. But in both groups there is a first prestage of enamel whose organic base does not dissolve during decalcification and which, immediately following its formation, may be stained (with a variety of dyes) so intensively that no structure is recognizable. In both groups also there is a second prestage of enamel restricted to a short period immediately prior to the completion of the mineralization. This second prestage permits recognition of structure both in reptiles and mammals. In the reptilian tooth anlage there occur here fine lines approximately parallel to the surface, which correspond to the contour lines of the fully formed mammalian enamel, and show that enamel forms in layers. At approximately a right angle to these lines, there are usually slightly curved, rod-like formations, by which a prism structure of the reptilian enamel is also indicated. In the fully formed enamel, the prism structure of the elements in question appears rather clearly in adequately ground thin sections of modern and especially fossil reptile teeth. Thus the reptilian enamel appears to be composed of prism-like structures which, in contrast to mammalian enamel, do not show sharply defined cross striation, and are not so sharply defined from one another.

In the development of mammalian teeth, it is known that during enamel formation the ameloblasts may contain in their interiors sharply circumscribed, selectively stainable secrete-droplets. In the ameloblasts of *Crocodylus,* such secrete-droplets could also be demonstrated; they react to staining with iron haematoxylin in the same way as the first prestage of enamel.

In several examples of reptile teeth it was shown that the dentine-enamel boundary does not follow the minute projections and depressions of the crown surface, but in the presence of more pronounced sculpturing runs parallel to the tooth surface.

Arrangement and mode of branching of the dentinal tubules may show considerable differences in the basal versus the other parts of the teeth.

Tooth cementum is present among the modern forms in crocodiles, among the fossil reptiles in the ichthyosaurs.

The mode of enamel formation in mammals had to be described earlier in connection with the reptiles because of the comparison. The following may here be added: To investigate the development of teeth in mammals I had available more varied and in many respects more favorable material, than I had for the reptiles. The processes of the development of teeth in reptiles, described above were first recognized in mammals. It was later found that comparable relations exist in reptiles.

For the graphic presentation of differences between the first and second prestages and the fully formed enamel in their reactions to acid and selective staining, the continuously growing gnawing teeth of rodents and lagomorphs proved to be particularly suitable objects. Since mineralization of a tooth begins at the tip and progresses toward the base, this process— in a functional gnawing tooth—is already completed not only at the tip but in a large portion of the tooth. In this area the enamel is totally dissolved during decalcification and nothing remains of its organic base. This empty space produced by decalcification is bordered by the zone of the second prestage of enamel, in which the organic ground substance is retained, and reveals its structure. Closer to the base there follows the first prestage of enamel, stained so intensively (with the use of the most different dyes) that it appears to be a structureless mass. A comparable sequence of the different stages of enamel formation could also be observed in developmental stages of teeth with terminal growth.

To gain information about the structure of the first prestage of enamel, a new procedure was used (Peyer, 1959) in which fixation and staining are avoided (p. 201). Phase contrast microscopy of such preparations revealed that the first prestage of enamel is not a structureless, cuticular secretion, but that the boundaries between the prestages of the individual enamel prisms are clearly visible.

The second prestage of enamel is also significant for understanding the process of enamel formation. A systematic search of places in the sections where the second prestage is visible in tooth preparations of different mammal groups, revealed that in this stage (which immediately precedes the end of mineralization) the forms of the future enamel prisms are already fully developed. In rodents and in lagomorphs these forms are, however, so complicated that the presently predominant theoretical view, that the mammalian enamel is a cuticular mass produced by a process of secretion, is hardly adequate to account for them. Our evidence suggests rather that the enamel prisms are first preconstituted by outgrowth of cell processes from the ameloblasts, which subsequently change to enamel prisms as dissolved mineral constituents are transported to the cell processes where the mineral matter is deposited.

The continuously growing gnawing teeth of the rodents and lagomorphs show further that in their formation the supply of material from the blood stream apparently takes place not only via pulp cavity but also from numerous blood capillaries by diffusion to the ectoderm of the tooth anlage. This is by no means a singular occurrence, because we could recognize in principle similar conditions also in the shark *Isurus*, the holostean *Lepisosteus*, in many teleosts, and, in a somewhat less striking but nevertheless certain instance, in a reptile.

With respect to the dentine we may mention that our observations on teeth of mammals, reptiles, amphibians, and fishes contradict a thesis published in 1957 by W. Warwick James, according to which the dentinal tubules are supposed to contain not processes of odontoblasts but only tissue fluid.

Deposition of tooth cementum on the enamel of the tooth crown is necessarily preceded by the destruction of the epithelial sheath that covers the enamel layer. To demonstrate the destruction of the epithelium and the invasion by mesodermal cells, sections through the deeply enamel-folded cheek teeth of the rabbit were particularly instructive, because in a single preparation all stages from the intact epithelium to the complete destruction appear side by side.

The significance of odontological characteristics in determining kinship relations among animals has been differently interpreted in the course of time. Many assignments or groupings based on dentitional features have proved to be untenable. Thus it was shown, for example, that *Daubentonia* (*Cheiromys*), the Aye-Aye of Madagascar, which formerly had been assigned to the rodents, belongs to the lemurs. The order Edentata turned out to be an unnatural grouping of forms that are not closely related to each other, and even the order Rodentia could not be retained in its former extent; the rabbits and their allies were removed and made the representatives of a separate order, Lagomorpha. Basically, these changes in the systematic grouping do not deny the taxonomic significance of dentition characters, because on more careful analysis it was recognized that neither *Daubentonia* nor the lagomorphs has a rodent dentition. In the classification of mammals, dentitional characters play indeed a most important role. Thus, for example, "jumping mice," despite similar differentiation of the limbs, are placed in different families on the basis of their dentitions. In much the same way, the dentition of the Litopterna shows that these extinct mammals of the South American Tertiary cannot be related to the horses, despite notably horse-like fore and hind limbs.

In the interpretation of the systematic position of fossil mammals, particularly from the early Tertiary, the obviously great significance of odontological features should not, however, lead to their one-sided over-evaluation; it should always be remembered that dentitional characteristics represent only one aspect of an animals' structure.

The odontological studies of the paleontologists contributed to the insight that numerous parallel developments have resulted in extremely similar end conditions, which were considered as evidence of kinship relations while only a few forms were known. In all instances, however, where the history of individual groups of vertebrates, especially of mammals, can be surveyed from the beginnings to the Present or to extinction, the more or less complete adaptation of the dentition to specific tasks appears as a historic achievement. In odontological features, as in all morphological studies, the serial grouping of morphological conditions may lead to an understanding of evolutionary processes only if the functional aspects of the problem are also investigated. Such a point of view cannot be regarded as teleological since it includes no designation of an aim, but rests merely on the proposition, based on our general experiences, that we recognize as meaningful attributes certain organizational relations and certain chemical processes that run their courses in organisms.

So far as we may now recognize, a survey of the evolution of the dentition in vertebrates results, as expected, in a correspondence with the insights reached from other features of organization. This correspondence is true also of the microscopic relations. As an example, the crossopterygians, from which the tetrapods have evolved, correspond with them also in the histological structure of the teeth, in that in both groups only orthodentine and true enamel are present. The actinopterygians, however, with the three tooth hard substances restricted to this group, have advanced on a phylogenetic side line that could no longer lead to the tetrapods.

Table of the geological designations [1]

Era	Period	Absolute ages in millions of years	
		Begin	Duration
Cenozoic	Quaternary	1	1
Age of mammals and man	Tertiary	63	63
Mesozoic	Cretaceous	135	71
Age of reptiles	Jurassic	181	45
	Triassic	230	48
Paleozoic	Permian	280	49
Age of lower vertebrates and extinct primitive invertebrates	Carboniferous	345	64
	Devonian	405	59
	Silurian	425	19
	Ordovician	500	74
	Cambrian	600	99

[1] Kulp, J. L. 1961. Geologic Time Scale. *Science* 133:1105–1114. The sequence of the geologic periods, with which changes in flora and fauna go hand in hand, has been determined during the past century and a half by the comparative study of positional relations of rock strata in a vast number of profiles, and by study of the rock sequences. The absolute age data have been determined by physicists by the decay rates of radioactive substances.

The delimitation of the boundaries of the periods is more or less conventional and influenced by regional factors. Of differences in terminology the following may be mentioned. The Carboniferous is divided by American geologists into two subgroups, the older Mississippian (whose characteristic rock types are limestones) and the younger Pennsylvanian (the "Great Coal Age" proper).

The Rhaetic, a transitional horizon between Triassic and Jurassic, is placed at the end of the Triassic by some, at the beginning of the Jurassic by others.

The epochs of the Tertiary period are as follows in sequence from the oldest (bottom) to the youngest:
Pliocene
Miocene
Oligocene
Eocene
Paleocene

Time table of tooth eruption in man and in the horse

a. Eruption of the milk teeth of Man

(after W. Meyer, 1951)

First milk incisor	6. – 8. month
Second milk incisor	8. – 12. month
Milk canine	15. – 20. month
First milk premolar	12. – 16. month
Second milk premolar	20. – 40. month

b. Eruption of the permanent teeth of Man

(after W. Meyer, 1951)

First incisor	6. – 9. year
Second incisor	7. – 10. year
Canine	9. – 14. year
First premolar	9. – 13. year
Second premolar	11. – 14. year
First molar	6. – 8. year
Second molar	10. – 14. year
Third molar	16. – 30. year

c. Eruption and change of teeth in the horse

(after Ellenberger-Baum, 1943)

Milk dentition

eruption of	I d 1	Prior to birth or in the first weeks thereafter.
eruption of	I d 2	Within 2–4, more rarely 4–8 weeks
eruption of	I d 3	Within 5–9 months
eruption of	C d	The C d are soon present, at the latest ½ year after birth, however, generally do not erupt.
eruption of	P d 1 P d 2 P d 3	Prior to birth or in the first weeks thereafter.

Permanent dentition

change of	I 1	Within 2½–3 years
change of	I 2	Within 3½–4 years
change of	I 3	Within 4½–5 years
eruption of	C	Within 3½–5 years
eruption of	P 1	Undetermined, usually in the first half year after birth.
change of	P 2	Within 2½ years
change of	P 3	Within 2½ years
eruption of	P 4	Within 3½–4 years
eruption of	M 1	Within 6–9 months, sometimes up to 14 months
eruption of	M 2	Within 2–2¼ years
eruption of	M 3	Within 3½–4½ years

The very small P 1 are common in the upper jaw, but extremely rare in the lower jaw. They have no predecessors in the milk dentition. As pointed out before, the premolars are counted from the back to the front in veterinary-anatomical works. In the table above, the usual mode of counting was employed.

More detailed data concerning the tooth replacement may be found for man in the human anatomical works, for example in W. Meyer (1951); for the horse and the domestic animals in Ellengerger and Baum (1943).

Bibliography

Abel, O. 1919. *Die Stämme der Wirbeltiere*. Berlin und Leipzig: W. de Gruyter.

Aichel, O. 1915. Das Problem der Entstehung der Zahnform. *Archiv. f. Anat. Suppl. Bd.*

Anthony, R. L. F. 1934. La dentition de l'oryctérope. Morphologie—développement—structure—interpétation. *Ann. Sci. Nat. Zool.,* Paris ser. 10, 17.

Bargmann, W. 1933. Die Zahnplatten von *Chimaera monstrosa. Zeitschr. f. Zellforsch. u. mikr. Anat.* 19.

———— 1937. Zur Frage der Homologisierung von Schmelz und Vitrodentin. *Zeitschr. F. Zellforschung u. mik. Anat.* 27.

———— 1941. Ueber den Feinbau der Zahnplatten von *Chimaera monstrosa. Anat. Anz.* 92, (13/14).

———— 1951. *Histologie und mikroskopische Anatomie des Menschen.* Stuttgart: G. Thieme.

Bauer, F. 1898. Die Ichthyosaurier des oberen weissen Jura. *Palaeontographica* 44.

Baumann, F. 1949. *Die freilebenden Säugetiere der Schweiz.* Bern: Hans Huber.

Beaumont, G. de 1960. Contribution à l'étude des genres *Orthacodus* Woodw. et *Notidanus* Cuv. (Selachii). *Schweiz. Pal. Abh.* 77.

De Beer, G. R. 1947. The differentiation of neural crest cells into visceral cartilages and odontoblasts in *Amblystoma,* and a reexamination of the germ-layer theory. *Proc. Roy. Soc.* (B) 134.

Bensley, Arthur. 1903. On the evolution of the Australian Marsupialia; with remarks on the relationships of the marsupials in general. *Trans. Linnean Soc.* London, Ser. 2, Zool., 11.

Besmer, A. 1947. Beiträge zur Kenntnis des Ichthyosauriergebisses. *Abh. Schweiz. Pal. Ges.* 65.

Bigelow, H. B. and W. C. Schroeder. 1948. Part I, Lancelets, Cyclostomes and Sharks, in *Fishes of the Western North Atlantic.* Mem. Sears Foundation for Marine Research No. 1, New Haven: Yale University.

1953. Part II, Sawfishes, Guitarfishes, Skates and Rays, Chimaeroids, in *Fishes of the Western North Atlantic*. Mem. Sears Foundation for Marine Research No. 1, New Haven: Yale University.

Bluntschli, H. 1911. Zur Phylogenie des Gebisses der Primaten mit Ausblicken auf jenes der Säugetiere überhaupt. *Vierteljahrschr. Naturforsch. Ges. in Zürich* 56.

1931. Die Gebiss- und Zahntheorien von Louis Bolk. *Fortschr. Zahnheilkunde* 7.

Bödecker, C. F. 1905. Eine Entkalkungsmethode für Gewebe, welche wenig organische Substanz enthalten, insbesondere Zahnschmelz. *Zeitschr. Mikrosk.*, 22.

Bogert, C. M. 1943. Dentitional phenomena in cobras and other elaphids with notes on adaptive modifications of fangs. *Bull. Amer. Mus. Nat. Hist.* 81.

Bolk, L. 1911. Ueber die Phylogenese des Primatengebisses und das Zukunftsgebiss des Menschen. *Zeitschr. f. Morph. u. Anthrop.* 20.

1917. Die Beziehung zwischen Reptilien, Beutler—und Plazentalierge-biss. *Zeitschr. f. Morph. u. Anthrop.* 20.

1913–1919. *Odontologische Studien.* I–III. Jena: G. Fischer.

Breder, C. M. 1942. The shedding of teeth by *Carcharias littoralis* (Mitchill). *Copeia.* 1942.

Brettnacher, H. 1939. Aufbau und Struktur der Holocephalenzähne. *Ztschr. f. mikr—anat. Forschung.* 46.

Broom, Robert. 1907. The dental formula of *Orycteropus. Nature* 1907.

Bullet, Ph. 1942. Beiträge zur Kenntnis des Gebisses von *Varanus salvator* Laur. *Vierteljahrsschr. Nat. Ges. in Zürich* 87.

Burckhardt, R. 1906. Die Entwicklungsgeschichte der Verknöcherungen des Integumentes und der Mundhöhle der Wirbeltiere, in *Handbuch der vergleichenden und experimentellen Entwicklungslehre der Wirbeltiere* II, i. Jena: Gustav Fischer.

Butler, P. M. 1939. Studies of the mammalian dentition—Differentiation of the postcanine dentition. *Proc. Zool. Soc. London* (B) 109.

1941. A theory of the evolution of mammalian molar teeth. *Amer. J. Sci.* 239 (6).

Bystrow, A. P. 1938a. Zahnstruktur der Labyrinthodonten. *Acta Zoologica* 19.

1938b. *Dvinosaurus* als neotenische Form der Stegocephalen. *Acta Zoologica* 19.

Campbell, C. B. G. 1966. Taxonomic Status of Tree Shrews. *Science* 153.

Casier, E. 1947. Constitution et évolution de la racine dentaire des Euselachii. *Bull. Mus. Roy. d'Hist. nat. de Belgique* 23.

Clark, R. S. 1926. *Rays and Skates, a revision of the European species.* Fisheries, Scotland, Sci. Invest.

Colbert, Edw. H. 1951. *The Dinosaur Book.* New York: American Mus. Nat. Hist.

Corse, J. 1799. Observations on the Manners, Habits and Natural History of the Elephant. Observations on the different species of Asiatic Elephants and their mode of Dentition. *Phil. Trans. Roy. Soc. London* 1799.

Crompton, A. W. 1962. On the dentition and tooth replacement in two bauriamorph reptiles. *Annals South Afr. Mus.* 46.

— 1963. Tooth replacement in the cynodont *Thrinaxodon liorhinus* Seeley. *Annals South Afr. Mus.* 46.

Davis, D. D. 1964. The Giant Panda: A morphological study of evolutionary mechanisms. *Fieldiana: Zoology Memoirs* 3.

Denison, R. H. 1958. Early Devonian fishes from Utah. III. Arthrodira. *Fieldiana: Geology* 11 (9).

Dependorf, Th. 1888. *Zur Entwicklungsgeschichte des Zahnsystems der Marsupialia.* Semon's Zool. Forsch. in Australien etc. Jena.

De Terra, P. 1911. *Vergleichende Anatomie des menschlichen Gebisses und der Zähne der Vertebraten.* Jena: Gustav Fischer.

Döderlein, L. 1921. Betrachtungen über die Entwicklung der Nahrungsaufnahme bei Wirbeltieren. *Zoologica* 27.

Eastoe, J. E. 1964. *Recent studies on the organic matrices of bone and teeth,* in *Bone and Tooth Symposium,* ed. H. J. J. Blackwood. New York: Macmillan.

Edmund, A. G. 1960. Tooth replacement phenomena in the lower vertebrates. Life Sci. Div. Contrib. 52, The Royal Ontario Museum, Toronto.

Ellenberger, W. and H. Baum 1943. *Handbuch der vergleichenden Anatomie der Haustiere.* 18. Aufl., bearbeitet von O. Zietzschmann, Eb. Ackerknecht und H. Grau. Berlin: Springer-Verlag.

Fahrenholz, C. 1915. Ueber die Verbreitung von Zahnbildungen und Sinnesorganen im Vorderdarm der Selachier und ihre phylogenetische Deutung. *Jenaische Zeitschr* 53.

Fourie, S. 1963. Tooth replacement in the gomphodont cynodont *Diademodon.* *S. Afr. J. Sci.* 59.

Fritsch, A. 1883–1901. Fauna der Gaskohle und der Kalksteine der Permformation Böhmens, Prag: Selbstverlag, in Commission bei Fr. Řivnáč.

Garman, S. 1913. The Plagiostomia (Sharks, Skates and Rays). *Mem. Mus. Comp. Zoology Harvard* 36.

Gazin, C. L. 1965. A study of the early Tertiary condylarthran mammal *Meniscotherium.* *Smithson. Miscel. Collect.* 149 (2).

Gesner, Conrad. 1551. *Historia animalium, L. I, de quadrupedibus viviparis.* Zürich: Froschauer .

Giebel, C. G. 1855. *Odontographie.* Leipzig.

Goodrich, E. S. 1909. *Vertebrata craniata,* Fasc. 1, Cyclostomes and Fishes, in Ray Lankester's *Treatise on Zoology,* Part IX, London: Adam and Charles Black.

Gregory, W. K. 1921. The origin and evolution of the human dentition. *Journ. Dental Research* 2, 3.

　　1951. *Evolution emerging. A Survey of changing Patterns from Primeval Life to Man.* New York: Macmillan.

Gregory, J. T. 1951. Convergent evolution: The jaws of *Hesperornis* and the mosasaurs. *Evolution* 5 (4).

Gregory, J. T., Peabody, F. E. and Price, L. I. 1956. Revision of the Gymnarthridae, American Permian Microsaurs. *Peabody Mus. Nat. Hist. Yale University Bull.* 10.

Gross, W. 1956. Ueber Crossopterygier und Dipnoer aus dem baltischen Oberdevon im Zusammenhang mit einer vergleichenden Untersuchung des Porenkanalsystems paläzoischer Agnathen und Fische. *Kun. Svenska Vetensk. Handlingar* 4, Ser. 5, 6.

　　1957. Mundzähne und Hautzähne der Acanthodier und Arthrodiren. *Palaeontographica* 109, Abt. A.

Günther, A. 1880. *An introduction to the study of fishes.* Edinburgh.

Guttormsen, S. E. 1937. Beiträge zur Kenntnis des Ganoidengebisses, insbesondere des Gebisses von *Colobodus. Schweiz. Pal. Abh.* 60.

Held, H. 1926. Über die Bildung des Schmelzgewebes. *Zschr. mikrosk.-anat. Forsch.* 5.

Helmcke, J. G. 1954. *Biokristallographische Einlagerung anorganischer Verbindungen in organische Hartsubstanzen.* Un. Intern. Cristallogr., Third Intern. Congr. Paris and Copenhagen: F. Bagges Hoftoqtr., pp. 61–62.

Hennig, E. 1906. *Gyrodus* und die Organisation der Pycnodonten. *Paleontographica* 53.

Hertwig, O. 1874a. Ueber Bau und Entwicklung der Placoidschuppen und der Zähne der Selachier. *Jenaische Zeitschr. Naturwiss* 8.

　　1874b. Ueber das Zahnsystem der Amphibien und seine Bedeutung für die Genese des Skelettes der Mundhöhle. *Arch. mikr. Anat. Suppl.* 11.

Hopson, J. A. 1964. Tooth replacement in cynodont, dicynodont and therocephalian reptiles. *Proc. Zool. Soc. London* 142 (4)

Huene, F. v. 1936. *Henodus chelyops,* ein neuer Placodontier. *Palaeontographica* 84.

Hürzeler, J. 1949. Neubeschreibung von *Oreopithecus bambolii* Gervais. *Schweiz. Pal. Abh.* 66.

1958. *Oreopithecus bambolii* Gervais, a preliminary report. *Verh. Nat. Ges. Basel* 69.

Huxley, J. S. 1872. *A manual of the anatomy of vertebrated animals.* New York.

Imms, A. D. 1905. On the oral and pharyngeal Denticles of Elasmobranch Fishes. *Proc. Zool. Soc. London* I.

Jaekel, O. 1889. Die Selachier aus dem ob. Muschelkalk Lothringens. Heft 4 *Geol. Spezialkarte von Elsass-Lothringen* 3.

Jacobshagen, E. 1923. Placoidorgane und Selachierzähne. Kritik der morphologischen Herleitung von Zement und Knochen nach O. Hertwig. Anat. Anz. 57, Erg. Heft.

Jain, S. L., Robinson, P. L., and Chowdhury, T. K. Roy. 1964. A new vertebrate fauna from the Triassic of the Deccan, India. *Quart. J. Geol. Soc. London* 120.

James, W. W. 1953. The succession of teeth in elasmobranchs. *Proc. zool. Soc. London* 123.

1955. The blood capillary system of the odontoblast layer of the dental pulp. *Journ. Anat.* 89, part 4.

1957. A further study of dentine. *Transact. Zool. Soc. of London* 29, Part I.

1960. *The Jaws and Teeth of Primates.* London: Pitman.

James, W. W. and Wellings, A. W. 1943. The dental epithelium and its significance in tooth development. *Proc. R. Soc. Med.* 37.

Jarvik, Erik. 1954. On the visceral skeleton in *Eusthenopteron,* with a discussion of the parasphenoid and palatoquadrate in fishes. *Kungl. Svenska Vetenskap, Akad. Handl.* 4th ser., 5 (1).

Jesson, Hans. 1966. Die Crossopterygier des oberen Plattenkalkes (Devon) der Bergisch-Gladbach-Paffrater Mulde (Rheinisches Schiefergebirge) unter Berücksichtigung von amerikanischem und europäischem *Onychodus*-Material. *Arkiv för Zoologi, Kungl. Svenska Vetenskap. Akad.* Serie 2, 18 (14).

Kälin, J. 1955. Crocodilia, in *Traité de Paléontologie.* Paris: Masson.

Kerr, T. 1955. Development and structure of the teeth in the dog fish, *Squalus acanthias* L. and *Scyliorhinus caniculus* (L). *Proc. Zool. Soc. London* 125.

1960. Development and structure of some actinopterygian and urodele teeth. *Proc. Zool. Soc. London* 133, Part 3.

Kiprijanoff, W. 1881. Studien über die fossilen Reptilien Russlands, I. *Mem. Ac. Sci. St. Petersb.* VII. Ser., 28.

Klaatsch, N. 1890. Zur Morphologie der Fischschuppen und zur Geschichte der Hartsubstanzgebilde. *Morphol. Jahrb.* 16.

Klunzinger, C. B. 1870–71. Synopsis der Fische des Rothen Meeres. *Verh. Zool.—Bot. Ges. Wien* 20, 21.

Köenigswald, G. H. R. von. 1965. Das Leichenfeld als Biotop. *Zool. Jahrb. Abt. Syst. Ökol. Geogr. Tiere* 92 (1).

Korvenkontio, V. A. 1934. Mikroskopische Untersuchungen an Nagerincisiven unter Hinweis auf die Schmelzstruktur der Backenzähne. *Ann. Zool., Soc. Zool.—Bot. Fennicae Vanamo* 2.

Kraus, B. S. and Jordan, R. E. 1965. The Human Dentition before Birth. Philadelphia: Lea & Febiger.

Krause, Rudolf. 1923. *Mikroskopische Anatomie der Wirbeltiere* III. Berlin & Leipzig: Vereinig. Wiss. Verl., de Gruyter.

Krüger, W. 1939. Unser Pferd und seine Vorfahren. *Verständl. Wissensch.* 41.

Kuhn-Schnyder, E. 1952. *Askeptosaurus italicus* Nopsca, in: B. Peyer, Die Triasfauna der Tessiner Kalkalpen. *Schweiz. Pal. Abb.* 69.

Kühne, W. G. 1956. The Liassic Therapsid *Oligokyphus*. London: British Museum (Natural History).

Kükenthal, Willy. 1889–1893. Vergleichend-anatomische und entwicklungsgeschichtliche Untersuchungen an Waltieren. Chapter VI, Bezahnung. *Jenaische Denkschr.* III, 2.

Küpfer, M. 1935. Beiträge zur Erforschung der baulichen Struktur der Backenzähne des Hausrindes (*Bos taurus*). *Denkschr. Schweiz. Nat. Ges.* 70.

Kvam, T. 1946. Comparative study of the ontogentic and phylogenetic development of dental enamel. *Norske Tandlaegforen. Tid.* 56, Suppl.
   1950. The development of mesodermal enamel on piscine teeth. Trondheim: *Det Kongelide Norske Videnskabers Selskab*.

Landolt, H. H. 1947. Ueber den Zahnwechsel bei Selachiern. *Revue suisse de Zool.* 54.

Leche, W. 1874–1900. Säugetiere, in Bronn, *Klassen und Ordnungen des Tierreichs.*
   1909, 1915. Zur Frage nach der stammesgeschichtlichen Bedeutung des Milchgebisses bei den Säugetieren. *Zool. Jahrb.* (Syst.) 28, 38.

Lehman, J. P. 1959. *L'évolution des vertébrés inférieurs*. Monographies Dunod, Paris: Dunod.

Lehner, J. 1931. Ein Beitrag zur Kenntnis vom Schmelzoberhäutchen (Cuticula dentis). *Zeitschr. mikr.-anat. Forschg.* 27.

Lehner, J. and Plenk, H. 1936. Die Zähne, in W. v. Möllendorff, *Handbuch der mikroskopischen Anatomie des Menschen* 5. Berlin: Julius Springer.

Leunis, J. 1883. [H. Ludwig] *Synopsis der Tierkunde*. Hannover: Hahn'sche Buchhandlung.

Levi, G. 1939. Étude sur le développement des dents chez les téléostéens. *Arch. Anat. micr. Paris* 35.

1939. Sulla calcificazione dello smalto nei teleostei. *Bull. d'Histol. appl.* 16.

Lison, L. 1941. Recherches sur la structure et l'histogenèse des dents des poissons dipneustes. *Arch. Biol.* 52.

1949. Recherches sur l'histogenèse de l'émail dentaire chez les sélaciens. *Arch. Biol.* 60.

1954. Les dents, in E. Grassé, *Traité de Zoologie* 12. Paris: Masson.

Marcus, H. 1931a. Zur Phylogenie der Schmelzprismen. *Zeitschr. Zellforsch* 12.

1931b. Zur Zahn-und Gebissentwicklung bei Gymnophionen, Krokodilen und Marsupialiern. *Morphol. Jahrb.* 68.

Markert, F. 1896. Die Flossenstrahlen von *Acanthias*. *Zool. Jahrb., Abt. f. Anat.* 9.

Marquard, E. 1946. Beiträge zur Kenntnis des Selachiergebisses. *Revue suisse de Zool.* 53.

Marsh, O. C. 1896. *The dinosaurs of North America.* 16th Ann. Rept. U. S. Geol. Survey, Washington.

1897. Recent observations on European dinosaurs. Amer. J. Sci. (IV) 4.

Mercati, Michele. 1717. Metallotheca.

Meyer, P. 1944. Beiträge zur Kenntnis des Gebisses von *Rana esculenta* L. mit besonderer Berücksichtigung des Zahnwechsels. *Vierteljahrsschr. Nat. Ges. in Zürich.*

Meyer, W. 1951. *Normale Histologie und Entwicklungsgeschichte der Zähne des Menschen.* München: Carl Hanser.

Miles, R. S. 1964. A reinterpretation of the visceral skeleton of *Acanthodes*. *Nature* 204.

Millot, J. et Anthony, J. 1958. *Anatomie de Latimeria chalumnae,* Tome 1 *Squelette et muscles.* Paris: Centre National de la Recherche scientifique.

Moss, M. L. 1964. Development of cellular dentine and lepidosteal tubules in the bowfin *Amia calva. Acta anat.* 58 (4).

Moss, M. L., Jones, S. J. and Piez, K. A. 1964. Calcified ectodermal collagens of shark tooth enamel and teleost scale. *Science* 145.

Moy-Thomas, J. A. 1934. On the teeth of the larval *Belone vulgaris* and the attachment of teeth in fishes. *Quart. Journ. micr. Sci.* 76.

Mummery, J. H. 1917. On the structure and development of the tubular enamel of the Sparidae and Labridae. *Phil. Trans. Roy. Soc. (B)* 208.

1924. *The microscopic and general anatomy of the teeth.* Oxford: Oxford Univ. Press.

Neumann, E. 1863. *Beitrag zur Kenntnis des normalen Zahnbein- und Knochengewebes*. Leipzig.

Nopsca, Franz. 1903. Neues über *Compsognathus*. *Neues Jahrb., Min. Geol., Pal. (Beil. Bd)* 16.

Odermatt, C. 1940. Beitrag zur Kenntnis des Gebisses von *Heloderma*. *Vierteljahrsschr. Nat. Ges. in Zürich* 85.

Orban, B. 1927. Schmelzlamellen und Schmelzbüschel. *Deutsche Monatsschr. Zahnheilk.* 45.

Ørvig, Tor. 1951. Histologic studies of Placoderms and fossil elasmobranchs. 1. The endoskeleton, with remarks on the hard tissues of lower vertebrates in general. *Arkiv för Zool., Kungl. Svenska Vetenskapsakad.* 2 Ser. 2, (2), (literature)

Ostrom, J. H. 1962. The cranial crests of hadrosaurian dinosaurs. Postilla, No. 62, New Haven

Owen, Richard. 1840–1845. *Odontography; or a treatise on the comparative anatomy of the teeth; their physiological relations, mode of development and microscopic structure in the vertebrate animals.* London: Hippolyte Bailliere.

Pappenheim, P. 1909. Pisces (inkl. Cyclostomata), Fische, in A. Brauer, *Die Süsswasserfauna Deutschlands* Heft 1. Jena: Gustav Fischer.

Parrington, F. R. 1936. On the tooth replacement in Theriodont Reptiles. *Phil. Trans. Roy. Soc. London* (B) 226.

1947. On a collection of Rhaetic Mammalian Teeth. *Proc. Zool. Soc. London* 116.

Parsons, Thomas and Willams, E. E. 1962. The teeth of amphibia and their relation to amphibian phylogeny. *J. Morph.* 110 (3).

Patterson, Bryan. 1949. Rates of evolution in taeniodonts, in *Genetics, Paleontology and Evolution*. Princeton: Princeton University Press.

1956. Early Cretaceous mammals and the evolution of mammalian molar teeth. *Fieldiana: Geology* 13 (1).

Patterson, C. 1965. The phylogeny of the chimaeroids. *Phil. Trans. Roy. Soc. London* (B) 249.

Peter, J. 1957. *Elektronenmikroskopische Untersuchungen an Schmelz und Dentin des Tümmlerzahns* (Tursiops tursio). Diss. Freie Univ. Berlin, Med. Fak.

Peyer, B. 1919. Die Flossenstacheln der Welse. *Anat. Anz.* 52.

1920. Zum Problem der Entstehung der Zahnform. *Anat. Anz.* 53.

1925. Die Ceratodusfunde, in Ergebnisse der Forschungsreisen Prof. E. Stromer's in den Wüsten Aegyptens. *Abh. Bayer. Akad. Wiss. math.-nat. Kl.* 30.

1929. Das Gebiss von *Varanus niloticus* L. und von *Dracaena guianensis* Daud. *Revue Suisse de Zool.* 36.

1931a. *Tanystropheus longobardicus* Bass. *Sp. Abh. Schweiz. Pal. Ges.* 50.

1931b. Hartgebilde des Integumentes, in L. Bolk, E. Göppert, E. Kallius, W. Lubosch. *Handb. der Vergl. Anatomie* I, Berlin und Wien: Urban and Schwarzenberg.

1937. Zähne und Gebiss, in L. Bolk, E. Göppert, E. Kallius, W. Lubosch, *Handb. der Vergl. Anatomie* 3. Berlin und Wien: Urban und Schwarzenberg.

1944. Die Reptilien vom Monte San Giorgio. *Nat. Ges. in Zürich. Neujahrsblatt.*

1945. Ueber Algen und Pilze in tierischen Hartsubstanzen. *Archiv Julius Klaus-Stift. Erg. Bd. zu Bd.* 20.

1946. Die schweizerischen Funde von *Asteracanthus* (*Strophodus*). *Schweiz. Pal. Abh.* 64.

1949. Die Genese von Schmelz, Zahnbein und Knochen. *Arch. Julius Klaus-Stift.* 24, Zürich.

1950a. *Geschichte der Tierwelt.* Zürich: Büchergilde Gutenberg.

1950b. Goethes Wirbeltheorie des Schädels. *Nat. Ges. in Zürich, Neujahrsblatt.*

1954. Ein Gebissfund von *Lepidotus* aus dem oberen weissen Jura von Thayngen, Kt. Schaffhausen (Schweiz). *Schweiz. Pal. Abhandl.* 70.

1955. *Helveticosaurus zollingeri* n.g.,n.sp. *Schweiz. Pal. Abh* 72.

1956. Über Zähne von Haramiyden, von Triconodonten und von wahrscheinlich synapsiden Reptilien aus dem Rhät von Hallau, Kt. Schaffhausen (Schweiz). *Schweiz. Pal. Abh.* 72.

1957. Ueber die morphologische Deutung der Flossenstacheln einiger Haifische. *Mittl. Nat. Ges. Bern, N.F.* 14.

1959a. Ueber die Vomerzähne von *Ceratodus parvus* und über die verschiedenen Altersstadien seiner Zahnplatten. *Vierteljahrsschr. Nat. Ges. in Zürich* 104.

1959b. Ein Verfahren zur Herstellung histologischer Präparate ohne Fixierung, Entkalkung und Färbung von Zähnen und Knochen samt den Weichteilen. *Anat. Anz.* 106 (21/24).

1963. *Die Zähne, Ihr Ursprung, ihre Geschichte und ihre Aufgabe.* Verständl. Wiss. *79*, Jul. Springer, Berlin.

Pickerill, H. P. 1913. The structure of enamel. *Dent. Cosmos.* 55.

Piveteau, Jean. 1937. Un amphibien du Trias inférieur. Pal. de Madagascar no. 23; *Annales de Paléontologie* 26.

1957. *Traité de Paléontologie* Tome VII, *Primates, Paléontologie humaine.* Paris: Masson.

Plenk, H. 1927. Ueber argyrophile Fasern (Gitterfasern) und ihre Bildungszellen. *Erg. d. Anat.* 27.

Quenstedt, F. A. 1882. *Bdellodus Bollensis* aus dem Posidonienschiefer bei Boll. *Jahresh. Ver. vaterl. Naturk. Württ.* 38.

Reich, P. 1907. *Das irreguläre Dentin der Gebrauchsperiode.* Jena: Gustav Fischer.

Reinhart, R. H. 1959. A review of the Sirenia and Desmostylia. *Univ. Calif. Publ. Geol. Sci.* 36 (1).

Remane, A. 1955. Ist *Oreopithecus* ein Hominide? *Akd. Wiss. und Lit. Math.-Nat. Kl., Nr. 12.*

Romer, A. S. 1945. *Vertebrate Paleontology.* Chicago: The University of Chicago Press. 3rd edit., 1966.

  1959. *Vergleichende Anatomie der Wirbeltiere.* Hamburg-Berlin: Parey.

  1961. Synapsid evolution and dentition. Intern. Coloq. on the evolution of mammals. *Kon. Vlaamse Acad. Wetensch. Lett. Sch. Kunsten Belgie,* Brussels, Part I.

Röse, C. R. 1893. Über die Zahnentwicklung der Krokodile. *Morphol. Arb.* 3.

  1897. Ueber die verschiedenen Abänderungen der Hartgewebe bei niederen Wirbeltieren. *Anat. Anz.* 14.

Russell, L. S. 1956. The Cretaceous reptile *Champsosaurus natator* Parks. *Bull.* No. 145, Nat. Mus. Canada, Ottawa.

Saal, R. v. 1930. Beobachtungen über den feineren Bau des menschlichen Zahnbeins. *Zeitschr. f. Zellforsch.* 11.

Scapino, R. P. 1965. The third joint of the canine jaw. *J. Morph.* 116 (1).

Schaffer, J. 1933. *Lehrbuch der Histologie und Histogenese.* Berlin and Wien: Urban & Schwarzenberg.

Schalch, F. and Peyer, B. 1919. Über ein neues Rhätvorkommen im Keuper des Donau-Rheinzuges. *Mitteil. Badisch. Geol. Landesanstalt* 8 (2).

Schmidt. W. J. 1948. Wandlungsvorgänge am Zahnbein der Fische. *Nachr. Giessener Hochschul-Ges.* 17.

Schmidt, W. J. 1949. Einige neuere Erkenntnisse an den Zahnsubstanzen. *Deutsch. Zahnärztl. Zschr.* 4.

Schmidt, W. J. and Keil, A. 1958. *Die gesunden und die erkrankten Zahngewebe des Menschen und der Wirbeltiere im Polarisationsmikroskop.* München: Carl Hanser.

Schultz, A. H. 1960. Einige Beobachtungen und Masse am Skelett von *Oreopithecus* im Vergleich mit anderen catarrhinen Primaten. *Z. Morph. Anthr.* 50, (2)

Schulze, F. E. 1869. Ueber cuticuläre Bildung und Verhornung von Epithelzellen bei den Wirbeltieren. *Arch. mikr. Anat.* 5.

Schweizer, Rolf. 1964. Die Elasmobranchier und Holocephalen aus den Nusplinger Plattenkalken. *Paleontographica,* Abt. A. 123.

Scott, J. H. and Symons, N. B. B. 1964. *Introduction to dental anatomy.* Edinburgh and London: Livingstone.

Serres, A. 1817. *Essai sur l'Anatomie et la Physiologie des dents ou nouvelle Théorie de la Dentition.* Paris.

Sicher, Harry. 1952. *Oral Anatomy,* 2d ed. St. Louis: Mosby.

Simons, E. L. 1960. The Paleocene Pantodonta. *Trans. Amer. Phil. Soc.* (N.S.) 50 (6).

Simpson, G. G. 1925. Mesozoic Mammalia. 3. Preliminary comparison of Jurassic mammals except multituberculates. *Amer. J. Sci.* 10, Ser. 5.

1931. A new classification of mammals. *Bull. Amer. Mus. Nat Hist.* 59.

1932. Fossil Sirenia of Florida and the Evolution of the Sirenia. *Bull. Amer. Mus. Nat. Hist.* 59 (8).

1936. Studies of the earliest mammalian dentitions. *Dental Cosmos* 78.

1945. The principles of classification and a classification of mammals. *Bull. Amer. Mus. Nat. Hist.* 85.

1948. The beginning of the age of mammals in South America. Bull. *Amer. Mus. Nat. Hist.* 91 (1).

1951. *Horses.* Oxford: Oxford Univ. Press.

1961. Evolution of the Mesozoic mammals. Intern. Colloq. on the evolution of mammals. *Kon Vlaamse Acad. Wetensch. Lett. Sch. Kunsten Belgie,* Brussels, Part I.

Simpson, G. G. and Couto, Carlos De Paula. 1957. The Mastodonts of Brazil. *Bull. Amer. Mus. Nat. Hist.* 112 (2).

Smreker, E. 1928. Ueber Anastomosen zwischen Dentinkanälchen und Zementkörperchen bei der Gemse. *Sitz. Ber. Akad. Wiss. Wien, Math. nat. Kl.*

Sognnaes, R. F. (ed.). 1963. Symposium *Mechanisms of hard tissue destruction.* Washington: Amer. Assoc. Adv. Sci.

Spalteholz, W. 1909. *Handatlas der Anatomie des Menschen.* Leipzig: S. Hirzel.

Stehlin, H. G. and Schaub S. 1951. Die Trigonodontie der simplicidentaten Nager. *Schweiz. Paläontol. Abhandl.* 67.

Steinhard, O. 1902. Ueber Placoidschuppen in der Mund-und Rachenhöhle der Plagiostomen. *Arch. Naturgesch.* 69.

Stensiö, E. A:Son. 1961. *Permian vertebrates* (an account of the Stensiö-Ørvig lepidomorial theory). Geology of the Arctic, Toronto: Univ. of Toronto Press.

1962. Origine et nature des écailles placoides et des dents. In: Problèmes actuels de Paléontologie. *Colloq. Internationaux du Centre Nat. Rech. Sci.,* No. 104, Paris.

Stephan, Pierre. 1900. Recherches histologiques sur la structure du tissu osseux des poissons. *Bull. Sci. France et Belge* 33 ser. 5 (2).

Stern, I. B. 1964. An electron microscopic study of the cementum, Sharpey's fibers and periodontal ligament in the rat incisor. *Amer. Journ. Anat.* 115 (3).

Stirton, R. A. 1940. Phylogeny of North American Equidae. *Univ. Calif. Publ. Bull. Dept. Geol. Sci.* 25.

——— 1959. *Life, Time and Man.* New York: Wiley.

Thomasset, J. 1930. Recherches sur les tissus dentaires des poissons fossiles. *Arch. d'Anat., d'Histol. et d'Embr.* 11.

Tobias, P. V. 1965. Early Man in East Africa, *Science* 149.

Tomes, Ch. S. 1875. On the structure and development of the teeth in Ophidia. *Phil. Trans. Roy. Soc. London* 165.

Tomes, Ch. S. 1923. *A Manual of Dental Anatomy, human and comparative.* London: Churchill.

Tomes, J. 1849. On the structure of the dental tissues of marsupial animals and more especially of the enamel. *Phil. Trans. Roy. Soc. London* 1849.

Traquair, R. H. 1898. Notes on Paleozoic fishes. *Ann. Mag. Nat. Hist* (ser. 7) 2.

Tretjakoff, D. 1926. Die Zähne der Plectognathen. *Zeitschr. f. Zool.* 127.

Treuenfels, P. 1896. Die Zähne von *Myliobatis aquila.* Diss. Basel.

Tucker, W. 1956. Studies on the trichiuroid fishes.—3. *Bull. Brit. Mus. (Natural History) Zool.* 4.

Tullberg, T. 1899. *Ueber das System der Nagetiere.* Upsala.

Vandebroek, G. 1964. Recherches sur l'origine des mammifères. *Ann. Soc. Roy. Zool. Belgique* 94.

Van Huysen, Grant. 1961. The microstructure of young dentine. *Norelco Reporter* 8 (5) Mount Vernon, N. Y.

Vogt, C. and Hofer, B. 1909. *Die Süsswasserfische von Mittel-Europa.* Dr. Schlüter and Mass, Halle, A. S.

Wagner, G. 1955. Chimaerische Zahnanlagen aus *Triton*-Schmelzorgan und *Bombinator*-Papille. Mit Beobachtungen über die Entwicklung von Kiemenzähnchen und Mundsinnesknospen in den *Triton*-Larven. *J. Embryol. exp. Morph.* 3.

Waldeyer, W. v. 1871. Bau und Entwicklung der Zähne, in Stricker's *Handbuch der Lehre von den Geweben* 1. Leipzig.

Walkhoff, O. 1924. *Die normale Histologie menschlicher Zähne.* Leipzig: Artur Felix.

Weber, M. 1928. *Die Säugetiere. Einführung in die Anatomie und Systematik der rezenten und fossilen Mammalia.* Jena: Gustav Fischer. Bd. I, 1927, Bd. II, 1928.

Weidenreich, F. 1926. Ueber den Schmelz der Wirbeltiere und seine Beziehungen zum Zahnbein. *Zeitschr. Anat. Entwickl.* 79.

1929. Dentin, in Kantorowicz' *Handwörterbuch der gesamten Zahnheilkunde* 1, Leipzig and Berlin: 1929.

Weil, L. A. 1888. Zur Histologie der Zahnpulpa. *Dtsch. Mschr. Zahnheilk,* 6.

Wheeler, R. C. 1958. *Textbook of Dental Anatomy and Physiology.* 3rd. ed. London: Saunders.

1962. *An atlas of tooth form.* 3rd. ed. London: Saunders.

Wheeler, W. H. 1961. Revision of the uintatheres. *Bull. Peabody Mus. Nat. Hist. Yale Univ.* 14.

Wellings, A. W. 1938. *Practical microscopy of the teeth and associated tissues.* London: Staples Press.

Widdowson, T. W. 1946. *Special or dental anatomy and physiology and dental histology.* Vols. I and II. London: Staples Press.

Wiedersheim, R. 1909. *Vergleichende Anatomie der Wirbeltiere.* Jena: Gustav Fischer.

Williams, J. L. 1882. Studies in the histogenesis of the teeth and contiguous parts. *Dental Cosmos* 24.

Winge, Herluf. 1893. Jordfundene og nulevende Pungdyr (Marsupialia). *E Mus. Lundi, Kjøbenhavn* 2 (2).

Woerdeman, M. W. 1920. Die Bolksche Dimer-Theorie. *Deutch. Zahnheilkunde.*

Wood, A. E. 1957. What, if anything, is a rabbit? *Evolution* 11 (4)

1962. The early Tertiary Rodents of the family Paramyidae. *Transact. Amer. Phil. Soc. Philadelphia* (N.S.) 52 (1).

1965. Grades and clades among rodents. *Evolution* 19 (1).

Woodward, M. F. 1896. On the teeth of the Marsupialia with especial reference to the premilk dentition. *Anat. Anz.* 12.

Woodward, A. Smith. 1889. *Catalogue of the fossil fishes in the British Museum (Natural History)* I. London.

1915. The use of fossil fishes in stratigraphical geology. *Quart. J. Geol. Soc. London* 71, Proc.

Wortman, J. L. 1903. Studies of Eocene Mammalia in the Marsh collection, Peabody Museum. Part II, Primates. *Amer J. Sci.* 15, 16.

Wurmbach, H. 1932. Das Wachstum des Selachierwirbels und seiner Gewebe. *Zool. Jahrb., Abt. Anat. and Ontog.* 55 (1).

Zangerl, R. 1933. Beitrag zur Kenntnis des feineren Baues der Dentinkanälchen. *Schweiz. Monatsschr. f. Zahnheilkunde* 43 (13).

1944. *Brachyuranochampsa eversolei,* gen. et. sp. nov., a new crocodilian from the Washakie Eocene of Wyoming. *Ann. Carn. Mus.* 30.

1966. A new shark of the family Edestidae, *Ornithoprion hertwigi* from the Pennsylvanian Mecca Quarry Shales of Indiana. *Fieldiana: Geology* 16 (1).

Zangerl, Rainer and Richardson, E. S. Jr. 1963. The paleoecological history of two Pennsylvanian black shales. *Fieldiana: Geology Memoirs* 4.

Zittel, K. A. v. 1923. *Grundzüge der Paläontologie* II, *Vertebrata*. Neubearbeitet von F. Broili und M. Schlosser. München und Berlin: R. Oldenborg.

    1902. *Textbook of Paleontology*. Vol. II. Transl. by Charles R. Eastman. London: Macmillan.

Index

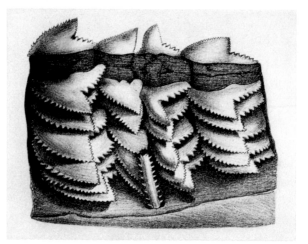

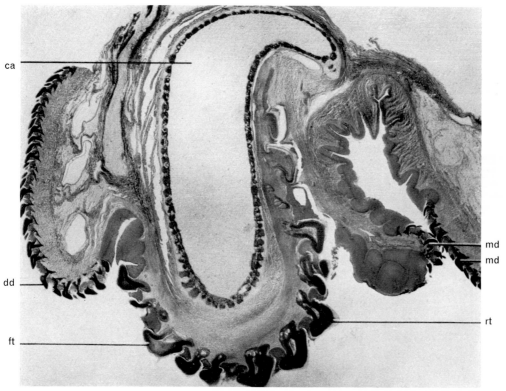

Pl. 1b Section through the upper jaw of the shark *Mustelus:* dd, dermal denticles; ca, jaw
cartilage; separated from it by connective tissue, the functional dentition teeth (ft) and, on
lingual side of the jaw the replacement teeth (rt) in process of formation. The youngest tooth
anlage is uppermost in the picture. The mucous membrane fold covering the replacement
teeth has come loose in its lower part. Here anterior-most patch of mucous membrane denticles
(md); following a denticle-free incurved part of the membrane is the denticulate part of the
mucous membrane of the roof of the mouth. Marginally in the jaw cartilage dark calcifications.
13:1.

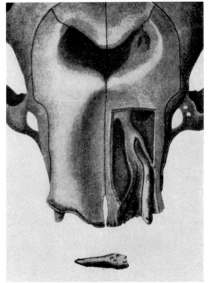

Pl. 2a Anterior view of the skull of a newborn Indian elephant. The left premaxilla was removed to show the presence of a milk tusk. After J. Corse from Peyer, *Die Zähne*, Verständliche Wissenschaft, vol. 79, Springer Verlag, Berlin (1963) (by permission).

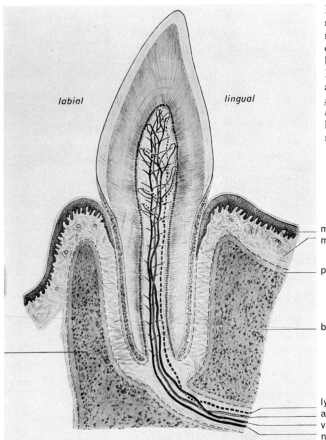

labial

lingual

mucous membrane

periosteum

bone

alveolar wall

lymph vessel
artery
vein
nerve

Pl. 2b Section through a mammal tooth: mucous membrane, gingiva, alveolar-dental membrane, and jaw bone, somewhat schematic. Modified from Ellenberger and Baum, *Handbuch der vergleichenden Anatomie der Haustiere*, 18th ed., Springer Verlag, Berlin (1943) (by permission).

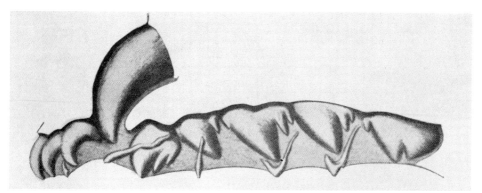

Pl. 3a Milk teeth and permanent dentition of a newborn seal, *Phoca vitulina*. After Weber (1927), from Peyer, *Die Zähne*, Verständliche Wissenschaft, vol. 79, Springer Verlag, Berlin (1963) (by permission).

Pl. 3b A cross row of teeth and replacement teeth of the upper jaw of the skate *Raja clavata;* palatoquadrate cartilage slightly deformed by drying. From Marquard (1946).

Pl. 3c Cross-section through the head of a *Triton alpestris* larva, into which material from the neural crest of *Bombina pachypus* has been implanted. Left, normal side with *Triton* cartilages and *Triton* tooth anlagen; right, operated side with chimerical tooth anlagen. From Wagner (1955).

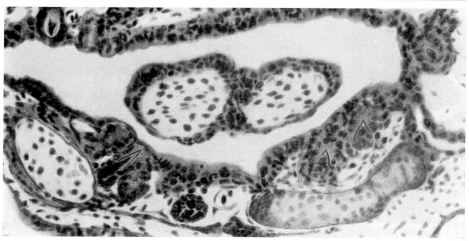

Pl. 4a   Lingual end of the dental lamina of the lower jaw of a *Squalus acanthias* embryo, showing two early tooth anlagen: a, enlarged ameloblasts of first and second tooth anlagen; dl, end of ectodermal dental lamina; ie, inner enamel epithelium; m, mesenchyme cells; oe, outer enamel epithelium; mp, mesodermal tooth papilla, a concentration of modified mesenchyme cells. 335:1.

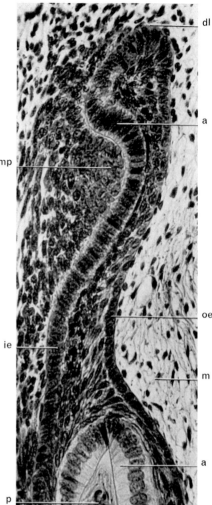

Pl. 4b   Reconstruction of the dentition of *Asteracanthus (Strophodus)*: A, upper jaw; B, lower jaw. From Peyer (1946).

Pl. 4c   Teeth of the acanthodian *Gomphodus;* left tooth spiral; right conical tooth. From Gross, Palaeontographica, Abt. A, *109*, Schweizerbartsche Verlagsbuchhandlung, Stuttgart (1957) (by permission).

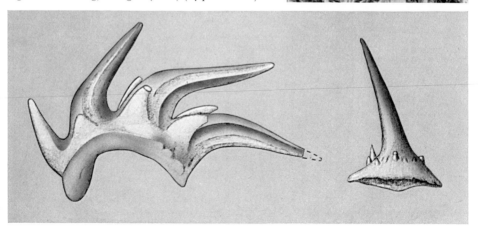

Pl. 5a   Dentition of the Indian skate *Rhina* sp. Tooth pavement in lower half of picture belongs to lower jaw. From Peyer, *Die Zähne*, Verständliche Wissenschaft, vol. 79, Springer Verlag, Berlin (1963) (by permission).

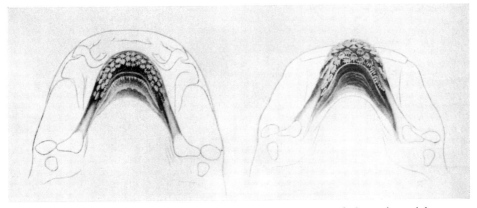

Pl. 5b   *Heterodontus francisci*, dentition of a very young specimen. Left, lower jaw; right, upper jaw. From Garman (1913).

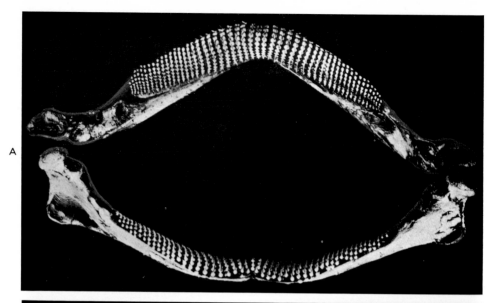

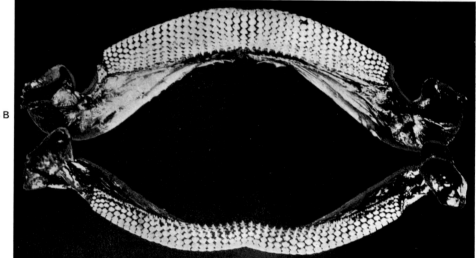

Pl.6 Sexual dimorphism of the dentition in the skate *Raja batis:* A, male; B, female. From Clark (1926) Fisheries, Scotland, Sci. Invest. (by permission).

Pl. 7a *Dalatias licha.* Interior view of the right half of the dentition. The teeth of the lower jaw are so arranged that the replacement of a single tooth is impossible; an entire longitudinal row of teeth must be changed at once. From Landolt (1947), after Peyer, *Die Zähne,* Verständliche Wissenschaft, vol. 79, Springer Verlag, Berlin (1963) (by permission).

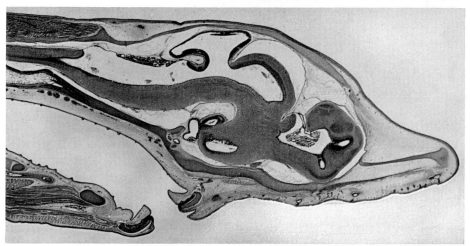

Pl. 7b *Squalus acanthias;* embryo of about 100 mm head-tail length (thread measure). Sagittal section through upper and lower jaws with the tooth anlagen. 6.45 : 1.

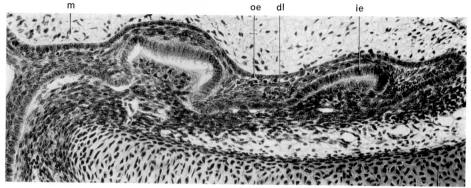

Pl.8a *Squalus acanthias;* embryo of about 100 mm head-tail length (thread measure). Sagittal section, lower jaw: ca, cartilage; dl, dental lamina; ie, inner enamel epithelium; oe, outer enamel epithelium; m, mesenchyme cells. 178:1.

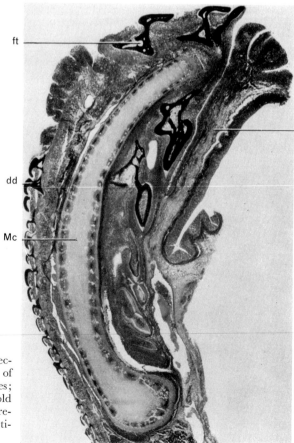

Pl.8b *Squalus acanthias,* adult. Section through a cross row of teeth of the lower jaw: dd, dermal denticles; ft, functional dentition tooth; f, fold of mucous membrane covering replacement teeth; mc, Meckel's cartilage. 17:1.

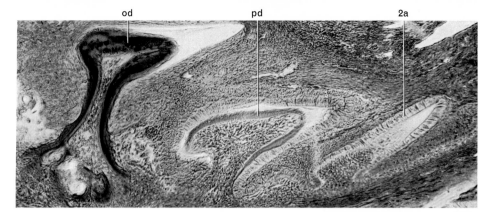

od   pd   2a

Pl. 9a *Scyliorhinus*, adult. Section through replacement tooth anlagen of the upper jaw: od, orthodentine; pd, predentine; 2a, second tooth anlage. 78:1.

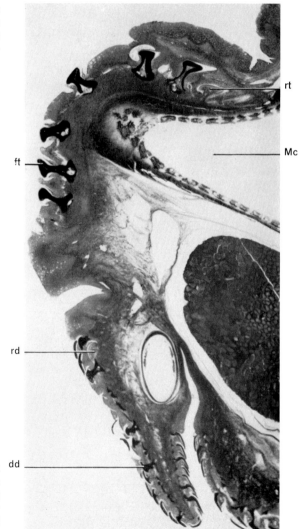

rt

Mc

ft

rd

dd

Pl. 9b *Scyliorhinus*, adult. Section through replacement tooth anlagen of the lower jaw: dd, dermal denticle; rd, replacement denticle; ft, functional tooth; rt, replacement tooth; Mc, Meckel's cartilage. 16:1.

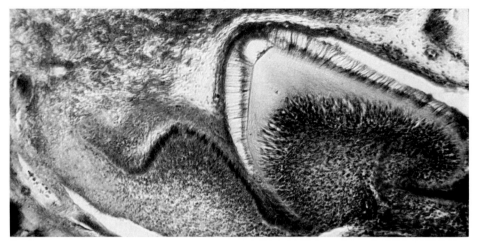

Pl. 10a *Mustelus*, adult. Section through youngest tooth anlage of a cross row of the upper jaw. 97:1.

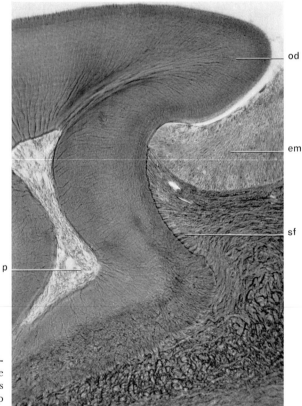

Pl. 10b *Raja clavata*, adult. Anchoring of the tooth in the connective tissue: em, epithelium of mucous membrane; od, orthodentine; p, pulp cavity; sf, Sharpey's fibers. 93:1.

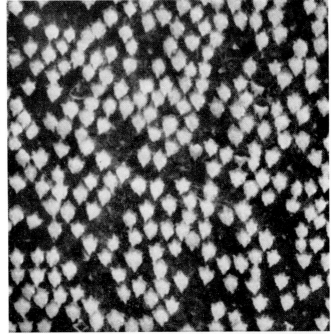

Pl. 11a *Hexanchus griseus.* Sample of a whole-mount preparation of the mucous membrane from the bottom of the mouth cavity. The dark spots represent areas where replacement of denticles was taking place. 6.5:1. From Peyer, *Die Zähne*, Verständliche Wissenschaft, vol. 79, Springer Verlag, Berlin (1963) (by permission).

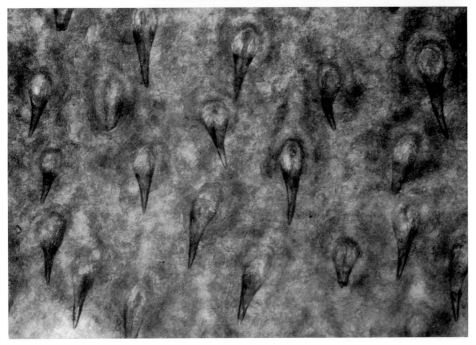

Pl. 11b Mucous membrane denticles of the skate *Raja clavata;* each denticle measures about 175 μ in overall length. Picture of mucous membrane cleared with KOH, stained with Light Green and preserved in glycerin. Transmitted light. The upper picture edge represents the anterior side of the specimen. 114:1.

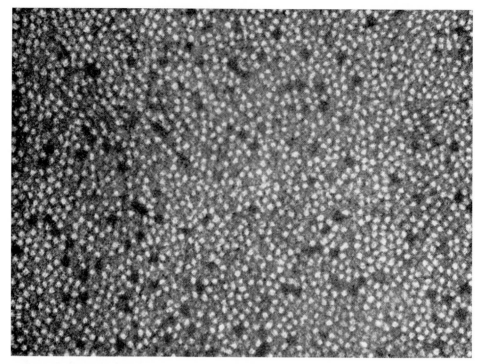

Pl. 12a *Carcharodon carcharias*, specimen 4.5 meters long. Radiograph of a section of mucous membrane from the mouth cavity studded with an average of 500 denticles per square cm. The dark spots correspond to areas where replacement of denticles was in progress. 5:1. From Peyer, *Die Zähne*, Verständliche Wissenschaft, vol. 79, Springer Verlag, Berlin (1963) (by permission).

Pl. 12b *Carcharodon carcharias*, special form of mucous membrane denticles. 48.2:1.

Pl. 13a *Carcharodon carcharias* specimen 4.5 meters long. Mucous membrane denticles of the mouth cavity, most common type. 46:1.

Pl. 13b *Heterodontus* sp. Radiograph of the mucous membrane denticles in the anterior lower region of the mouth cavity. The light, triangular areas in the upper left and right corners of the picture are the X-ray shadows of the edges of the lower jaw cartilages, between which the dried mucous membrane is stretched out. 5.9:1.

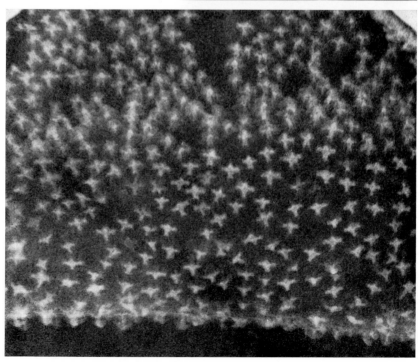

Pl. 14a *Prionace glauca;* mucous membrane denticles of the mouth cavity. The upper edge of the picture corresponds to the anterior side. 72:1.

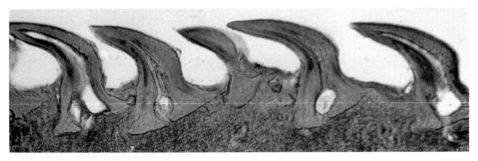

Pl. 14b *Carcharodon carcharias*, section through mucous membrane denticles from the middle of the roof of the mouth. Epithelium between the denticles only partly preserved. The points of the denticles are obliquely bent backward. 55:1.

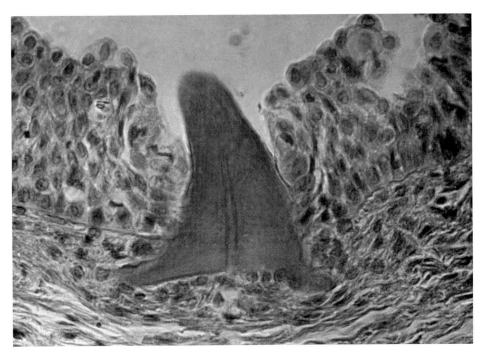

Pl. 15a Mucous membrane denticle of the floor of the mouth in the skate *Raja clavata* in vertical section. 565:1.

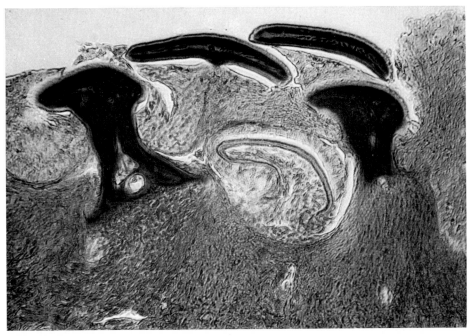

Pl. 15b *Scyliorhinus* adult; higher magnification from Pl. 9b. Anlage of a dermal denticle between two functional denticles. 128:1.

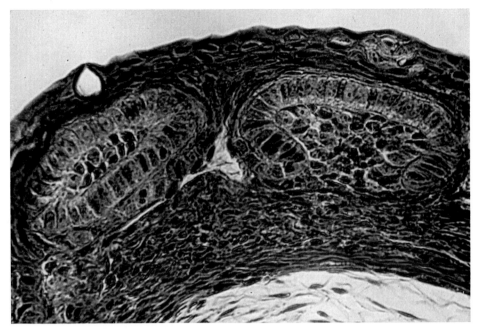

Pl. 16a *Scyliorhinus*, anlagen of dermal denticles of an embryo of 90 mm head-tail length (thread measure). Vertical section. 495:1.

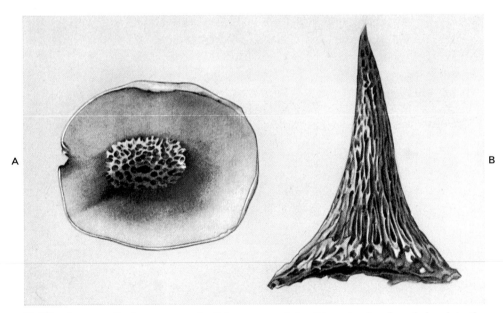

A   B

Pl. 16b *Isurus* sp. Replacement teeth of dry-preserved dentition: A, view from below into the wide pulp cavity of a replacement tooth—the formation of trabecular dentine has begun beneath a coat of orthodentine in the pointed portion of the tooth; B, slightly older replacement tooth, coat of orthodentine removed, the pulp cavity is filled with trabecular dentine. 0:0. From Marquard (1946).

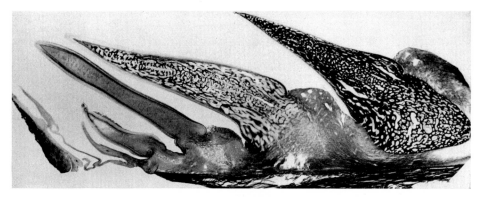

Pl. 17a *Carcharodon carcharias*. Labio-lingual vertical section through the replacement tooth anlagen in a cross row of the lower jaw. Oldest anlage at lower left of picture. Picture shows "sudden" appearance of trabecular dentine. 3.1:1.

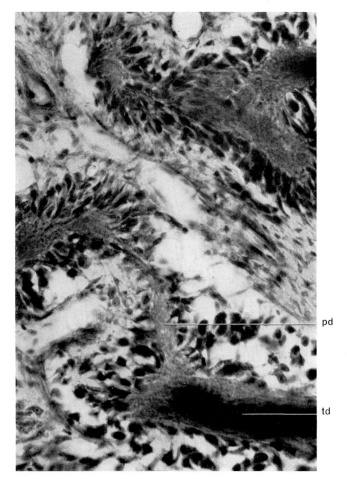

Pl. 17b *Prionace glauca*, development of the trabecular dentine: pd, predentine; td, trabecular dentine. 355:1.

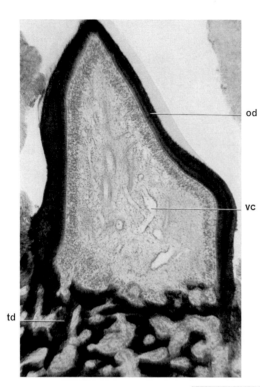

Pl. 18a *Sphyrna zygaena*, hammerhead shark: od, orthodentine; td, trabecular dentine near base; vc, vascular canal. 38:1.

Pl. 18b *Prionace glauca*, adult. Lower jaw with dentition teeth and tooth anlagen, dermal denticles and their anlagen: an2, second smallest tooth anlage; ca, calcifications near surface of Meckel's cartilage; dd, dermal denticles; ft, functional dentition tooth; ct, connective tissue pad enclosed by epithelium of mucous membrane forming a protective fold over the developing dentition teeth. 13.5:1.

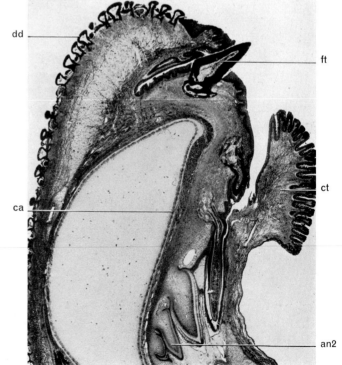

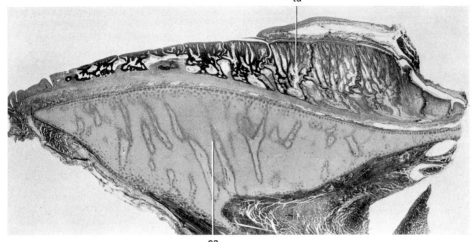

Pl. 19a Very young specimen of the eagle ray *Myliobatis aquila*. Upper jaw in sagittal section: ca, calcifications within palatoquadrate cartilage; td, trabecular dentine. 8:1.

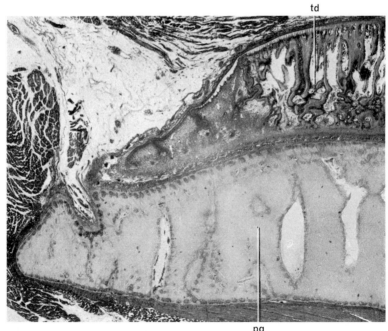

Pl. 19b Very young specimen of the eagle ray *Myliobatis aquila*. Upper jaw in transverse vertical section: pq, palatoquadrate; td, trabecular dentine. 15.6:1.

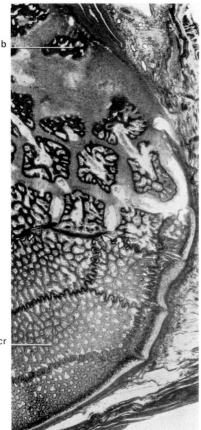

b

cr

Pl. 20a Very young specimen of the eagle ray *Mylio-batis aquila*. Upper jaw in about horizontal section: b, base of fully developed tooth; cr, crown of a replacement tooth. 11.3:1.

Pl. 20b *Prionace glauca*. Portion of a labio-lingual vertical section through a cross row of tooth anlagen in the lower jaw. Note the difference in the size of the ameloblasts of the third tooth anlage (an3) and the second (an2): o, odontoblasts of the third anlage; pd, predentine; p2, p3, pulpal cells of the second and third tooth anlagen. 333:1.

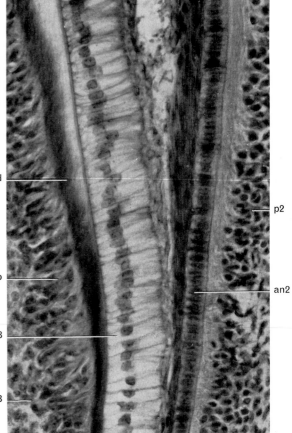

pd

o

an3

p3

p2

an2

Pl. 21a *Isurus glaucus*, adult. Very young replacement tooth slightly decalcified; paraffin section. Shows peripheral initial zone. Orientation: tooth point left, tooth base right. Upper edge of picture corresponds to outside of pointed-conical tooth: fi, fibrils extending into the peripheral initial zone from the basal membrane; fb, collagenous fiber bundles, both radial and tangential in orientation; p, cells of pulp cavity inside the odontoblasts. 390:1.

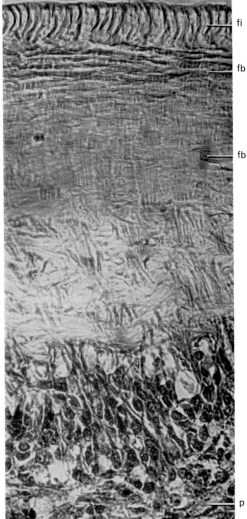

Pl. 21b Young replacement tooth anlage in the upper jaw of the skate *Raja clavata;* peripheral initial zone. Orientation: upper edge of picture corresponds to outer tooth edge which, in the oldest functional tooth in Pl. 3b, extends diagonally ventrad toward the point of the tooth: a, ameloblasts; ep, enamel pulp; piz, peripheral initial zone; m, mesenchymal tissue surrounding the tooth anlage; o, odontoblasts. 390:1.

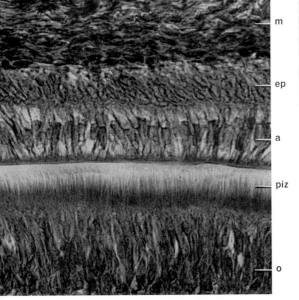

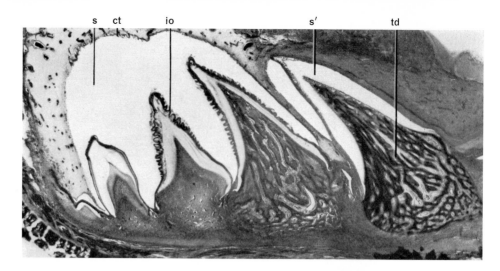

s ct   io   s'   td

Pl. 22a Five replacement tooth anlagen in the lower jaw of an adult *Isurus glaucus*, followed labiad by three functional teeth not shown. In the two oldest replacement teeth there is trabecular dentine. Only in the third and in the fourth youngest anlagen is the outer enamel epithelium folded. The surrounding connective tissue is richly supplied with capillaries, some of which enter folds of the outer enamel epithelium: io, inner and outer enamel epithelium; s, s', artificial shrinkage spaces; td, trabecular dentine; ct, connective tissue containing capillaries. 10.5:1.

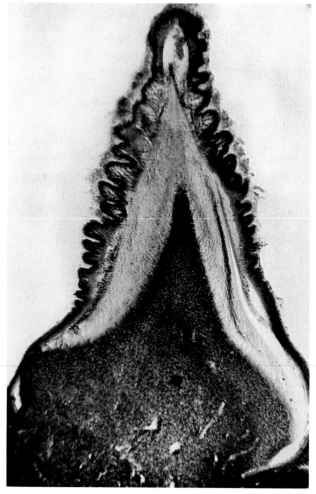

Pl. 22b Detail from 22a— third youngest replacement tooth in higher magnification. 41:1.

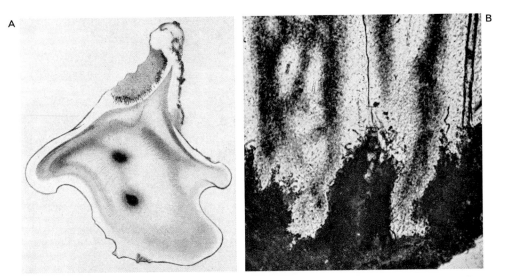

Pl. 23a   Borings in teeth of modern and fossil elasmobranchs: A, tooth of a skate *(Raja)* that served as food fish; B, tooth of *Asteracanthus (Strophodus)* from the late Jurassic. From Peyer (1945 and 1946).

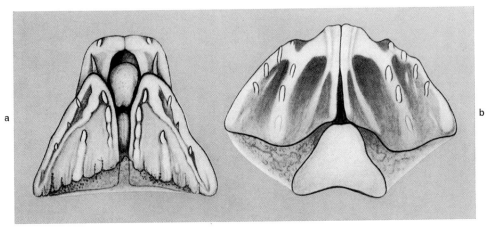

Pl. 23b   *Chimaera monstrosa:* a, upper; b, lower tooth plates. From Bargmann (1933).

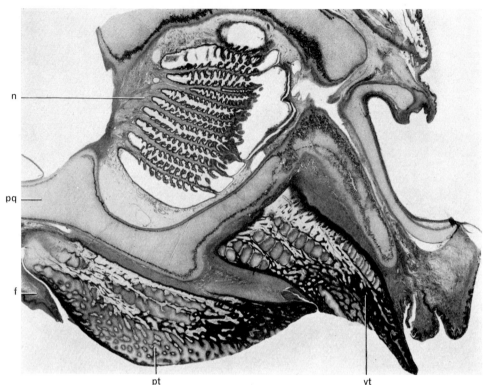

Pl. 24a *Chimaera monstrosa*. Sagittal section through the upper tooth plates: f, fold of mucous membrane covering posterior end of palatine tooth plate; n, nasal tract; pq, palatoquadrate; pt, palatine tooth plate; vt, vomerine tooth plate. 7.2 : 1.

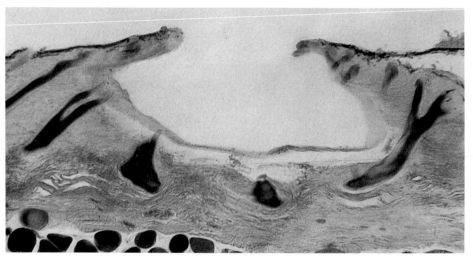

Pl. 24b *Chimaera monstrosa*. Cross-section through the canal at the point of branching of the lateral line in the head region. Note dermal denticles surrounding the canal. 83 : 1.

Pl. 25a *Chimaera monstrosa*. Dermal denticles from a portion of a vertical longitudinal section through a mixopodium. 51:1.

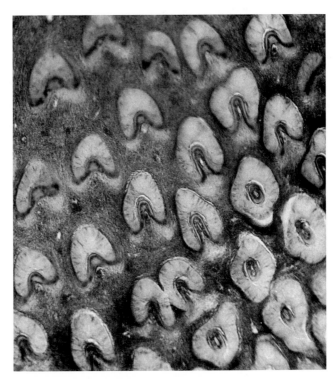

Pl. 25b *Chimaera monstrosa*. Dermal denticles in horizontal section from a mixopodium. 57:1.

Pl. 26a Teeth and replacement teeth of the ganoid fish *Lepidotes maximus* from the Upper Jurassic. After Peyer (1954).

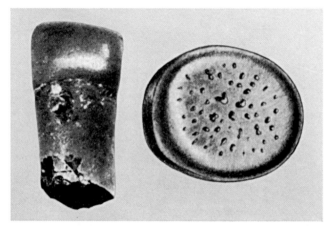

Pl. 26b Teeth of the ganoid fish *Sargodon tomicus* from the Rhaetic. Left, incisor-shaped tooth seen from the outside; right, pavement tooth in crown view. From Guttormsen (1937).

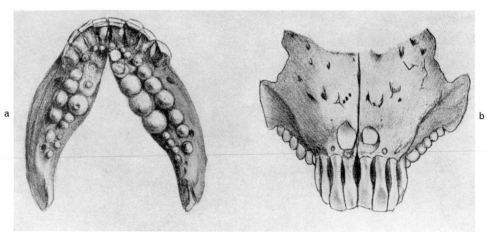

a   b

Pl. 26c Lower jaw of *Sargus rufescens* (a); upper jaw (premaxilla) of *Sargus vetula* (b) with incisor-shaped anterior teeth. After Owen, from Peyer, *Die Zähne*, Verständliche Wissenschaft, vol. 79, Springer Verlag, Berlin (1963) (by permission).

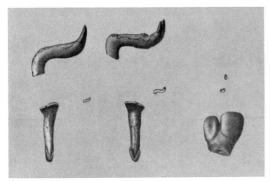

Pl. 27a Teeth of loricariids from the Tertiary of Iquitos, with S-shaped curve and bicuspid cutting blade. From Peyer (1937), in Bolk-Göppert-Kallius-Lubosch, *Handbuch der vergleichenden Anatomie der Wirbeltiere*, Verlag Urban & Schwarzenberg, Wien-Berlin (1931 to 1939) (by permission).

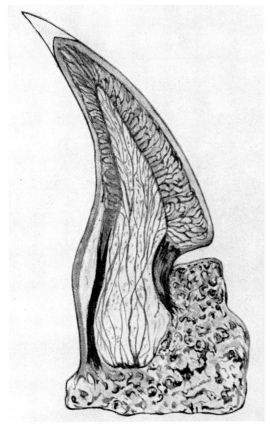

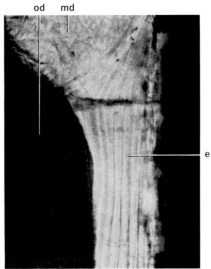

Pl. 27b Movable attachment of the large fang teeth of the hake *Merluccius*. The posteriorly curved tooth tilts backward during ingestion of prey, is subsequently erected by elastic ligaments. Forward tilting is prevented by shape of bony implacement surface. After Mummery, from Peyer, *Die Zähne*, Verständliche Wissenschaft, vol. 79, Springer Verlag, Berlin (1963) (by permission).

Pl. 27c Highly enlarged portion from a vertical section through a tooth of *Lepidotes elevensis*. Orientation: upper edge of picture apical, right edge corresponding to outside of tooth. The growth lines in the enamel layer show that it must have increased in thickness from the inside outward: md, modified dentine; e, true enamel; od, orthodentine. 245:.1 From Peyer (1954).

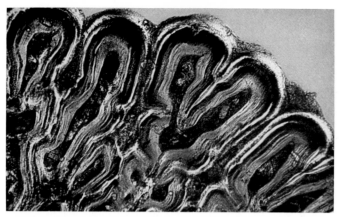

Pl. 28a Horizontal section through a tooth of *Lepisosteus*, polarized. The enamel enters only a short distance between the projections of the tooth surface, while the dentine is folded in labyrinthine fashion. In the black-and-white photograph the very significant difference in the mode of birefringence of enamel and dentine does not show clearly. 63:1.

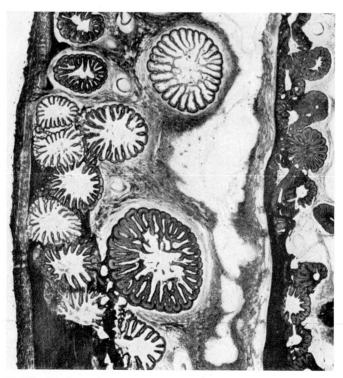

Pl. 28b Horizontal section through a jaw of *Lepisosteus*. The smaller teeth are radially folded much as the larger teeth. A few very young tooth anlagen are cut obliquely or nearly vertically. 7:1. From Peyer, *Die Zähne*, Verständliche Wissenschaft, vol. 79, Springer Verlag, Berlin (1963) (by permission).

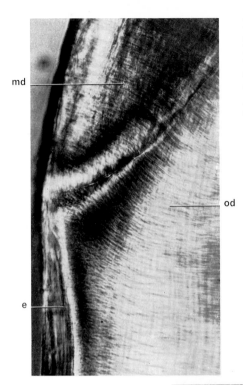

md

od

e

Pl. 29a Vertical section through a tooth of *Lepisosteus*. Orientation: Upper edge of picture apical; left edge of picture corresponding to outside of tooth. Shown is the place where the basal portion of the cap of modified dentine (md), the true enamel (e), and the orthodentine (od) come together. 265:1. (Compare this with Color Pl. III c, d.)

Pl. 29b Vertical section through a replacement tooth anlage of *Lepisosteus*. At bottom of picture pulp cavity (p) with odontoblasts (o), surrounded by a narrow, bright seam of predentine (pd). This is covered by a broad zone of orthodentine (od) apically capped by a zone of modified dentine (md) in process of development. There follows a bright gray inner and outer enamel epithelium enclosing an enamel pulp (ep); to the outside there follows darker, vascular connective tissue (vc). Cylindrical ameloblasts (a′) greatly enlarged over cap of modified dentine; not so (a″) in vicinity of the orthodentine, where they deposit true enamel. 83:1.

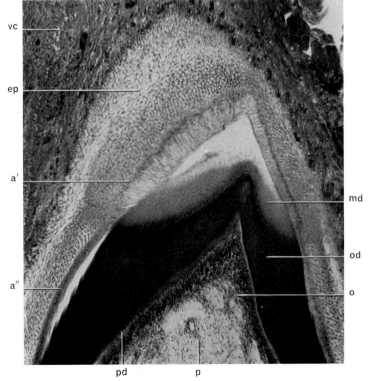

vc

ep

a′

a″

md

od

o

pd   p

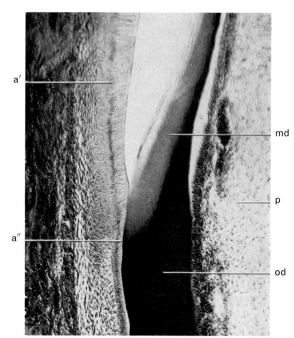

a′

a″

md

p

od

Pl. 30a Portion of a vertical section through a tooth anlage of *Lepisosteus*, showing the difference in height between ameloblasts in region of modified dentine and those bordering the orthodentine. Designations as in Pl. 29b. 97:1.

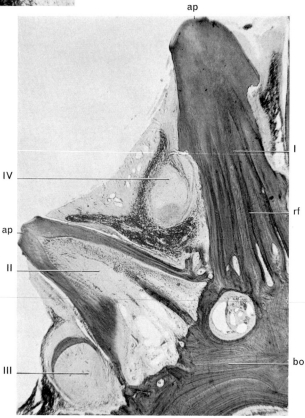

ap

IV

ap

II

III

I

rf

bo

Pl. 30b Labio-lingual, vertical section through a lower jaw of *Lepisosteus* with an old tooth (I) in state of resorption, an older (II) and two younger replacement tooth anlagen (III and IV): ap, apical tooth portion after decalcification, which resulted in loss of modified dentine cap; rf, dentinal lamellae of the radially folded tooth; bo, bone. 37.5:1. (See also Color Pl. IVc.)

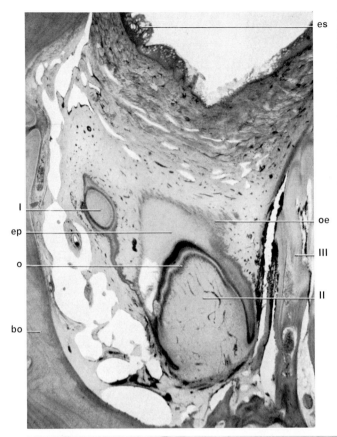

es

I

ep

o

bo

oe

III

II

Pl. 31a A labio-lingual vertical section through the lower jaw of *Lepisosteus* with three developmental stages of teeth I, II and III. Of III, the fully developed tooth, only the marginal portion is shown. The immature anlage II reveals the enamel pulp (ep) and the interdigitation of the outer enamel epithelium (oe) with the adjacent vascular connective tissue; es, epidermis; o, odontoblasts; bo, bone. 23:1.

Pl. 31b Labio-lingual vertical section through a lower jaw of *Lepisosteus*, showing the interdigitation of projections of the outer enamel epithelium (oe) with capillaries (v) of the adjacent connective tissue (ct) at the apical end of the enamel pulp (ep). 200:1. (See also Color Pl. IV b.)

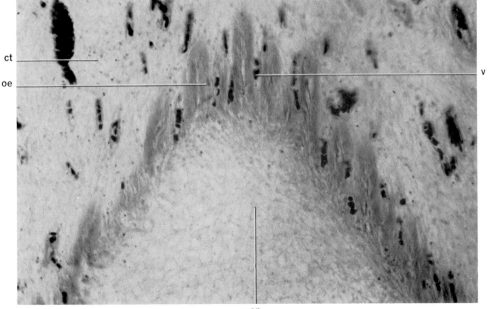

ct

oe

v

ep

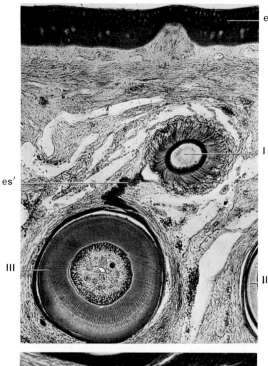

es

es′

I

III

II

Pl. 32a Labio-lingual horizontal section through an upper jaw of *Amia:* es, epidermis; I, II, III, three tooth anlagen of different ages; es′, strand of epithelium that connects I with III. 88:1. (See also Color Pl. Vc.)

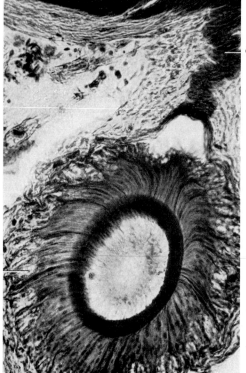

es′

is

Pl. 32b More highly magnified portion of 32a: es′, strand of epithelium leading to the older tooth anlage; is, interstitial spaces at the periphery of the outer enamel epithelium. 270:1.

Pl. 33a Labio-lingual vertical section through an upper jaw of *Amia;* part of a young tooth anlage. Upper edge of picture apical: o, odontoblasts; pd, predentine; md, modified dentine; ud, unmineralized dentine; ie, inner enamel epithelium; oe, outer enamel epithelium; is, interstitial spaces at periphery of outer enamel epithelium; v, vessels of the adjacent connective tissue (ct); p, pulp cavity. 305:1.

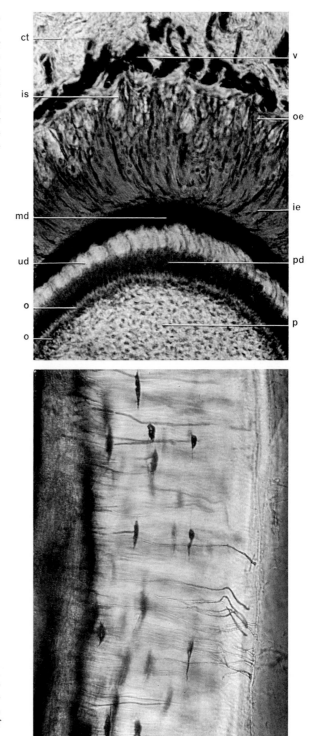

Pl. 33b Osteal dentine of *Amia.* Portion of a vertical section near the basal end of tooth wall. Upper edge of picture apical; right edge of picture corresponds to outside of tooth. 305:1.

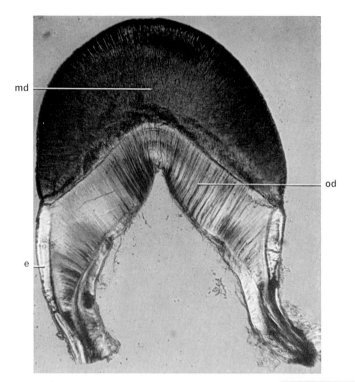

md

od

e

Pl. 34a Vertical ground thin-section through
a pavement tooth of *Labrus turdus*, polarized: md, cap of modified dentine; od, orthodentine; e, enamel. 43:1.

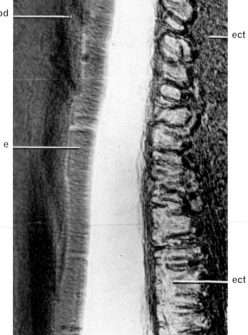

od

ect

e

ect

Pl. 34b *Crenilabrus pavo*, more highly enlarged
portion from Pl. 37a, showing the structure of
the organic ground substance of the enamel:
e, organic ground substance of the enamel;
ect, ectoderm; shrinkage space between the
two; od, orthodentine. 500:1.

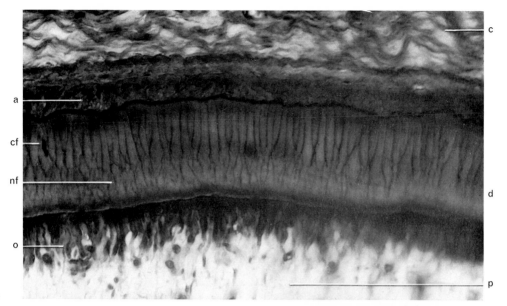

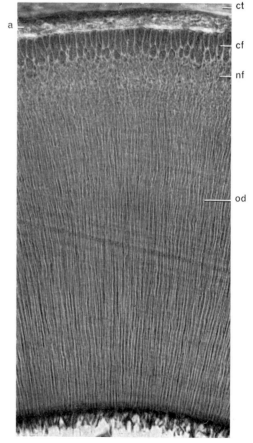

Pl. 35a Horizontal section through a lower jaw of the angler fish *Lophius piscatorius;* young tooth anlage: p, pulp cavity; o, odontoblasts; d, dentine, in which dentinal tubules have not yet been formed; cf, coarser radial fibers that extend from the periphery and often unite along their course; nf, inwardly adjacent network of finer fibers; a, ameloblasts; ct, connective tissue. 425:1.

Pl. 35b Horizontal section through a lower jaw of the angler fish *Lophius piscatorius;* an older tooth anlage. The radial fibers and the adjacent network of very fine fibers now form merely a peripheral seam; the tooth wall consists mainly of orthodentine (od) containing dentinal tubules: a, ameloblasts; ct, connective tissue. 290:1.

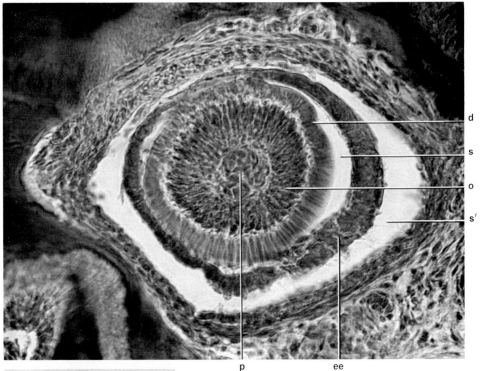

d

s

o

s'

p   ee

Pl. 36a Horizontal section through an upper jaw of *Trigla;* young tooth anlage: p, pulp cavity; o, odontoblasts; d, beginning of the formation of dentine; ee, enamel epithelium; s and s' artificial shrinkage spaces. 475:1.

Pl. 36b Section through a lower jaw of the teleost *Pomadasys;* an older tooth anlage. In the pulp cavity, cut obliquely in the section, there are numerous vessels. In the thick dentine wall, near the tooth surface dark streaks extend diagonally across dentine. 85:1. (See also Color Pl. VI b.)

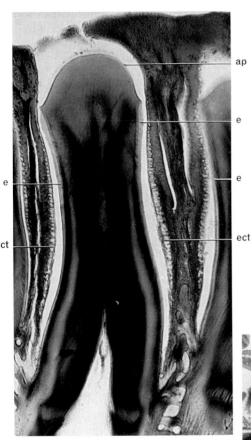

Pl. 37a Vertical section through teeth of *Crenilabrus pavo:* ap, upper edge of the orthodentine and not the tip of the tooth. The point that consisted of modified dentine was totally dissolved during decalcification of the preparation. Organic ground substance of the enamel (e), different from that of the mammalian enamel, is retained during decalcification. Ectoderm (ect). 71:1.

Pl. 37b Vertical section through upper throat teeth of the labrid *Labrus turdus:* ft, functional tooth; rt, replacement tooth anlage; p, pulp cavity; od, orthodentine; ie, boundary of the inner enamel epithelium; voe, capillaries entering between protuberances of outer enamel epithelium; os, osteoid tissue. 23:1.

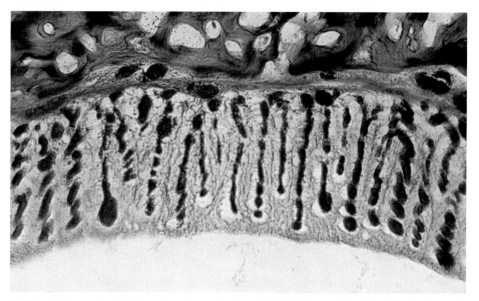

Pl. 38a *Labrus turdus*, highly enlarged portion from Pl. 37b. Penetration of capillaries from the connective tissue surrounding the tooth anlage between the protuberances of the outer enamel epithelium. 138:1.

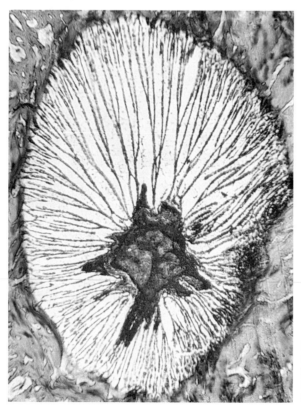

Pl. 38b Horizontal section through an upper jaw of *Sparus auratus;* young tooth anlage. In the center ectoderm, surrounded by threads of the so-called stroma. 44:1.

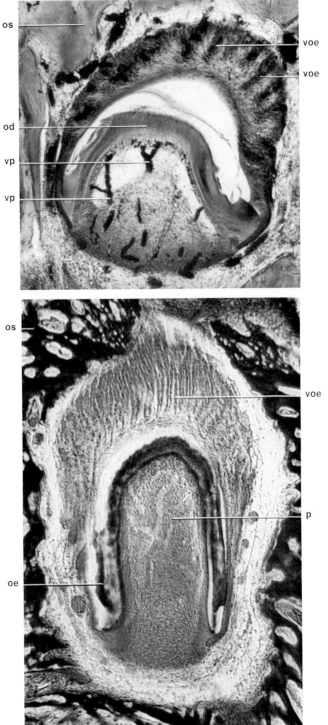

Pl. 39a Vertical section through a tooth of *Pomadasys;* young tooth anlage. At this stage the fine capillaries of the pulp cavity are about equal in size and number to those entering between the protuberances of the outer enamel epithelium: vp, vessels of the pulp cavity; voe, vascular capillaries entering between the protuberances of the outer enamel epithelium; od, orthodentine; os, osteoid tissue. 118:1.

os

voe

voe

od

vp

vp

os

voe

p

oe

Pl. 39b Section through a tooth of *Tetraodon;* young tooth anlage: p, pulp cavity; voe, interdigitation of vascular capillaries of the connective tissue with the outer enamel epithelium; oe, outer enamel epithelium; os, osteoid tissue. 114:1.

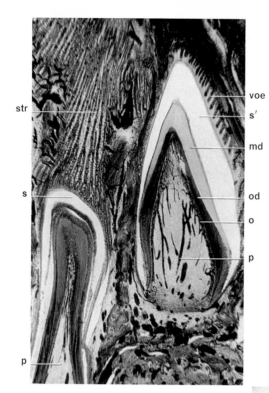

str

s

p

voe

s'

md

od

o

p

Pl. 40a Section through a lower jaw of *Sargus sargus*. The illustrated teeth are nearly vertically sectioned: p, pulp cavity; o, odontoblasts; od, orthodentine; md, modified dentine; voe, vascular capillaries entering between projections of the outer enamel epithelium, better developed on right side of tooth anlage; str, threads of the stroma; s, s', shrinkage spaces. 33:1.

II

III

I

td

Pl. 40b Vertical section through a lower jaw of the pike *Esox lucius*. Functional tooth, nearby three obliquely cut replacement tooth anlagen—I, II, III; td, trabecular dentine. 11.5:1.

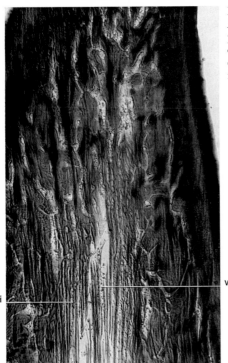

Pl. 41a   Vertical section through an upper jaw of *Esox lucius*. Upper edge of picture apical; upper part of right edge of picture corresponds to the outer side of the tooth. Formation of trabecular dentine: v, finest capillaries; fi, connective tissue fibrils. 316:1.

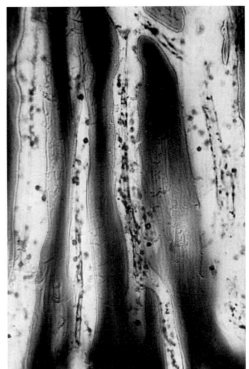

Pl. 41b   Vertical section through a lower jaw of *Esox lucius*. Vascular canals in the trabecular dentine. 310:1.

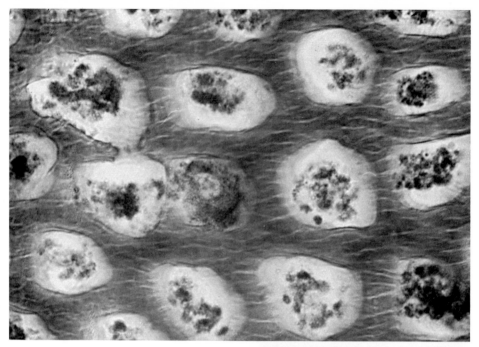

Pl. 42a Horizontal section through a lower jaw of *Esox lucius*. Course of the dentinal tubules in the trabecular dentine. 535:1.

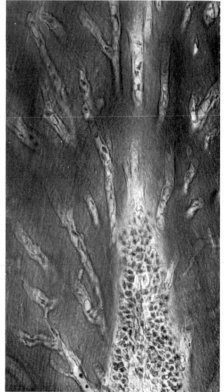

Pl. 42b Labio-lingual vertical section through a tooth of the hake *Merluccius merluccius*. Upper edge of picture apical. Vasodentine containing small canals that carry blood capillaries. 320:1.

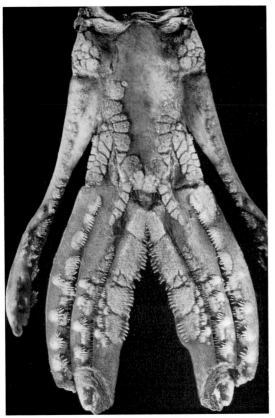

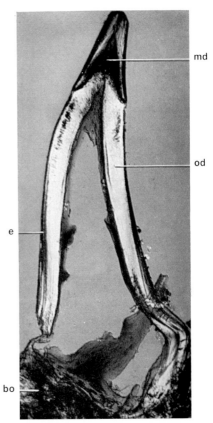

Pl.43a Throat teeth of the chondrostean fish *Polypterus*. 1.8:1. From Peyer, *Die Zähne*, Verständliche Wissenschaft, vol.79. Springer Verlag, Berlin (1963) (by permission).

Pl.43b Vertical ground thin-section through a tooth of *Polypterus*, polarized: md, modified dentine; od, orthodentine; e, enamel; bo, bone. 22.5:1.

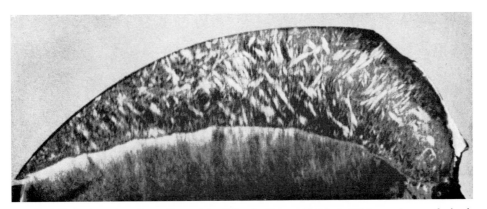

Pl.43c Vertical section through a tooth of the fossil ganoid fish *Lepidotes maximus*, polarized. At bottom orthodentine; above it a cap of modified dentine covered, on the right side of the picture, by a thin layer of bright, true enamel. 18:1. From Peyer (1954).

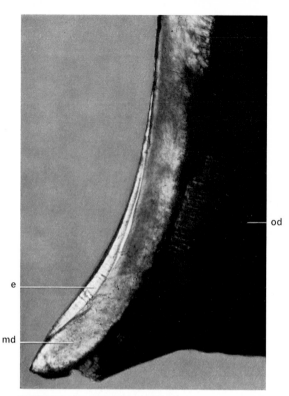

e

md

od

Pl. 44a Labio-lingual vertical section through crown of an incisor-shaped tooth of *Sargodon tomicus*, polarized. The illustrated portion shows only the lingual side of the section on which the modified dentine is covered by the lighter, more brilliant, true enamel: e, enamel; md, modified dentine; od, orthodentine. 74:1.

Pl. 44b Vertical section through a pavement tooth of a pycnodont from the Lower Cretaceous of Texas; polarized. In the center the dark orthodentine, whose dentinal tubules are visible; above it, lighter, the cap of modified dentine; left and right along the margin the strongly birefringent true enamel which also encloses the base of the modified dentine. 22:1.

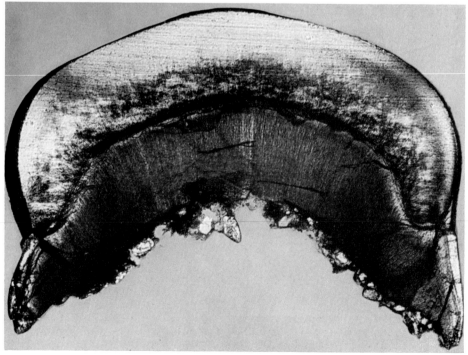

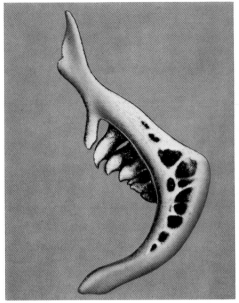

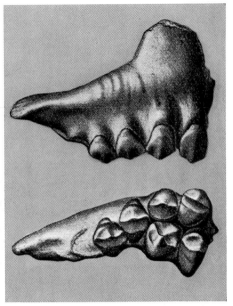

Pl.45a Lower pharyngeal bones with teeth of
Barbus fluviatilis. From Vogt and Hofer, *Die
Süsswasserfische von Mittel-Europa*, Schlüter and
Mass, Halle (1909) a. S.

Pl.45b Tooth-bearing premaxilla of the
characinid *Myletes*, from the late Tertiary of
the Upper Amazon. From Peyer (1937), in
Bolk-Göppert-Kallius-Lubosch, *Handbuch der
Vergleichenden Anatomie der Wirbeltiere*, Verlag
Urban & Schwarzenberg, Wien-Berlin (1931
to 1939).

md

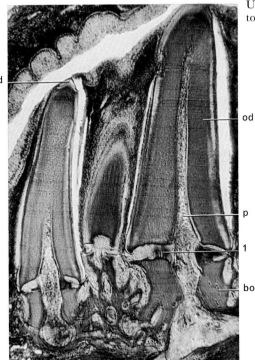

od

p

1

bo

Pl.45c Attachment of the teeth of the
marine eel *Conger* by connective tissue
fibrils that run from the tooth to its bony
pedestal: bo, bony base; 1, ligament; md,
modified dentine (mainly dissolved); od,
orthodentine; p, pulp cavity. 37:1.

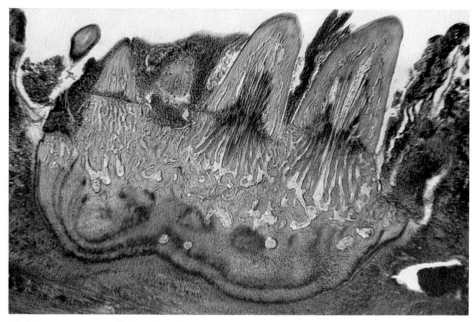

Pl. 46a Throat teeth of the pike, *Esox lucius*. 40 : 1. (See legend below.)

Pl. 46b Gill arch denticles of *Sparus auratus*. As in teleosts, generally, teeth of the gill arches are not directly connected to their bony skeleton, but occupy their own little bones that may assume a variety of shapes in different genera. 63 : 1.

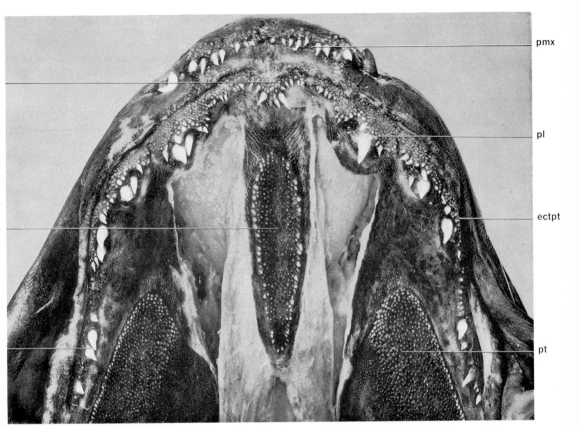

pmx

pl

ectpt

pt

Pl. 47 Anterior portion of the palate of the modern coelacanth *Latimeria chalumnae:* pmx, premaxilla; mx, maxilla; v, vomer; psph, parasphenoid; pl, palatine; ectpt, ectopterygoid; pt, pterygoid. From J. Millot and J. Anthony, *Anatomie de* Latimeria chalumnae, vol. 1, Centre National de la Recherche Scientifique, Paris (1958).

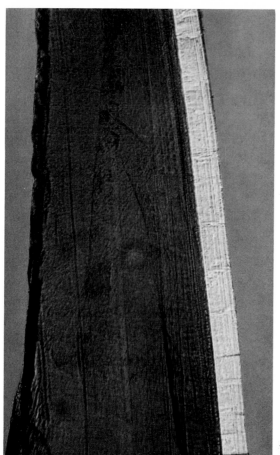

Pl. 48a   Vertical ground section through a tooth of *Onychodus sigmoides*, which, according to its tooth structure, probably belongs to the crossopterygians; from the Middle Devonian of Delaware. Upper edge of picture apical, right edge corresponds to outside of tooth. 35:1. (See also Color Pl. VI d.)

Pl. 48b Toothplates of the modern lungfish *Neoceratodus forsteri;* left, upper jaw with a small vomerine tooth and large palatal plates; right, lower jaw. After Stromer v. Reichenbach, from Peyer (1959).

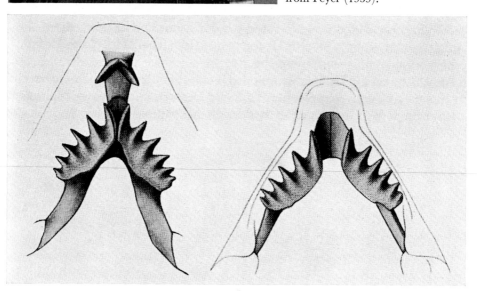

Pl. 49a Juvenile stage of a tooth plate of the fossil lungfish *Ceratodus parvus* from the Rhaetic. From Peyer (1959).

Pl. 49b Juvenile stage of a left vomer tooth of the fossil lungfish *Ceratodus parvus:* A, anterior, outer surface; B, posterior, inner surface; C, coronal surface; D, view of the tooth base. 33:1. From Peyer (1959).

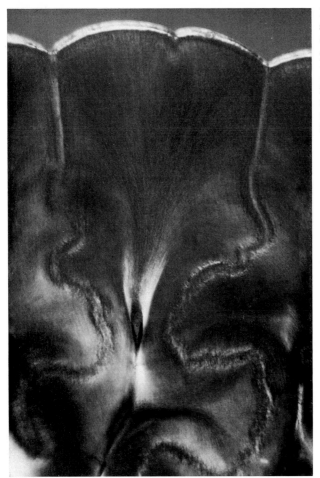

Pl. 50a Horizontal ground section through a small tooth of the stegocephalian *Masto-donsaurus* from the Rhaetic of Hallau, polarized. The enamel (top of picture) strongly birefringent; the first-formed dentine lamellae somewhat lighter than the later-formed dentine. 93:1.

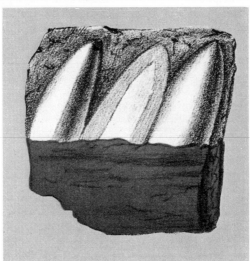

Pl. 50b Three superficially smooth teeth of *Microbrachis pelicani* from the Lower Permian gas coal of Nyran; the middle tooth cut open to show the wide, simple pulp cavity. 60:1. From Fritsch (1883).

Pl. 51a Basal, slightly oblique horizontal ground section through a tooth of the microsaur *Euryodus primus* from the Permian of Oklahoma. Note that the wall is not folded, but differentiated into radial struts. 33:1.

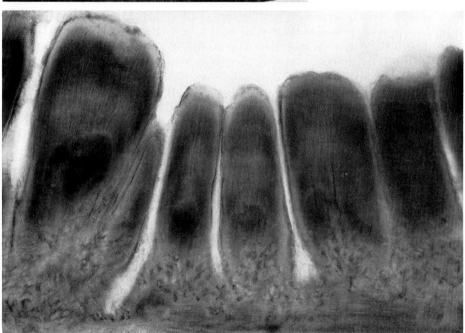

Pl. 51b Enlarged detail of section in 51a, showing absence of true folding of the tooth wall. 174:1.

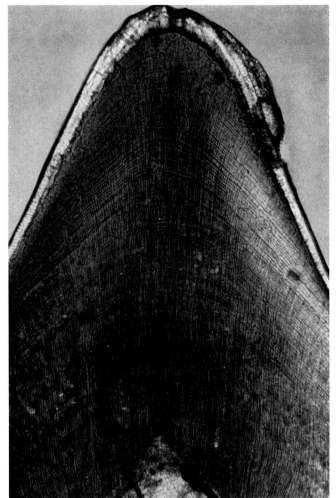

Pl. 52a Vertical ground section through a tooth of the microsaur *Euryodus primus* from the Permian of Oklahoma, polarized. Strong birefringence of the enamel; growth lines in the dentine. 94:1.

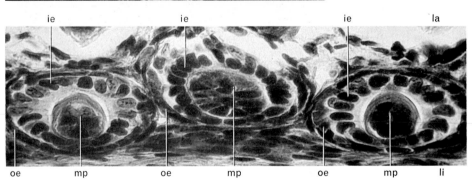

Pl. 52b Horizontal section through a mandible of *Salamandra maculosa*. Young tooth anlagen only; cross sections of functional teeth would lie above the picture: la, labial; li, lingual; oe, cells of outer enamel epithelium; ie, cells of the inner enamel epithelium; mp, mesodermal tooth papilla. 330:1.

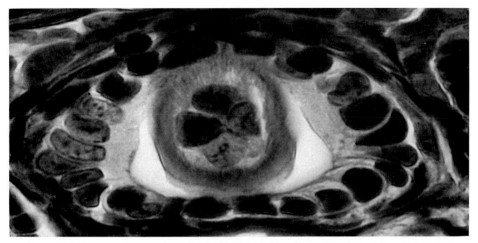

Pl. 53a *Salamandra maculosa*, lower jaw, horizontal section. Portion of Pl. 52b. 900:1.

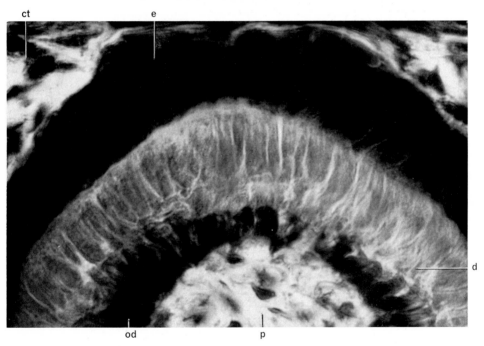

Pl. 53b Horizontal section through upper jaw of *Rana esculenta;* young tooth anlage: p, pulp cavity; od, odontoblasts; d, dentine in process of formation, traversed by radial fibers; e, inner and outer enamel epithelium; ct, connective tissue. 1030:1.

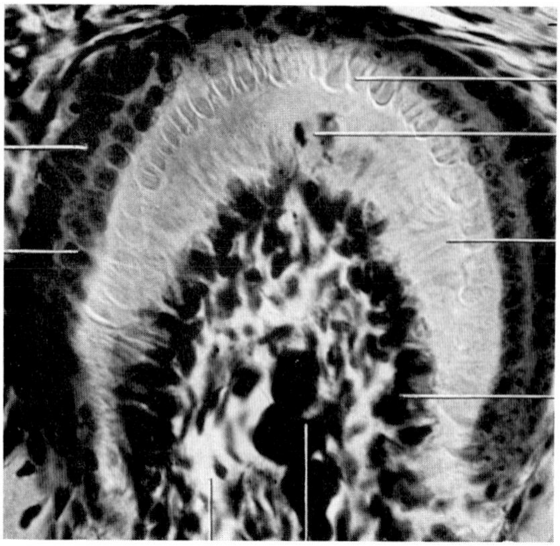

ve
ct
f
dc
oe
d
ie
od
p   pv   do

Pl. 54a Vertical section through upper jaw of *Rana esculenta;* tooth anlage: do, dorsal; ve, ventral; p, pulp cavity; pv, vessel; od, odontoblasts; d, dentine in process of formation; dc, displaced, probably mesodermal, cells; ie, inner enamel epithelium; oe, outer enamel epithelium; ct, connective tissue; f, radial fibers. 382:1.

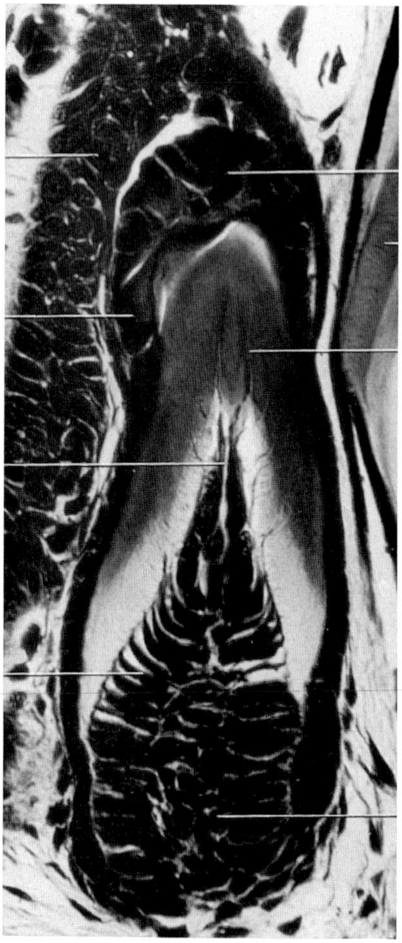

dl
oe
D
ie
d
odp
od
p

Pl. 54b Cross-section through the head of an axolotl; tooth anlagen: p, pulp cavity; od, odontoblasts; odp, processes of the odontoblasts entering the dentine; d, dentine; D, dentine of a neighboring tooth anlage; ie, inner enamel epithelium; oe, outer enamel epithelium; dl, dental lamina. 332:1.

Pl. 55a Cross-section through the mandible of an axolotl. Fully-developed tooth, firmly fixed to the substrate by a bony pedestal, and three replacement tooth anlagen. 106:1.

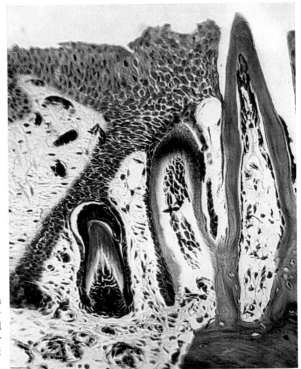

Pl. 55b Portion of a cross-section through the head of *Rana esculenta;* tooth anlagen of different ages and parts of bony pedestals. The lower edge of the picture faces almost ventrad. 136:1.

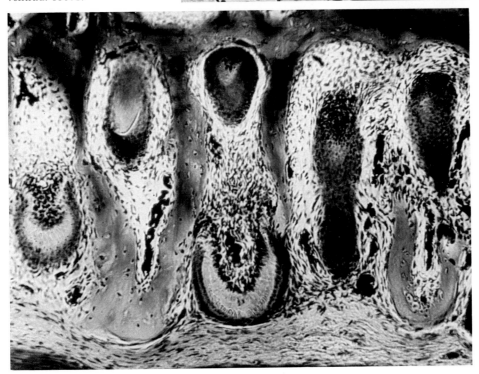

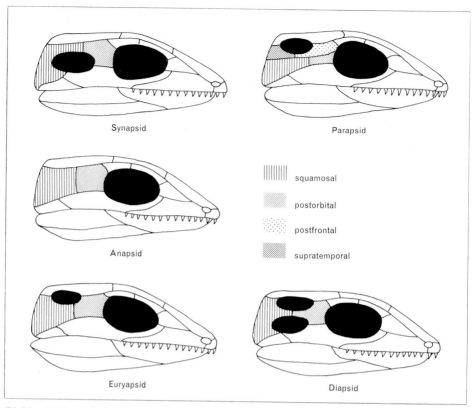

Pl. 56a Differentiation of the temporal region in reptiles; schematic. From Colbert, *The Dinosaur Book*, McGraw-Hill Book Company (1951) (by permission).

Pl. 56b Portion of the lower jaw of an alligator, seen from the outside, partially opened to demonstrate tooth replacement. Note that openings through which replacement teeth enter the interiors of their predecessors lie on the lingual side of the teeth. From Owen (1840–45).

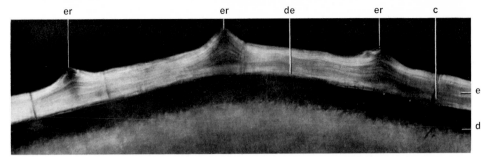

Pl. 57a Horizontal ground section through a tooth of a recent crocodile, polarized: d, dentine; e, enamel; c, crack extending through enamel at right angle to tooth surface; er, fine ribs of the enamel surface. The course of the dentine-enamel boundary (de) is not influenced by the minute sculpturing of the enamel surface. 98:1.

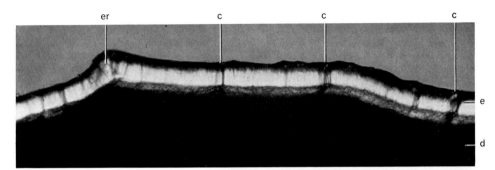

Pl. 57b Horizontal ground section through the tooth of a carnosaur from the Rhaetic of Hallau; polarized: d, dentine; e, enamel; c, cracks in the enamel at right angles to surface; er, broad rib. The course of the enamel-dentine boundary follows this sculpturing of the tooth surface. 99:1.

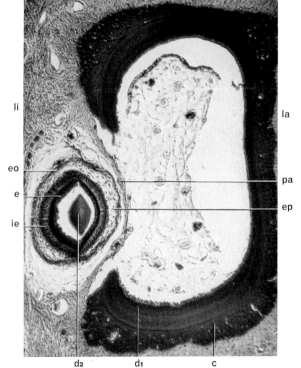

Pl. 57c Horizontal section through the mandible of a young crocodile: la, labial; li, lingual; d_1, dentine of the older tooth; c, cementum; pa, partition between the old tooth and the younger tooth anlage; ie and oe, inner and outer enamel epithelium; ep, enamel pulp; e, enamel in process of formation; d_2, dentine of the younger tooth anlage. 90:1.

Pl. 58a Horizontal section through the lower jaw of a young crocodile: la, labial; li, lingual; c₁, layer of cementum of the oldest tooth; d₁, dentine of the oldest tooth; d₂, dentine of the tooth anlage of medium age; ie and oe, its inner and outer enamel epithelium; ep, enamel pulp; mp, mesodermal tooth papilla of the youngest anlage; bo, jaw bone. The tooth anlage of medium age has already entered the interior of the oldest tooth; pa, partition between old and replacement teeth. 61:1.

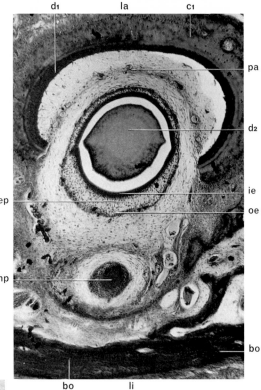

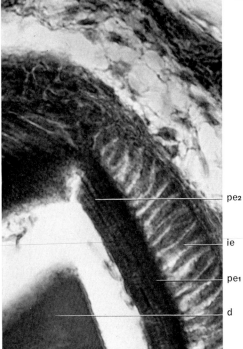

Pl. 58b Horizontal section through the lower jaw of a young crocodile; enlarged detail from 58a: ie, inner enamel epithelium (ameloblasts); pe₁, first prestage of enamel, showing no structure; pe₂, second prestage of enamel, showing layering parallel to surface and a fine structure oriented at a right angle to it; d, dentine. 760:1.

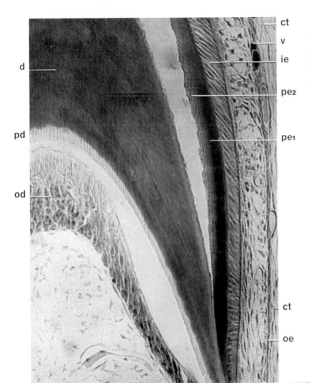

Pl. 59a Labio-lingual vertical section through the upper jaw of a young crocodile: ct, connective tissue; oe and ie, outer and inner enamel epithelium; pe_1 and pe_2, first and second prestages of enamel; d, dentine; pd, predentine; od, odontoblasts; v, vessel. 268:1.

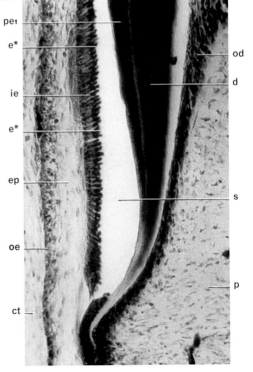

Pl. 59b Labio-lingual vertical section through the upper jaw of a young crocodile. The preparation shows particularly the occurrence (during amelogenesis) of droplets of a substance within the ameloblasts, e*, whose chemical behavior toward histological stains is identical with that of the first prestage of enamel (pe_1); ep, enamel pulp; p, pulp cavity; s, shrinkage space. Other designations as in 59a. 283:1.

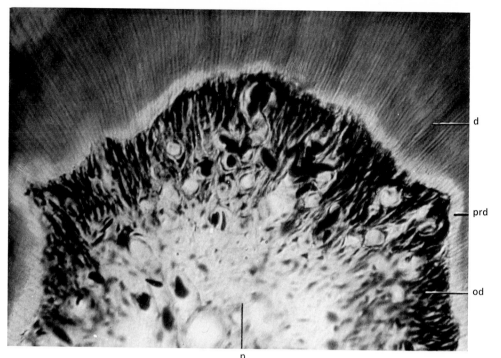

Pl. 60a Horizontal section through the upper jaw of *Varanus salvator*. The preparation shows the course of the odontoblast processes within the dentine tubules: p, pulp cavity; od, odontoblasts; prd, predentine; d, dentine. 422:1.

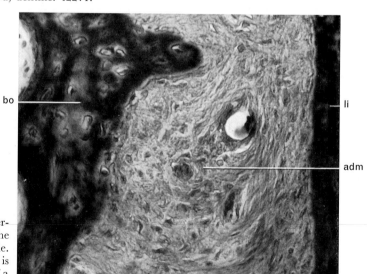

Pl. 60b Labio-lingual vertical section through the upper jaw of a crocodile. Upper edge of picture is apical: li, lingual wall of a functional tooth covered by a layer of cementum; adm, alveolar-dental membrane; bo, bony inner wall of the alveolus. 373:1.

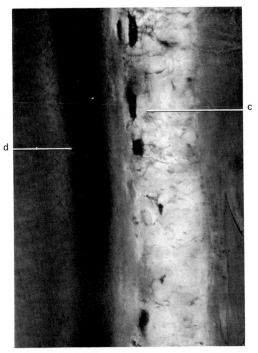

Pl. 61a   Vertical ground section through a tooth of a modern crocodile. Upper edge of picture is apical: d, dentine (dark); c, cementum. 408:1.

Pl. 61b   Vertical ground section through a tooth of *Diadectes;* polarized: d, dentine; above this (in the picture), enamel in the basal part of which there is a layering or bedding that runs almost parallel to the surface, corresponding to the "lines of Retzius" in mammalian enamel. The alternation of light (a) and dark (b) streaks, at right angles to the surface, is brought about by the regular change of the optical orientation of neighboring groups of structural elements. 585:1.

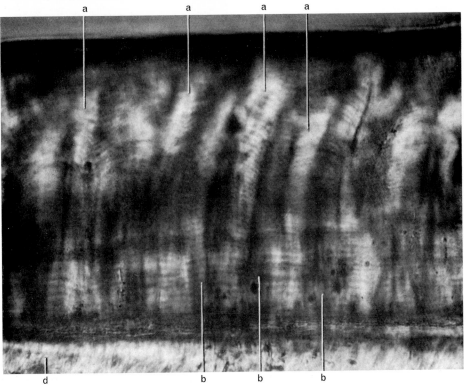

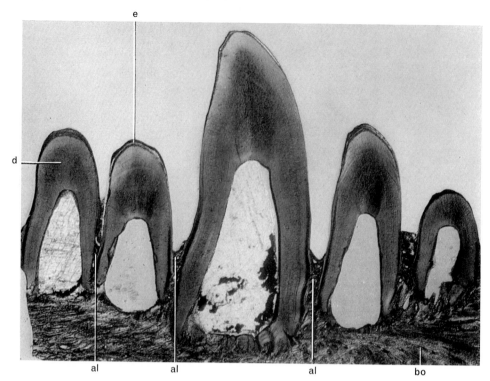

Pl.62a Vertical ground section through a tooth-bearing jaw fragment of the cotylosaur *Labido-saurus* from the Permian of Oklahoma: e, enamel; d, dentine; al, bone of the alveolar walls; bo, jaw bone. 17.5:1.

Pl.62b Portion from radiograph of the lower jaw of a large mixosaur from the Triassic of the Monte San Giorgio, Tessin, Switzerland. Here the teeth do not stand in a continuous groove, but in individual alveoli. 1.27:1. From Besmer (1947).

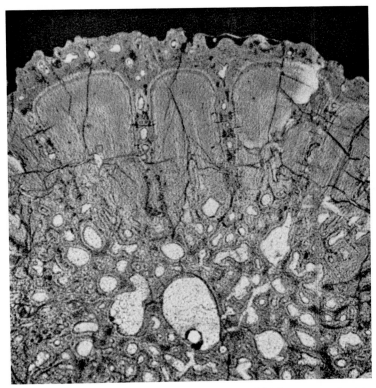

Pl.63a Vertical ground section through a tooth of *Ichthyosaurus acutirostris:* showing part of the folded dentine wall with outer cover of cementum and filling of the basal-most portion of the pulp cavity with cementum. From Besmer (1947).

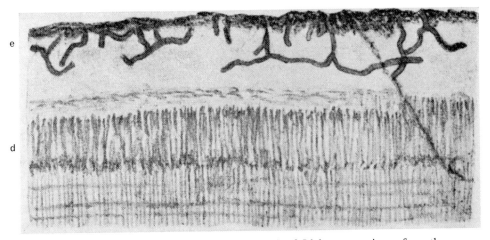

Pl.63b Transverse ground section through a tooth of *Ichthyosaurus trigonus* from the uppermost Jurassic. In the enamel layer, bore holes produced by the so-called *Mycelites ossifragus* enter from the outside: e, enamel; d, dentine. After Bauer (1898), from Peyer (1945). Much enlarged.

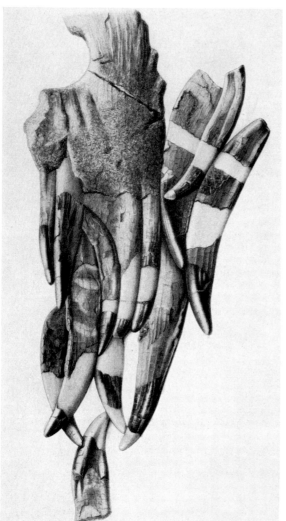

Pl. 64a   Snout of the placodont *Helveticosaurus* from the Triassic of the Monte San Giorgio, Tessin, Switzerland. 1:1.62. From Peyer (1955).

Pl. 64b   Lower jaw of a large specimen of *Tanystropheus;* all teeth are single-cusped. 1.15:1. From Peyer (1931).

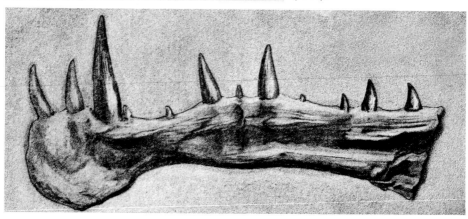

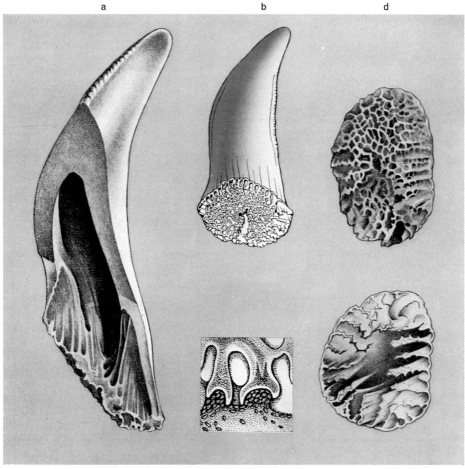

a   b   d

e   c

Pl. 65a   Tooth development of *Varanus salvator:* a, replacement tooth opened at the mesial side, dentine folds of the labial and lingual wall; b, replacement tooth, viewed from labial side, and the obliquely positioned base that has been closed except for a small aperture; c, younger, and d, older stage in closure of basal aperture by dentine folding; e, mode of fixation of the fully grown tooth on the jaw. Different magnifications. From Bullet (1942).

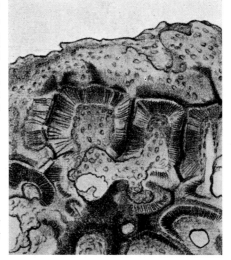

Pl. 65b   *Varanus salvator;* remains of incompletely resorbed teeth overgrown by bone and gradually being resorbed. 90:1. From Bullet (1942).

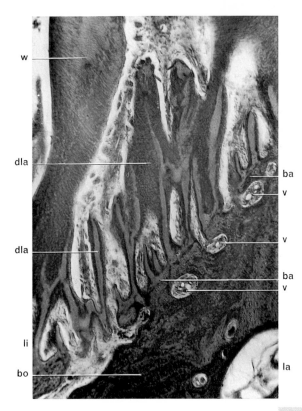

Pl. 66a Labio-lingual vertical section through the upper jaw of *Varanus salvator*. Upper edge of picture is apical: li, lingual; la, labial; w, medial wall of the tooth; dla, dentine lamellae that secondarily form the closure of the tooth base and become connected to the bone of attachment (ba) of the jaw; v, vascular canals; bo, bone of jaw. 70:1.

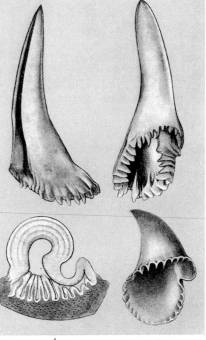

Pl. 66b Tooth development of the poisonous lizard *Heloderma horridum:* a and b, replacement tooth in oblique anteromedial and in oblique ventral view (venom groove is seen in a); c, intermediate stage of development of a replacement tooth; d, horizontal ground section in area of maximal depth of venom groove. Labial tooth wall is folded, lingual wall is not. Different magnifications. From Odermatt (1940).

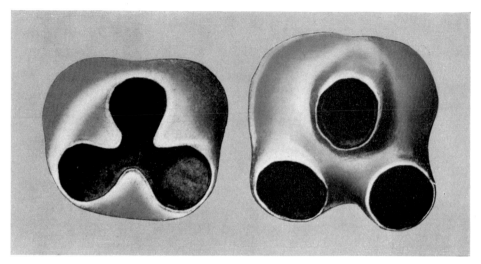

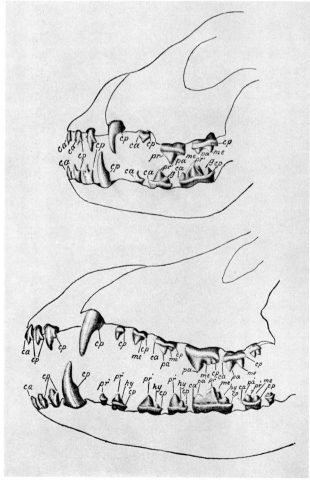

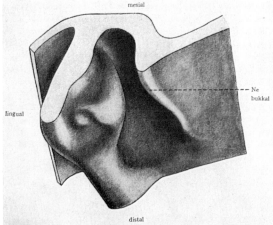

mesial

lingual

— Ne
bukkal

distal

Pl.68a Accessory lamina occurring during tooth development of man. After a wax plate model made from serial sections. From W. Meyer, *Normale Histologie und Entwicklungsgeschichte der Zähne des Menschen*, Carl Hanser Verlag, München (1951) (by permission).

A   A

soh   soh

Pl.68b Enamel membrane of a human tooth: A, ameloblasts; soh, enamel membrane; enamel has been entirely dissolved during decalcification. From W. Meyer, *Normale Histologie und Entwicklungsgeschichte der Zähne des Menschen*, Carl Hanser Verlag, München (1951) (by permission).

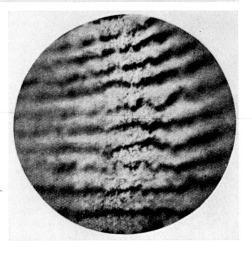

Pl.68c Surface of a human tooth. Imbrication lines emphasized by rubbing with graphite. After Pickerill from Tomes, *A Manual of Dental Anatomy, Human and Comparative*, J. and A. Churchill Ltd., London (1923) (by permission).

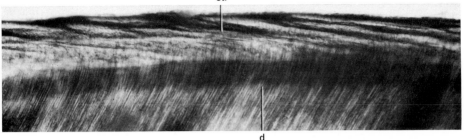

Pl.69a Striation of Retzius (str) in the enamel layer near the growing end of a lower incisor of a squirrel; d, dentine. 125:1.

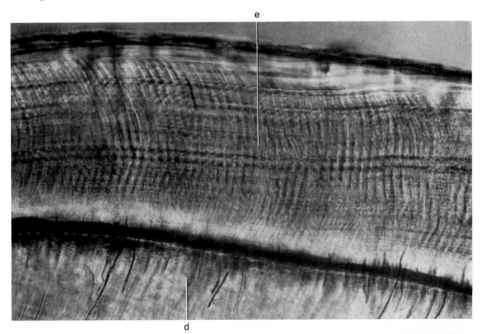

Pl.69b Striation of Retzius in the enamel of a lower premolar of the cat.
Right edge of picture apical: e, enamel;
d, dentine. 428:1.

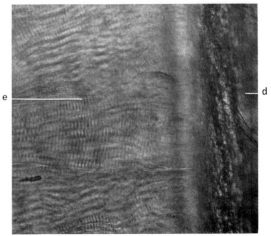

Pl.69c Transverse striation of the prisms
in the enamel of a lower canine of the
cat. Upper edge of picture apical: d,
dentine; e, enamel. 345:1.

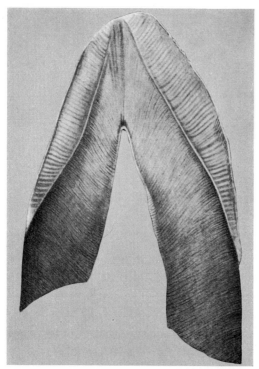

Pl. 70a Striation of Hunter-Schreger of the enamel; polished ground surface of a human canine in reflected light. Near surface of enamel on right side of picture the oblique striation of Retzius is visible. 7.7 : 1. After Lehner-Plenk, *Handbuch der mikroskopischen Anatomie des Menschen.* Springer Verlag, Berlin (1936) (by permission).

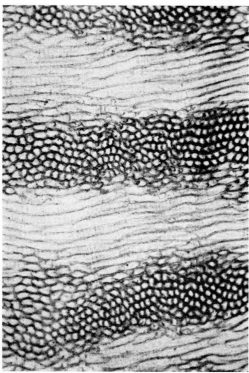

Pl. 70b Parazones and diazones of the enamel layer. In the parazones predominantly longitudinal sections, in the diazones primarily cross sections of enamel prisms. From W. Meyer, *Normale Histologie und Entwicklungsgeschichte der Zähne des Menschen.* Carl Hanser Verlag, München (1951) (by permission).

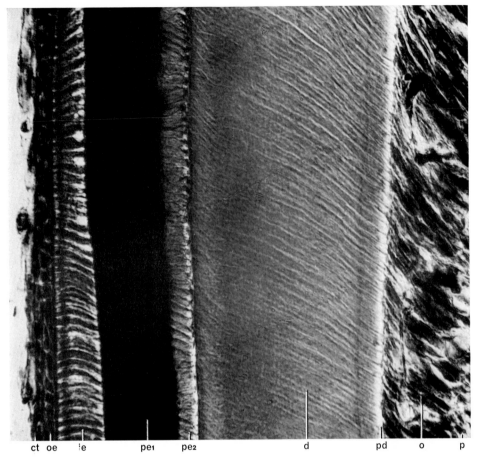

ct oe ie pe₁ pe₂ d pd o p

Pl. 71a Vertical section through an upper milk premolar of a young cat. Upper edge of picture apical: ct, connective tissue; oe, outer enamel epithelium; ie, inner enamel epithelium (ameloblast layer); pe₁, first prestage of enamel; pe₂, second prestage of enamel; d, dentine; pd, predentine; o, odontoblasts; p, pulp cavity. 447:1.

Pl. 71b Enamel formation in a pig embryo: dt, dentine tubules. Between the ameloblasts and the precursors of the enamel prisms there are granular inclusions. After Held, from Peyer (1937), in Bolk-Göppert-Kallius-Lubosch, *Handbuch der Vergleichenden Anatomie der Wirbeltiere*, Verlag Urban & Schwarzenberg, Wien-Berlin (1931–1939) (by permission).

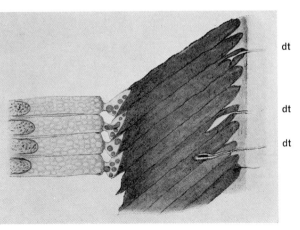

dt

dt

dt

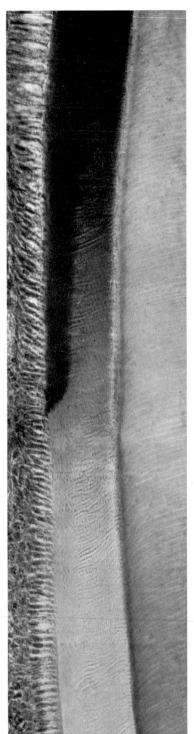

Pl. 72 Longitudinal section through an upper incisor of a mouse. Orientation: the functional end of the tooth lies off the bottom side of the picture, the permanently growing basal end off the top edge. Thus the first prestage of enamel, which shows no structure, is on the upper side of the picture; the second prestage, in which the organic base of the enamel prisms may be recognized in the picture, follows below. Even farther below, beyond the picture, follows the forward end of the tooth, in which the enamel was totally dissolved during decalcification. 332:1.

Pl. 73a Horizontal section through a milk tooth of a newborn infant. Upper picture edge apical: p, pulp cavity; d, dentine (dark line along its left edge is predentine); pe₂, second prestage of enamel; pe₁, first prestage of enamel; ie, inner enamel epithelium; si, stratum intermedium; ep, enamel pulp. Preparation in the Anatomical Institute, University of Zürich. 376:1.

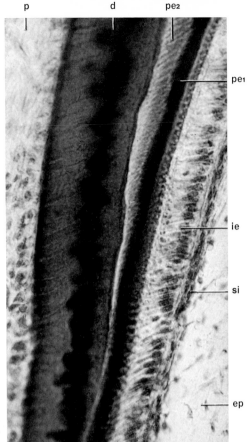

p   d   pe2

pe1

ie

si

ep

Pl. 73b Cross-section through an upper incisor of a hare close to the posterior end. Upper edge of picture is dorsal. Near bottom of picture dentine: pe₂, second prestage of enamel showing the complicated arrangement of the organic base of the enamel prisms; ie, inner enamel epithelium whose ameloblasts show, largely in connection with amelogenesis, specific staining of the cell bodies; ep, enamel pulp. 538:1.

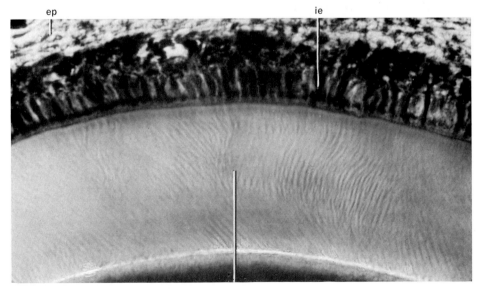

ep   ie

pe2

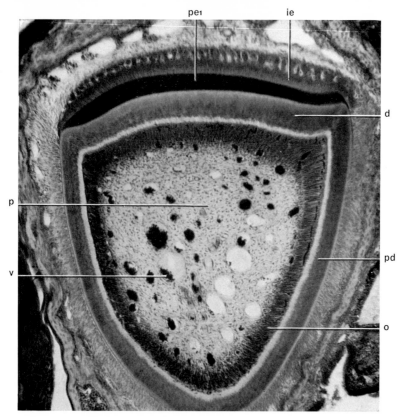

Pl. 74a Cross-section through the middle portion of a gnawing tooth of a young hamster. Upper edge of picture is dorsal (in relation to the whole head), left edge is lateral. The enamel cover, as in most rodents, is restricted to the labial face of the incisor: p, pulp cavity with vessels (v); o, odontoblasts; pd, predentine; d, dentine; pe₁, first prestage of enamel; ie, inner enamel epithelium; farther dorsad, outer enamel epithelium, with blood vessels entering between cells. 100:1.

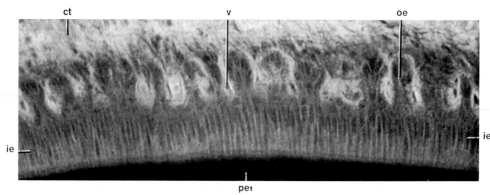

Pl. 74b More highly magnified portion of 74a: v, capillaries; oe, outer enamel epithelium; ct, connective tissue; other designations as above. 423:1.

Pl. 75a Tufts of enamel prisms; ground thin-section of human tooth; Fuchsin stain. 144:1.
From W. Meyer, *Normale Histologie und Entwicklungsgeschichte der Zähne des Menschen*, Carl
Hanser Verlag, München (1951) (by permission).

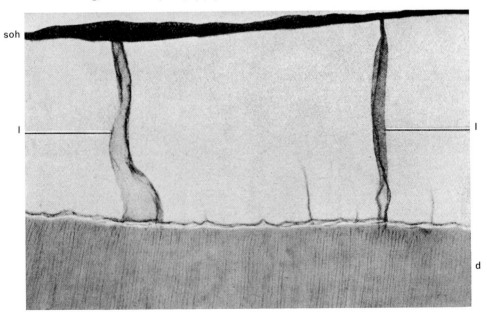

Pl. 75b Enamel lamellae, decalcified cross-section of a human tooth; Fuchsin stain: soh,
enamel surface membrane covered with tartar; l, lamellae; d, dentine. 180:1. From
W. Meyer, *Normale Histologie und Entwicklungsgeschichte der Zähne des Menschen*, Carl Hanser
Verlag, München (1951) (by permission).

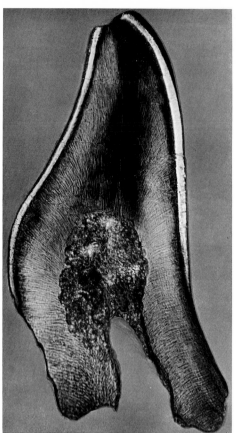

Pl. 76a Vertical ground thin-section through a cheek tooth of a triconodont from the Rhaetic of Hallau, polarized. The cusp that follows to the left of the picture is not illustrated because it was defective. 80:1.

Pl. 76b Vertical ground thin-section through an anterior tooth of a probable triconodont from the Rhaetic of Hallau, polarized. 110:1.

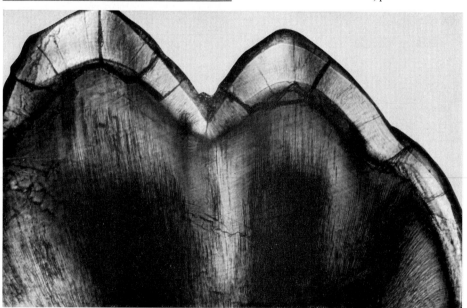

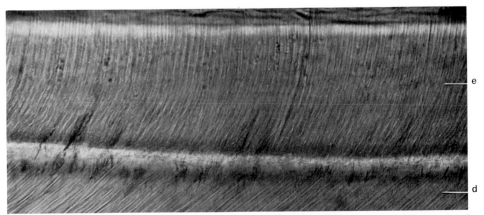

Pl. 77a Vertical ground thin-section through a lower molar of the mole: e, simple form of enamel prisms; d, dentine. 460:1.

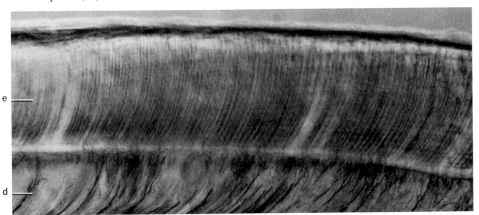

Pl. 77b Vertical ground thin-section through an upper tooth of a bat: e, enamel; d, dentine. 390:1.

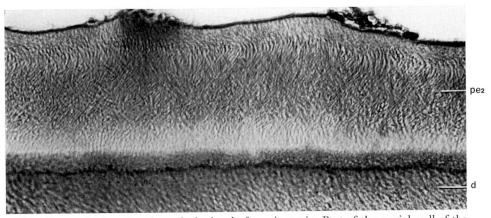

Pl. 77c Parasagittal section through the head of a guinea pig. Part of the mesial wall of the last premolar near its base; pe₂, second prestage of enamel, shows complicated form of future enamel prisms; d, dentine. 460:1.

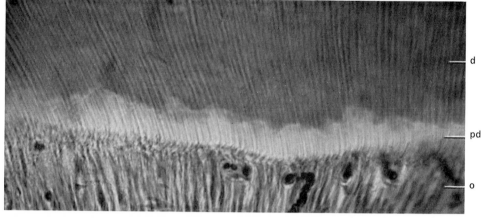

d

pd

o

Pl. 78a Cross-section through the head of a young hamster; portion of a vertically cut upper cheek tooth: o, odontoblasts, that send their cytoplasmic processes into the predentine (pd) and from there into the dentine (d). Minute vessels from pulp cavity enter between the odontoblasts. 500:1.

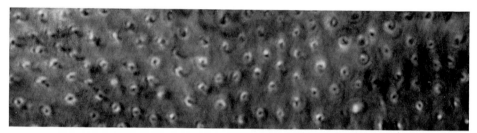

Pl. 78b Cross-section through the head of a young hamster. Dentine tubules cut transversally, with cross cut processes of odontoblasts in their centers. 1420:1.

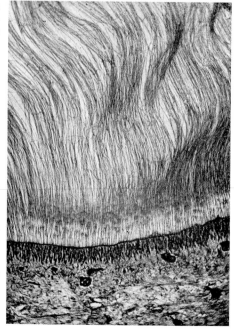

Pl. 78c Processes of odontoblasts of a human tooth, after decalcification with 50 percent nitric acid and staining of a frozen section with acid Fuchsin. Adjacent is a portion of the pulp cavity. From W. Meyer, *Normale Histologie und Entwicklungsgeschichte der Zähne des Menschen,* Carl Hanser Verlag, München (1951) (by permission).

Pl. 79a Interglobular dentine of a human tooth. 500:1. From W. Meyer, *Normale Histologie und Entwicklungsgeschichte der Zähne des Menschen*, Carl Hanser Verlag, München (1951) (by permission).

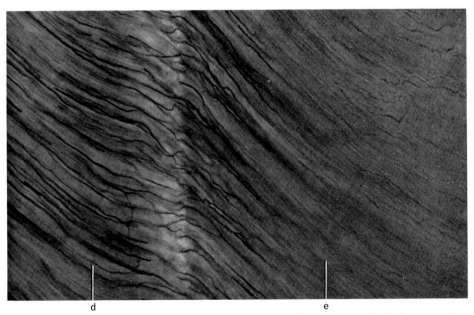

d   e

Pl. 79b Vertical section through a cheek tooth of *Procavia*. Numerous dentinal tubules entering the enamel: d, dentine; e, enamel. 420:1.

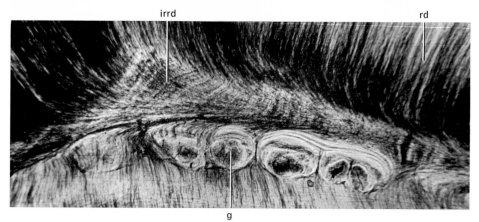

Pl. 80a Vertical section through a cheek tooth of a very old seal. The narrow portion of the pulp cavity that forms the root canal is formed by globular structures (g), surrounded by irregularly arranged dentinal tubules (irrd); rd, regularly arranged dentinal tubules. 44:1.

Pl. 80b Vertical section through a freshly shed, lower I_2 of a six-year-old girl. Basal resorption of the dentine; Howship's lacunae. 482:1.

e

d

c

m

m

Pl.81a Vertical ground thin-section through the tooth of a chamois: d, dentine; e, enamel; c, cell-containing cementum, above that cell-free cementum. 107:1.

Pl.81b Vertical longitudinal ground thin-section through the lower cheek tooth series of a hare. Shown here is a place in the deep enamel fold of the second molar which shows the destruction of the enamel epithelium by the entrance of mesodermal cells (m), a process that precedes deposition of crown cementum on the enamel surface. 88:1.

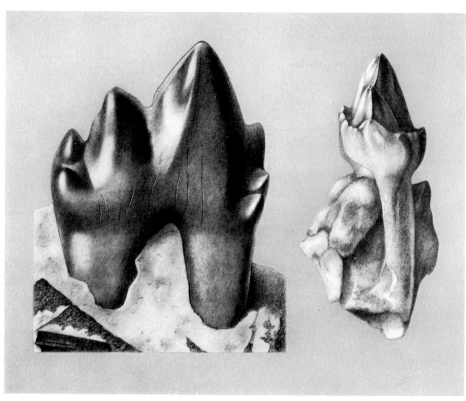

Pl. 82a Two triconodont teeth from the Rhaetic of Hallau, Switzerland. 24:1. From Peyer (1956).

Pl. 82b Right upper half of dentition of the vampire bat *Desmodus rufus*. From Peyer, *Die Zähne*, Verständliche Wissenschaft, vol. 79. Springer Verlag, Berlin (1963) (by permission).

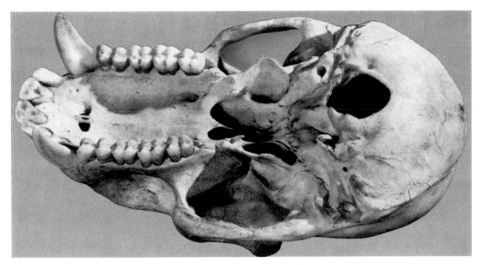

Pl. 83a   Skull of *Cynopithecus niger* seen obliquely from below. From Warwick James, *The Jaws and Teeth of Primates*, Pitman Medical Publication Co., London (1960) (by kind permission of the publisher and the executors of the estate of the late Mr. Warwick James).

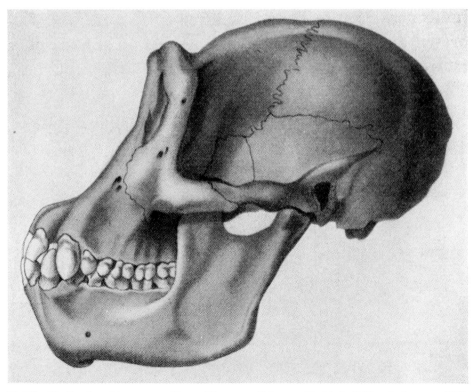

Pl. 83b   Skull of a chimpanzee. From Piveteau, *Primates*, *Traité de Paléontologie*, tome VII, Masson et Cie, Paris (1957) (by permission).

Pl.84a *Oreopithecus bambolii*, upper jaw. 2.25:1. After Hürzeler, from Pivetau, *Primates*, *Traité de Paléontologie*, tome VII. Masson et Cie, Paris (1957) (by permission).

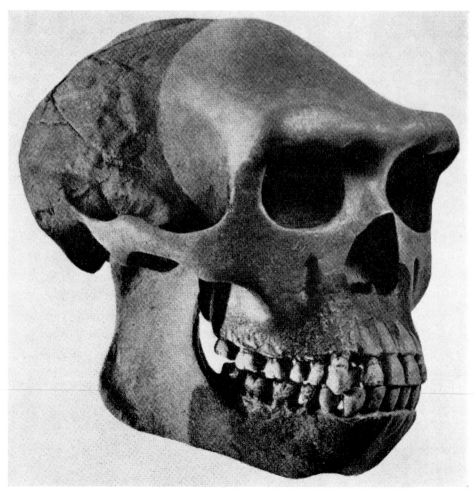

Pl.84b *Pithecanthropus*. Reconstruction of the skull. 1:1.6. After Weidenreich, from Piveteau, *Primates*, *Traité de Paléontologie*, tome VII. Masson et Cie, Paris (1957) (by permission).

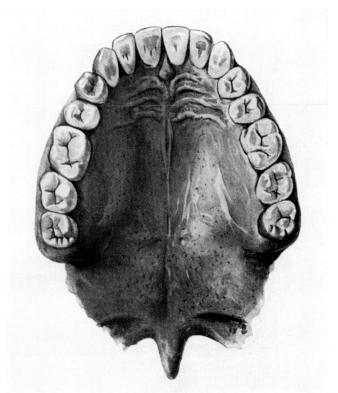

Pl. 85 Permanent denti-
tion of man, upper and
lower jaws. From Spalte-
holz, *Handatlas der Anatomie
des Menschen*, S. Hirzel Verlag, Leipzig (1909) (by permission).

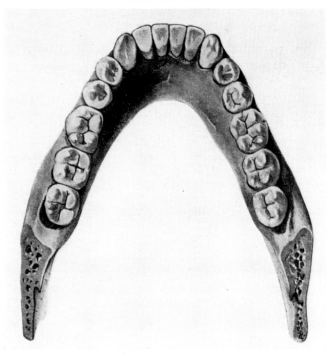

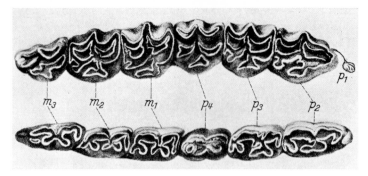

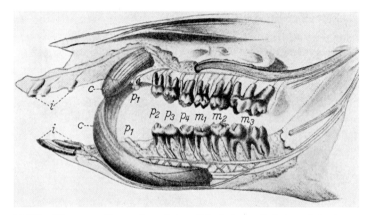

Pl.86a   Upper and lower cheek teeth of the horse. The premolars have become molar-like. From Peyer, *Die Zähne*, Verständliche Wissenschaft, vol.79. Springer Verlag, Berlin (1963) (by permission).

Pl.86b   Upper and lower jaw of the wild pig in medial view: i, incisors; c, canines; p, premolars; m, molars. From Peyer, *Die Zähne*, Verständliche Wissenschaft, vol.79. Springer Verlag, Berlin (1963) (by permission).

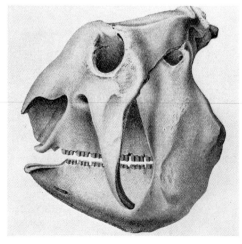

Pl.86c   Skull of the Pleistocene *Glyptodon*. After Burmeister from Weber, *Die Säugetiere*, Gustav Fischer Verlag, Jena (1928) (by permission).

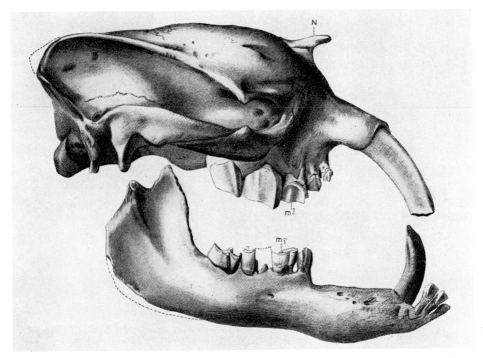

Pl. 87a *Astrapotherium*, last representative of a small South American mammalian order, from the Miocene of Patagonia: m¹, first molar above and below; N, nasal bone. 1:6.2. After Scott and Abel, from Weber, *Die Säugetiere*, Gustav Fischer Verlag, Jena (1928) (by permission).

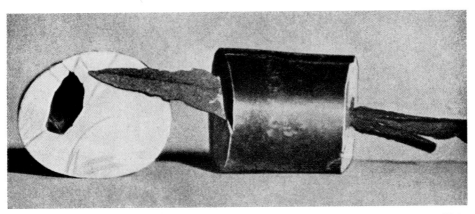

Pl. 87b Spear point in the dentine of an elephant tusk. From Peyer, *Die Zähne*, Verständliche Wissenschaft, vol. 79. Springer Verlag, Berlin (1963) (by permission).

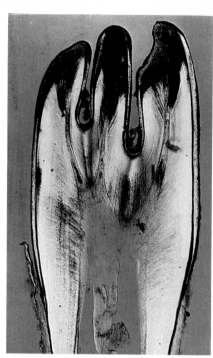

Pl. 88a   Vertical ground thin-section through a lower incisor of *Procavia syriaca*. 14.8 : 1.

Pl. 88b   *Desmostylus*, a subungulate from the Miocene of California and Japan; molar. Photo courtesy of Dr. Muller, Stanford University, California. 1.5 : 1. From Peyer, *Die Zähne*, Verständliche Wissenschaft, vol. 79. Springer Verlag, Berlin (1963) (by permission).

DESCRIPTIONS OF THE COLOR PLATES

Color Plate I

a) Denticles of the mucous membrane of the mouth of the smooth dogfish *Mustelus*, early stage of development. In the rose-colored ectoderm large slime cells. In the lower left-hand corner of the picture, above the dark connective tissue, the narrow Malpighian layer is indistinctly recognizable. The large ameloblasts of the tooth anlage are light, their nuclei reddish; above the ameloblasts the cells of the outer enamel epithelium. The very thin layer of predentine is blue, the cells of the pulp cavity are reddish. 200:1.

b) Denticles of the mucous membrane of the mouth of the shark *Carcharodon* in sagittal section. The points of the denticles are directed obliquely backward. The third denticle from left is not yet fully developed. Dentine red, the connective tissue beneath the denticles dark; the incompletely preserved ectoderm that lies between the individual denticles rose-colored. 29:1.

c) Denticles of the mucous membrane of the mouth of the shark *Mustelus;* direction of section only approximately horizontal, its plane lies on the right side of the picture within the dark-colored connective tissue beneath the ectoderm. The fully developed, bright red denticles are cut partly apically, partly basally; the denticle anlagen are cut more or less basally. In the latter the predentine is blue, the ectodermal formational tissue light rose. 46.5:1.

d) Denticles of the mucous membrane of the mouth of *Mustelus*. Slightly older developmental stage than in (a). In the ectoderm, slime cells and Malpighian layer are recognizable. On the left side of the picture, the ameloblasts are in contact with the blue predentine, on the right side separated from it by a shrinkage space. Same staining as in (a). 178:1.

e) Dermal denticles of the shark *Prionace glauca* in vertical section. Between two fully developed denticles a young anlage. Staining as in (a) and (d). 95:1.

f) Denticle of the mucous membrane of the mouth of the shark *Mustelus*. Staining as in (a) and (d). The picture shows that the formation of dentine extends into the dark-colored meso-dermal territory beneath the ectoderm. Furthermore, in addition to the broad basal communi-cation, there is just barely visible a narrower lateral opening leading into the pulp cavity, as is commonly the case in dermal and mucous membrane denticles of sharks. 205:1.

g) Dentition tooth of the skate *Raja clavata*. Vertical section through an older developmental stage. At bottom of picture the red odontoblasts; above them the bluish-colored dentine in which the light dentinal tubules are visible. Above the dentine, what I call the peripheral initial zone, because, according to my view, in agreement with that of Röse, the teeth of selachians possess no enamel. In the character of the staining a reddish inner zone may be distinguished from a light blue outer portion which contains delicate fibers that become thinner toward the periphery. Uppermost in the picture the ectoderm, whose structure has become indistinct at this stage. 250:1.

Color Plate II

a) Tooth of the ganoid fish *Dapedius*, from the Rhaetic of Hallau. Vertical thin-section, po-larized. In the picture below the orthodentine with its dentinal tubules; right and left, the dentine is surrounded by a sharply distinguished bright whitish layer of true enamel. The rounded apical tooth portion is formed of a cap of modified dentine that appears reddish-yellow in the picture. Basally, it is overlain for a short distance by the enamel layer. 90:1.

b) Pavement tooth of the ganoid fish *Colobodus* from the upper Triassic (so-called Lettenkohle) of Crailsheim, Württemberg. Vertical thin-section, polarized. The layer of true enamel is much thicker and more extensive than in *Dapedius*. The modified dentine (dark in the picture) is restricted to a small area on top of the tooth crown. The matrix fill of the pulp cavity contains many strongly birefringent crystals. 18.5:1.

c) Tooth of the ganoid fish *Birgeria* from the Rhaetic of Hallau. Vertical thin-section, polarized. The illustrated portion shows only the area where the true enamel (left, bright yellowish-white), orthodentine (right, dark red) and the modified dentine (upper part of the picture, light blue) meet. 250:1.

Color Plate III

a) Tooth of the ganoid fish *Sargodon* from the Rhaetic of Hallau. Vertical section parallel to the cutting edge of an incisiviform tooth, polarized. The main mass of the tooth is formed by orthodentine (brown in the picture) which is covered right and left by a thin layer of true enamel. The tooth crown is covered by a thick coat of modified dentine (bright whitish in the picture). 15.6:1.

b) Tooth of the gar pike *Lepisosteus*. Vertical thin-section, polarized. The cap of modified dentine dark brown, followed beneath by the white enamel that covers the orthodentine which appears in the picture partly green, partly yellow-brown. 31.5:1.

c) Tooth of *Lepisosteus*. Microtome section. To the right the rose-colored pulp cavity with the odontoblasts. Toward the left a thin blue zone of predentine and a broader, dark red zone of orthodentine. Above this is a light blue streak, extending obliquely upward, of modified dentine in process of formation and separated from the rose-colored ameloblasts by an open space. In the area of the modified dentine, the cylindrical ameloblasts are enormously enlarged, but the ameloblasts (beneath them in the picture), where they deposit enamel on the orthodentine, are of normal height. At the left, blue vascular connective tissue. 87:1.

d) Vertical section through a tooth anlage of medium age of *Lepisosteus*. In the lower center of picture, the reddish pulp cavity with the odontoblasts. The latter are bounded above by a thin blue zone of predentine followed by a broader dark red zone of orthodentine, in its turn covered apically by a light blue cap of modified dentine. Here again it is apparent that the ameloblasts have become enlarged only in the immediate vicinity of the modified dentine, but remain normal next to the orthodentine on which they deposit enamel. The section shows, furthermore, a true so-called stellate reticulum between the inner and outer enamel epithelium, as well as the interfingering of capillaries (colored more intensively red) and the cells of the outer enamel epithelium (pale rose). Uppermost in the picture, stained blue, vascular connective tissue. 57:1.

Color Plate IV

a) Portion of a vertical section of the lower jaw of *Lepisosteus*. On the left, pale red, a very young tooth anlage; in the middle an anlage of medium age and along the right margin the side of a fully formed tooth. In the middle tooth anlage, in spite of the modest magnification, the blue predentine and the dark red orthodentine are visible, as well as the interfingering of the capillaries with the outer enamel epithelium. Uppermost in the picture the pale rose-colored ectoderm of the mucous membrane. 22:1.

b) Vertical section through a tooth anlage of *Lepisosteus*. Below, the rose-colored enamel pulp; above, the blue-stained vascular connective tissue. At the boundary between the two, the interfingering of capillaries with projections of the outer enamel epithelium. 235:1.

c) Vertical section through a jaw of *Lepisosteus*. Between two old teeth that are already affected by resorption, a tooth anlage of medium age. Left, a notably younger anlage in which almost the entire future dentine is still at the stage of predentine and has thus been stained blue. The point of the tooth near the right margin corresponds to the boundary between orthodentine and modified dentine. The tooth point proper, consisting of modified dentine, has been dissolved during decalcification of the specimen. 39:1.

Color Plate V

a) Tooth of *Amia calva*, a modern holostean. Vertical thin-section, polarized. The orthodentine blue-green on the left, mainly yellow-brown on the right. The cap of modified dentine yellow on the left, blue on the right. The enamel that overlies the orthodentine does not show very well in this picture. 74:1.

b) Section through a fully formed tooth of *Amia calva*, and a young tooth anlage nearby to the left. In the latter only the inner and outer enamel epithelium is in the section plane. Epithelium of the mucous membrane of the mouth light red, the enamel epithelium of the young tooth anlage even lighter; dentine of the fully grown tooth and a little bone (lower left corner) dark red. Connective tissue blue. 18.5:1.

c) Horizontal section through the upper jaw of *Amia calva*. At the bottom (light rose) the epithelium of the skin; at the top (also light rose) the epithelium of the mucous membrane of the mouth; between them more or less horizontally cut tooth anlagen of different ages, some of which are connected to one another by strands of ectodermal tissue. Connective tissue dark green. 15:1.

d) Ground thin-section through a pavement tooth of the acanthopterygian *Labrus turdus*. The teeth of this fish are also composed of enamel, orthodentine and modified dentine. In the lower half of the picture the orthodentine (partly green, partly yellow-brown) is identifiable by the presence of dentinal tubules; it is sharply set off from the bright whitish enamel on either side. The tooth crown is formed by a thick cap of modified dentine (deep brown). 28.5:1.

Color Plate VI

a) Horizontal section through a young tooth anlage of the teleost fish *Pomadasys*. Innermost the pulp cavity with cross sections of vessels, and the odontoblasts. The latter are surrounded by a narrow blue zone of predentine and a broader belt of dentine in process of formation and containing fibers. This is followed in outward direction by a ring of vividly red-stained ectodermal cells. At bottom, part of another tooth anlage. 255:1.

b) Vertical section through a tooth of the teleost fish *Pomadasys*. In the lateral tooth wall within the dentine appears a red streaking that extends obliquely downward and outward, probably the result of the presence of less highly mineralized and hence better stainable fibers in that area. The same phenomenon was observed also in other teleosts, for example, in *Labrus turdus*. In the obliquely cut pulp cavity, branches of very small vessels. 70:1.

c) Horizontal section through a rather young tooth anlage of the European catfish *Silurus glanis*. At center bottom the pulp cavity, with the odontoblasts surrounded by a small seam of blue predentine. To the outside of the predentine there follows a thick zone of red-stained dentine. In the inner part of this zone dentinal tubules are present, but barely visible in the picture; in the outer portion dark fibers enter the interior from the periphery, many of them uniting along the way; a network of finer fibers adjoins them pulpward. In younger stages the fiber zone makes up the entire dentine coat; in the fully developed tooth it constitutes merely a thin outer zone. 240:1.

d) Polarized vertical ground thin-section through a tooth of the Devonian fish *Onychodus*, which, according to its tooth structure, probably belongs to the crossopterygians; see p. 114. The light enamel (right side of picture) is strongly differentiated from the orthodentine by its strong birefringence. It shows a layering nearly parallel to the surface, comparable to the striations of Retzius of the mammalian enamel and, except for obvious cracks, a fine structure oriented at a right angle to the surface. In the dark red dentine to the left, a layer of interglobular spaces. 260:1.

e) Vertical thin-section through a tooth plate of a juvenile stage of the fossil lungfish *Ceratodus parvus*, from the Rhaetic of Hallau, polarized. In the section a sharp crest of the plate, denticulate as in carboniferous dipnoans, was cut all along its extent; the largest, last-formed denticle is on the left side of the picture. In the valleys between some of the denticles, remains of the thin enamel cover have been preserved (thin whitish edge). In polarized light the presumed original independence of the individual denticles is indicated. Beneath the tooth plate is bone tissue. 15.5:1.

Color Plate VII

a) Vertical section through an older tooth anlage of *Rana escuienta*, surrounded by connective tissue (light whitish in the picture). The tooth enamel was totally dissolved during decalcification of the specimen. The space it originally occupied is sharply circumscribed by its surroundings. 280:1.

b) Horizontal section through an older tooth anlage of *Varanus salvator*. At bottom the pulp cavity with the layer of odontoblasts; above them a blue zone of predentine, followed above by the light gray dentine. Uppermost in the picture ameloblasts and, between them and the dentine, the uniformly red-stained first prestage of the enamel. 629:1.

c) Vertical thin-section through the tooth of a crocodile from the Lower Cretaceous of Texas, polarized. At bottom some dentine; above this the vividly multicolored enamel layer, in which groups of vertically oriented (relative to the tooth surface) structural elements show a regular change in the optical orientation, and thus of the color. On right side of picture a crack that penetrates the enamel and extends into the dentine. 78:1.

d) Horizontal sections through two stages, nearly equally old, in the tooth development of *Rana esculenta*. Innermost the pulp cells with their large nuclei, surrounded by the dark-stained odontoblasts. Adjacent the brown (in this picture) predentine and the darker dentine, the latter surrounded by a broad ring of black ectodermal cells. At the top of the right picture the beginning of the broad connection of this ectoderm with the epithelium of the mucous membrane of the mouth. In the stage shown, the fibers that originate from the basal membrane penetrate the entire thickness of the dentine, but in later stages, they form merely a thin peripheral seam, followed inward by a thick sequence of normal dentine. 285:1.

Color Plate VIII

a) Vertical section through a milk premolar of the cat, polarized. At bottom some dentine, above it the enamel layer in which a regular alternation of red and green streaks of color is oriented at a right angle to the surface. This alternation is related to the different course of entire bundles of enamel prisms which brings about a different optical orientation of the crystal axes. In places the cross striation of the prisms is visible. 303:1.

b) Portion from a vertical section through a milk premolar of a young cat. At bottom the pulp cavity with the dark brown odontoblasts, above them a narrow zone of intensely stained blue-green predentine and adjacent a broad belt of lighter-stained dentine. Following upward, the two prestages of enamel. The slightly older second prestage is sharply set off from the dentine by its red stain; in it the organic bases of the individual, future enamel prisms are clearly recognizable. The first prestage, adjacent to the ameloblasts shows no structure, however, and is uniformly dark (aside from a slightly lighter band that is exceptional in the present preparation). The ameloblasts are clearly visible, because they are separated by lighter interstices. Above them are the less distinct dark cells of the outer enamel epithelium. They are approached by vessels of the surrounding connective tissue which forms the upper edge of the picture. 230:1.

c) Portion from a labio-lingual vertical section through the anlage of a milk tooth in the lower jaw of a human newborn infant. The portion shown lies nearly at the basal end of the lingual wall of the anlage. Upper margin is apical. Along the left edge the margin of the pulp cavity with the odontoblasts is bordered at the right by a thin blue seam of predentine. Then follows a broad band of red dentine and the two prestages of the enamel, and even farther to the right the ameloblasts. The somewhat older, second prestage, in which prismatic structure is already visible, lies on the dentine, but it is separated from this by a narrow artificial crack. The younger, just-formed first prestage is closely attached to the ameloblasts. It is uniformly dark red and shows no structure. In the ameloblasts the nuclei are marked by red stain. Further to the right there follow meager remains of the outer enamel epithelium. These are enclosed by undifferentiated connective tissue (light greenish in the picture). 256:1.

PLATE I

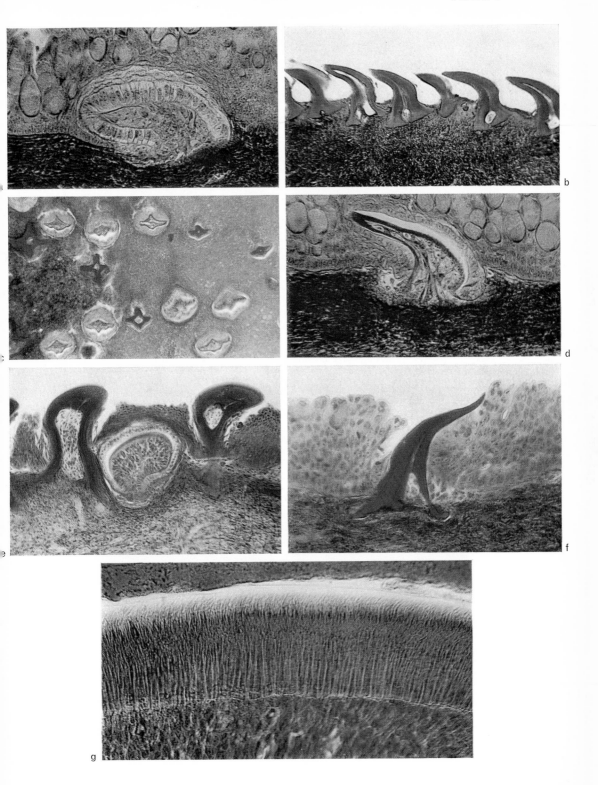

PLATE II

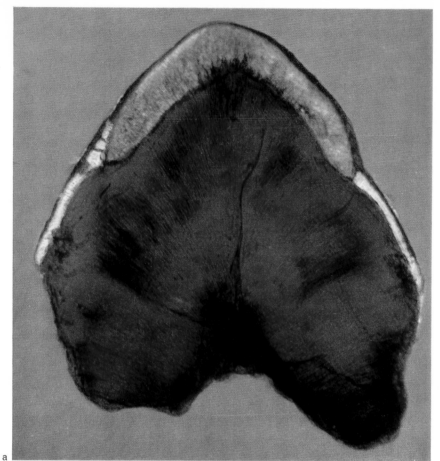

a

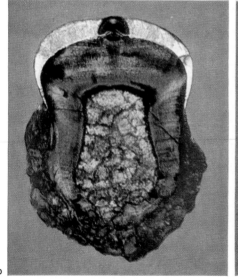

b

c

PLATE III

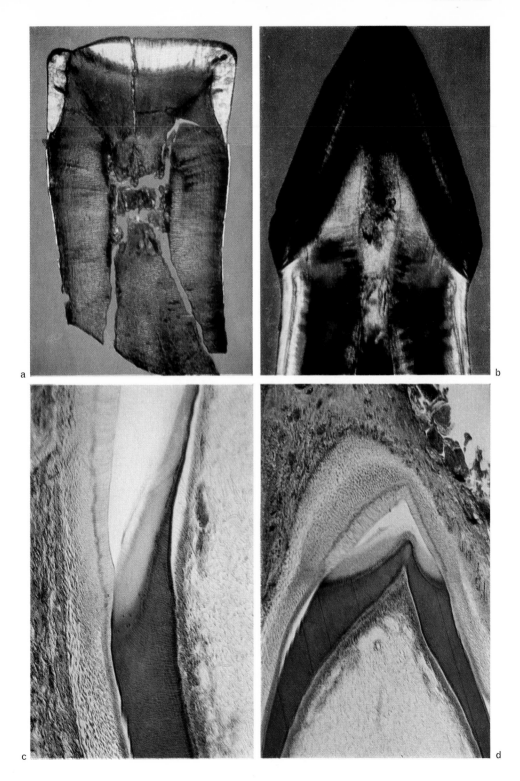

PLATE IV

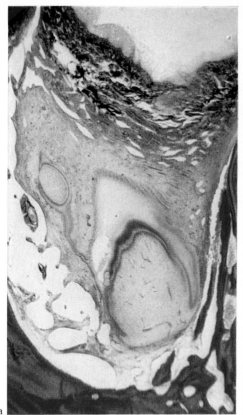

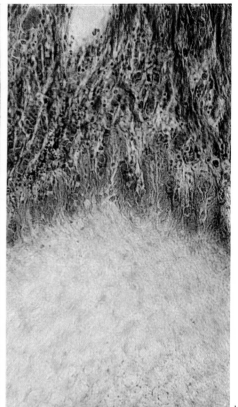

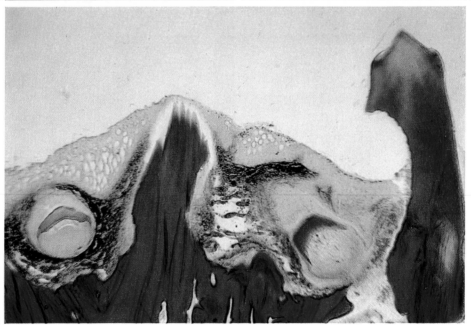

PLATE V

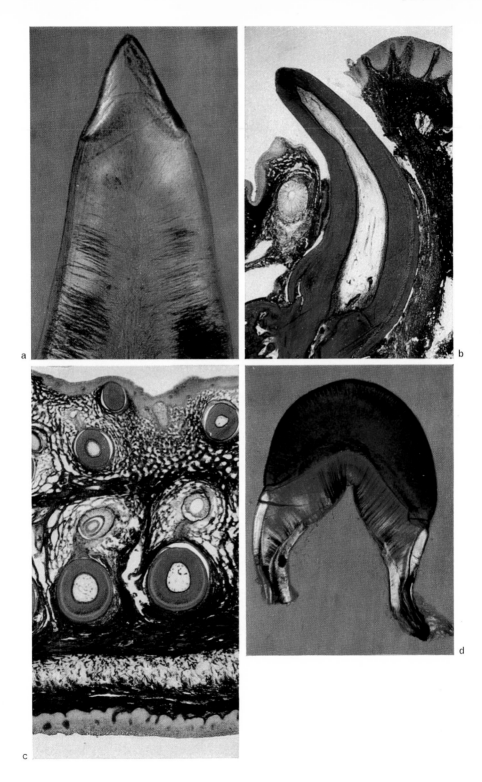

PLATE VI

PLATE VII

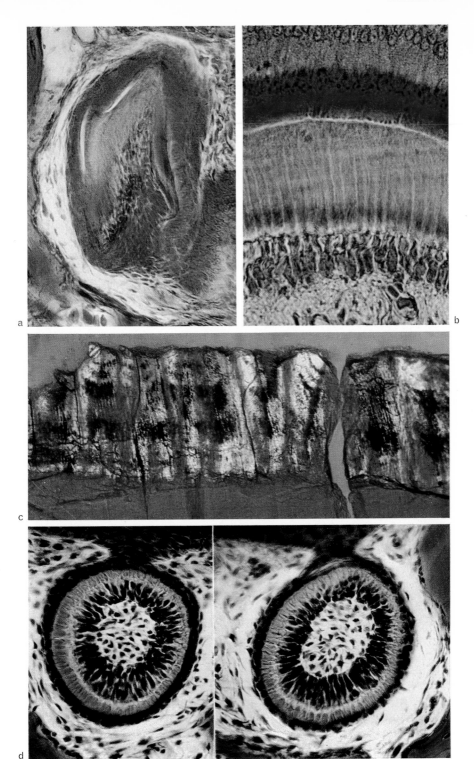

PLATE VIII

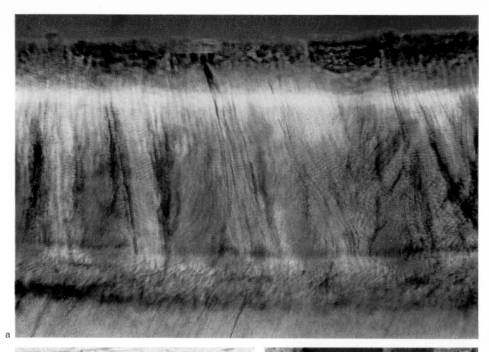

a

b

c